Fax sent from Navajo County Sheriff's Office. 1245 hours, Tuesday, June 19, 2002

The Rodeo fire burning in the Cibecue area of the White Mountain Apache Indian Reservation is located five miles northeast of Cibecue and approximately 20 miles southwest of Show Low. The U.S. Forest Service and B.I.A. Ft. Apache Forestry are aggressively working the fire with ground crews and air support. Local area Fire Departments and Law Enforcement are working closely with the Forest Service monitoring this situation.

THERE IS AN EVACUATION ORDER FOR THE RESIDENTS OF PINEDALE, LINDEN AND CLAY SPRINGS AT THIS TIME. EVACUATE IMMEDIATELY!

An evacuation center is being set up at the Show Low Intermediate School (OLD Show Low High School) at 500 E. Old Linden Road in Show Low. Tune to a local radio station for further information.

Thank you. Gary Butler, Sheriff, Navajo County.

Partial funding for this project provided by

Bison Homes, Gary & Ronna Martinson

$1.00 from the sale of every book goes to

The Fallen Firefighter Memorial

Administered by

The Wildland Firefighter Foundation
http://www.wffoundation.org/

Oct.'12

Rondie,

God's best to you!

THE
MONSTER
REARED HIS
UGLY
HEAD

THE STORY OF THE RODEO-CHEDISKI FIRE
AND FIRE AS A TOOL OF NATURE

JIM PAXON

Foreword by Arizona Governor, Janet Napolitano

Cedar Hill Publishing

The Monster Reared His Ugly Head – The Story of the Rodeo-Chediski Fire and Fire As a Tool of Nature

Cover design, editing and book layout by Rebecca Hayes, Cedar Hill Publishing

Contributing content editor, Ken Palmrose

Published in the United States by
Cedar Hill Publishing
www.cedarhillpublishing.com

ISBN-13: 978-1-933324-94-4

Library of Congress Control Number 2007937281

To order copies in bulk or contact the author, please visit his website:

www.paxonthefireguy.com

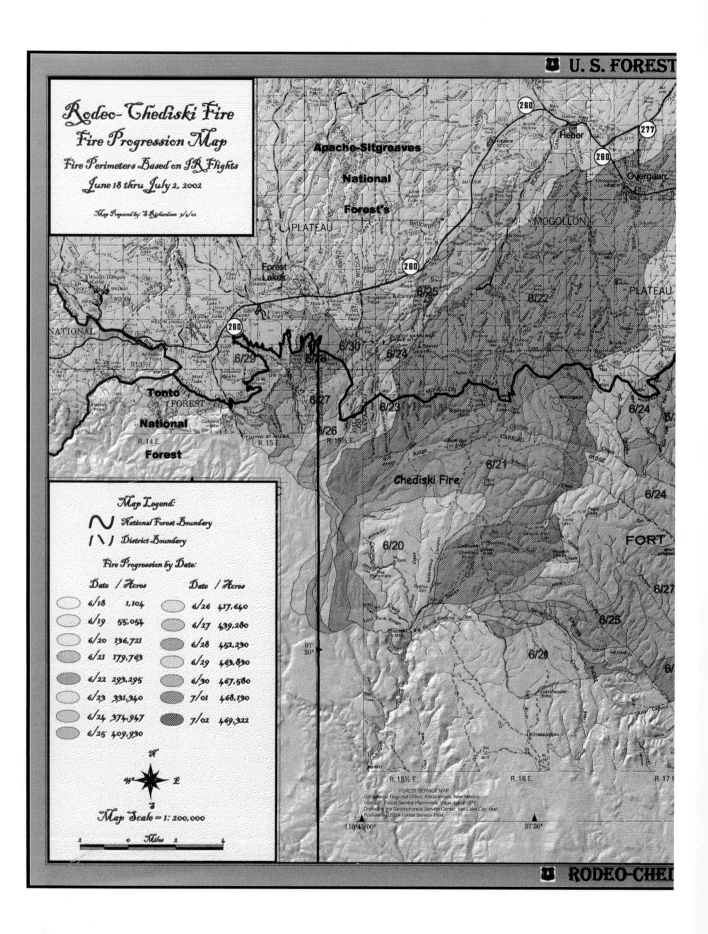

Rodeo-Chediski Fire
Fire Progression Map
Fire Perimeters Based on IR Flights
June 18 thru July 2, 2002

Map Prepared by: S. Richardson 9/4/02

Map Legend:

〜 *National Forest Boundary*
/\\/ *District Boundary*

Fire Progression by Date:

Date	/ Acres	Date	/ Acres
6/18	1,104	6/26	417,640
6/19	55,054	6/27	439,280
6/20	136,721	6/28	452,230
6/21	179,763	6/29	463,830
6/22	293,295	6/30	467,580
6/23	331,340	7/01	468,130
6/24	374,947	7/02	469,322
6/25	409,930		

Map Scale = 1: 200,000

Miles

U. S. FOREST

RODEO-CHE

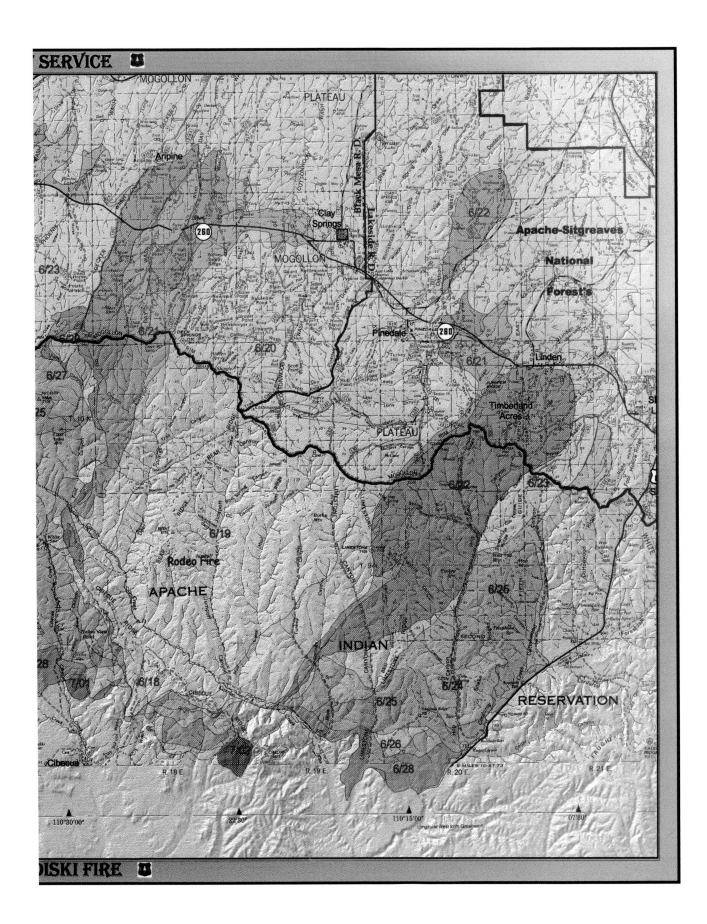

ACKNOWLEDGMENTS

I have had a lot of fun writing this, my first literary adventure, although, now that it is done, I may need an exorcism. There are so many people that I need to thank, but in short, I thank:

My maternal granddad, Poppa Garrett, for enrolling me in his life curriculum, "Preparation for Manhood" with grandfatherly advice and all the many wise homilies that stuck and that I continue to use. I can't really call them "Paxisms" as some of the news media did; rather they are "Poppa-isms." They make so much sense and are so simple, yet memorable. As in my spoken dialogue, many of them found their way into the text, as you will surely recognize.

Doc Smith for being the "fire sage" and mentor to me. I could call Doc on anything at anytime and he always gave me thoughtful responses. He posed questions that made me seek answers from sources far and wide.

Dr.'s Covington, Pyne and Swetnam for their ever expanding knowledge of fire and its interaction with this planet and the humans who occupy it... and for allowing me to summarize some of their findings in my colloquial "plain speak." I do hope that the salient points remained consistent and true to their research and conclusions.

Ken Palmrose, my humble "amateur" contributing editor, who worked tirelessly to change my prose, just enough to make sense, instead of reading with the same Texas twang in which I attempt to communicate verbally. Ken was adept at taking the "twang" out but keeping the gist of what I said. Seems I write much as I speak. Sometimes that is difficult to comprehend in the written word, *ya'll*, and you cannot see my hands waving and the smiles/expressions.

Jean Burr for the contribution of the photo of the monster's face in the smoke plume on June 19th, which she has graciously allowed me to use for the cover of the book.

Guy Atchley, Paul Bead, Kolleen Bean, Jerry Beddow, Tom Beddow, Jean Burr, Brian Buswell, Steve Campbell, Jeff Clark, Kathy Collins, Rick Fernau, Varnell Gatewood, Jerry Handorf, George Leech, Ron Moody, Ken Palmrose, Debbie Paxon, Boris Poff, Dewayne Saxton, Shane Shannon, Duane Swanson, John Thompson, Karen Wattenmaker, Paul Watson, Darin Whiting, Sandy Whiting, Lloyd Wilmes, Apache County Sheriff's Office, Arizona Department of Public Safety—Highway Patrol, New Mexico Division of Forestry, Phoenix Fire Department, Show Low Fire Department, Sunset Magazine, the Arizona Republic, the Maverick Newspaper, the White Mountain Independent News, the Ecological Restoration Institute at N.A.U., the Bureau of Indian Affairs and the U.S. Forest Service for contributing their photos and allowing me to present them to you in this tome.

Fire truly is the most awesome, beautiful force in Nature. It is also the most fearsome. I would hope that these photos promote some understanding and respect for fire, the fourth element of primeval Earth (the other three being Earth, wind and rain). If you and I need to understand one thing, it is that fire is not the enemy. Disrespecting fire, however, will make it our enemy.

George Leech for repeated assistance in timelines, dispatch records, reports, summaries, identification of photos and time for several personal interviews.

All of those who took time to share information and their personal stories with me. More than 60 interviews over the course of two years helped immensely in making this book true to the "simple truth standard" that Poppa Garrett instilled in me. It is my best effort at fact and accuracy.

Every wildland and structural firefighter who has "been there" and will go again, anytime called to serve his/her fellow man. Let us not forget how heroic yet humble and giving firefighters are.

My wife, Debbie, just for putting up with me and even more so, since I have been so obsessed with getting this book published. Her support has been total, consistent, and loving. What a blessed man I am.

Gary and Ronna Martinson of Bison Homes for helping me get this book in front of you.

Becky Hayes at Cedar Hill Publishing for actually making this book appear out of the pile of "stuff" that I gave her to sort out. Her challenges were huge and unimaginable.

FOREWORD

I began my tenure as Governor or Arizona in January 2003, with forest health and the protection of our forested communities among my top priorities. Arizona's forests are not healthy; the June 2002 Rodeo-Chediski fire in the White Mountains brought that message home, loud and clear. The Rodeo-Chediski Fire was a historic event and is Arizona's largest and most damaging wildfire… to date.

Jim Paxon was the national spokesman on that fire and the man who kept us all informed in a "blow-by-blow" commentary that ran for the two weeks of the fire event. We relied on his updates to tell us what was happening in the battle with the "monster" and the actions that firefighters were taking to save communities. Jim not only lived the fire, he became the voice of the fire and the face that we associated with our firefighters working on the firelines. Now, he shares his insights and experiences with us in the same straight talk that he used when on the fire.

Even now, years after the Rodeo-Chediski Fire, there are still many unanswered questions. Jim has delved into dispatch logs, unit summaries and personal reports, seeking answers. In addition, he has interviewed more than 50 individuals, many of whom participated in or were directly affected by the "battle against the monster." Each chapter of the book shows his findings. In the final *Chapter 16 – Reflections*, Jim shares his conclusions and some sobering predictions.

Wildfires have no political affiliation; they are neither Democrat nor Republican. We've learned many lessons from the Rodeo-Chediski Fire. For example, we now have much better coordination with all agencies' participation in fire and emergency planning. Since the fire, we have improved communications and we now have state-of-the-art equipment for both our rural and urban firefighting partners.

After the Rodeo-Chediski Fire, I established the Governor's Forest Health Advisory and Oversight Councils. These two councils brought all parties to the table to attack fire and land management issues, working through divergent interests to seek ways to thin forests, implement the "Firewise" program, bolster rural fire departments and protect communities in fire-risk zones. It is an ever-evolving process, but we as a state have begun to identify and implement workable solutions.

Jim has been an active part of our response, and took time from the Arizona Wildfire Academy to emcee my Forest Health Conferences each year.

Jim is one of the founders of the Arizona Wildfire Academy (AWA) held each March in Prescott, at the Embry Riddle Aeronautical University. The AWA has made fire education available to small departments. We know that there will be other "mega-fires" like the Rodeo-Chediski… we just don't know where or when. The AWA is helping us be better prepared for the inevitable.

Most Arizonans remember that Jim and his sweetheart, Debbie, had just gotten married a few days before the Rodeo Fire erupted. They did get their honeymoon in October, after the close of a long, hard fire season, covering the western U.S. Arizona is proud that the Paxons are now Arizona residents, with a cabin in Show Low.

Jim's reputation for telling it like it is is evident throughout this book. So, too, is his obvious care and compassion for people. Many of the stories related here are compelling and riveting. We also get some glimpses into the influences that shaped Jim's life in the sayings (or homilies) of his granddad, Poppa Garrett. Many of these became known as "Paxon-isms," and are remembered from Paxon's briefings, even to this day.

Lastly, this book has a compilation of some of the greatest, most amazing fire photographs ever seen. The awesome power of Mother Nature and the terrifying grandeur of mega-fires are seen up close.

The Monster Reared His Ugly Head is a good read, and worthy of a spot on your coffee table. Enjoy!

Janet Napolitano, Governor of the State of Arizona

INTRODUCTION

Mountain Time…it has nothing to do with standard or daylight savings… It has to do with getting the "city knots" out of your nervous system and unwinding the stress, so that you can see the beauty of God's finest creation in these mountains, streams and pine forests, said to be the hair on the face of the mountain and of course the true "residents" of the land, here long before the European settlers arrived. It also has to do with having a job, but not letting that dominate your life when there are more important things like family, and huntin' and fishin.'

Life on the mountain means taking the time to get to know your neighbors, even though they may not be of the same race, ethnic background, religion or speech accent as are you. As soon as you and I discover our ecological insignificance and temporary nature, then we are better able to fit into the overall mountain community that includes the streams, forests and wildlife. The mountain beckons to us and is the reason for wanting to be "here." Sometimes it takes a few years and a few life-changing experiences to understand. The Rodeo-Chediski Fire was such an experience, though many are still seeking understanding.

As I grow older and especially in the four years since Arizona's largest, "baddest" and most costly forest fire, I have realized that we humans are really not the author of our own destiny… some at best are recorders, while too many are mere observers and often unwilling pilgrims drug down this ol' road called life. How you and I respond to challenges writes the "real" story, both personally and collectively. Some face the hills and turns with a sense of adventure while others approach the challenge with fatigue and dread. The mountain knows our struggles and only demands that we help each other. That is truly the idea behind the survival of communities. Break Mother Nature's rules and she will make us stay after class. Her punishment is often harsh with few second chances to make things right.

In June 2002, the people of the White Mountains faced a road that few could have conceived, even in their wildest dreams. The Rodeo-Chediski Fire forever changed individuals and their communities. Many lost much, but neighbors became closer to neighbors once again. Many reached out to each other with empathy, compassion and a helping hand, reminiscent of a simpler time. So many individuals and communities extended kindnesses that I have fallen woefully short of giving them credit, but they did not act to receive notice. It was almost a "living Norman Rockwell painting," a living picture of what America is supposed to be. This book is of them and for them.

I was part of a wonderful fire team and organization, Humphrey's Type I Incident Management Team. Most of the 40 members of that team had worked together for ten years or more and in many ways, were like extended family. *This is not their story.*

Larry Humphrey, a larger than life "Popeye" kind of character, who is the consummate fire practitioner, was our Incident Commander and leader. The decisions that he considered were deep and life changing for so many. Although he readily took input from his team, government officials and many members of the public, the responsibility for decisions made rested on his shoulders. I have the highest respect for him and what he did on the Rodeo-Chediski. *This is not his story*.

I have a 34 + year history in fire, beginning as a grunt/dirt digger on the fireline, working in the dirt and ash, living in the same, through the final 13 years of my fire career as a Type I Information Officer… an interpreter of sorts, telling people what happens on fires and how we are attacking them. There are many accounts of the Rodeo-Chediski and I take issue with none of them. ***This IS MY story***. In it, I attempt to convey to you what happened in the two plus weeks of battle with "the Monster," through my eyes. I have incorporated vignettes and personal experiences of more than 60 people who have shared "their story" with me.

Without being trite, to me, life is much like a horse ride. There are broncs and there are solid, dependable mounts. There are mountains with steep slopes and box canyons with impassable walls, but there are always *good rides*, wherever the trail may lead. Sometimes the "storms" we encounter along the way, make that particular ride even more memorable. So it is with firefighting.

And so it was with Fire Information on the Rodeo-Chediski Fire. A wild ride it was, with plenty of buck and pitch, squeal and bawl. The monster reared his ugly head many times and as a result, many a precipice and canyon wall did we run up against, but we P.I.O.s (Public Information Officers) escaped without too many bad wrecks and only a few scrapes. We had a job to do and that was to tell the world what was happening on the Rodeo-Chediski Fire. Even though the message was often bad, we attempted to give hope to the citizens of the White Mountains and the world, by telling in simple language exactly what firefighters were doing to make the situation better. It was our job to make *order out of chaos*, for that is the mantra of "P.I.O.s"…and we did our best. Poppa Garrett used to tell me that without valleys there would be no peaks. Peaks are the place where we can witness the sun rising on God's glorious creation. Nothing could be finer, but often we must climb out of the valley to reach the peak.

History was made on the mountain back in '02… so read on and hear the story of the battle against this Monster as seen through this ol' Fire Guy's eyes. As always, God's best to you!

TABLE OF CONTENTS

Ten minutes to evacuation – 6:50 p.m., June 22, 2002 – Show Low. Photo by Steve Campbell.

CH 1: THE ANCIENT ONES AND FIRE

*"When we view land as a community to which we belong,
then and only then, may we begin to use the land with love and respect."*
Aldo Leopold, Sand County Almanac

The Mogollon Rim is a 400-mile escarpment that stretches from southwest of present day Flagstaff across Northeastern Arizona, into Western New Mexico, where it terminates at the majestic 10,770-foot tall Mogollon Baldy, in the Gila National Forest. Most of the Mogollon Rim is 6,000-foot elevation or more.

Above and adjacent to the Rim is the world's largest continuous stand of Ponderosa Pine forests. One of Arizona's gems, the Rim offers grand vistas along its entire length. This is mountain and mesa country, complete with forests, meadows and woodlands, sparkling streams and blue sky. It is a place where one longs to spend time and take in the natural splendor, solitude and peace that abound.

Taking time to enjoy the grandeur of the Rim is a re-creative experience. So it has been for centuries, although, for some, the Ancient Ones, it was a place to toil and attempt to eke a living from the land. Continued survival was the only measure of success in this wild and beautiful setting. Still, can you imagine an animal skin-clad, ancient hunter with handmade bow and arrows, stopping on the Rim in pursuit of game, taking a deep breath at the magnificence of the view and thinking that life was good, even as harsh as life was in those times? They knew nothing different, but the mountain knew, as it knows now. The mountain has changed little in the last 1,000 years, only in those who call it home. [1.a]

The ancient ones were here before time remembered. Some call them the "Anasazi," although in Navajo, that is loosely translated to "the oldest enemies." Their close cousins were the Mogollon to the southeast and the Patayan and Hohokam to the southwest. The territories and periods of these ancient peoples, although distinct and different, were intermingled.

The cultures of the period also shared much in the ways of shelter construction, subsistence, lifestyle and religion. The names of these historic settlements are familiar to many today... Kinishba, Walnut Canyon, Wupatki, Tusayan, Casa Grande, El Morro, Mesa Verde, Chaco Canyon, the Mimbrenos Gila Cliff Dwellings, Canyon de Chelly, Betatakin, Bandelier, and others. They lived in the Southwest for thousands of years before their social structure broke down and the "Great Drought" (of 36 years, starting in 1250 A.D.), drove them downstream to amalgamate with other societies or left them to suffer death and extinction in place.

Masonry wall of cliff dwelling on ledge, protected by cliff overhang. Gila Cliff Dwellings. Photo by USFS, Gila National Forest.

Once they vacated the Mogollon Rim and the lands of the Southwest, the cliff dwellers were never to return, but they are the primary ancestors of the modern Pueblo nations and many of the mountain dwellers that inhabit the historical Southwest, including the Hopis and the Pueblos of Northern New Mexico.

Navajos and Apaches came shortly after the Ancient Ones and occupied the same area. The Ancient Ones and their groundwork of civilization, culture and religion that was formulated, lived and passed on influence current Native American nations and much of their histories. One thing is certain: They depended on fire to survive. Because of fire's role in their lives, they understood.

Whether you refer to them as Anasazi, Mogollon, or by other names, these Ancient Ones had well-developed cultures. Extended families made up most villages with 10-20 people on average. An unusually large community consisted of several families with a total of 50 individuals or so.

They were farmers, hunters and gatherers who were also skilled masons. They built homes in the nooks and overhangs of cliffs, which were hard to reach, secure from invaders and protected from the elements. Modest walls of rock and mud masonry were built out from the cliff faces, closing up ledges for habitation. There is evidence that primitive forms of logging occurred with the use of beams over entryways and poles for wall framing in later structures. Interior walls separated rooms.

The Ancient Ones developed agricultural systems and used natural flows from snow runoff and summer rains to irrigate planted crops. In the rich soil of alluvial fans and creek-side floodplains, they grew squash, gourds, corn and beans. Seed for crops and farming technology may have been gained from neighbors to the South, the Hohokam and the natives in the Mexican highlands. The farming near the Rim was more difficult, as water for crops was limited to spring runoff and reliance on spotty summer rains. Also, agrarian conditions along the Mogollon Rim were much harsher, due to elevation and shorter growing seasons.

In addition, the Ancient Ones had no beasts of burden, nor the technology of wheels and metal implements. Planting, cultivation, harvesting and storage were all done strictly by hand and by family.

Though they had no written language, they left a rich history of masonry structures. Their housing and ceremonial structures, pottery and artifacts tell a story, which has only begun to be revealed by the investigations archaeologists. The enduring nature of the Ancient Ones' building practices and the conditions in the arid Southwest have protected and preserved art, artifacts, baskets, and ceramic pots, and even stored corn and other grains for more than 800 years. [1.b]

The Ancient Ones were also gatherers and hunters. They harvested prickly pears, yucca flowers and other cactus fruit, juniper berries, pinyon nuts, acorns, mesquite beans and even grass seed stalks. As hunters, they ate most anything that they could catch or kill. They lived on small game and birds that were taken with bow and arrow, thrown clubs or trapped. Deer, antelope and wild turkey were considered delicacies that brought rewards and approval to the successful hunter. By approximately 600 A.D., turkeys had been domesticated and were raised in small community flocks for their feathers and for a continuing source of meat, when wild game was hard to find.

These people had made baskets for several centuries. In later periods, Ancient Ones were potters. The development of fired clay pots, ollas, plain pots for cooking, and painted and decorated pots for trade and ceremonial use, are highlights of the era. Harvested crops and proceeds from gathering were dried and stored, short term in covered baskets, and longer term in large clay jars. Food from storage was cooked in stews and soups throughout the winter as needed.

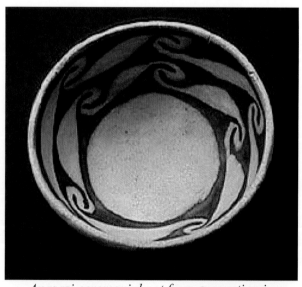

Anasazi ceremonial pot from excavation in Arizona. Photo by Kolleen Bean.

2

As multi-faceted societies, all of these ancient ones claimed descent and lineage from the mother's side of a family. Matriarchs passed down the family name and dictated inheritance, position and authority. It is only natural, then, that all these societies uniformly worshipped the land as "Mother Earth." All things came from her and closely paralleled societal views of human mothers.

Drought, expanding populations with dwindling food supplies, and mysterious social pressures caused the Anasazi communities to begin to unravel about 1270 A.D. Some groups migrated east to Chaco Canyon or southwest to the Phoenix Basin or north to the Colorado Plateau and the land of the Hopi. By 1300 A.D., the area of the Mogollon Rim was virtually vacant and uninhabited.

The disappearance of an entire society and the demise of an entire population remains a mystery. Archaeologists and anthropologists maintain that the Hopi and the Northern Pueblo Nations are the descendents of the Ancient Ones and still carry many of the traditions, culture and religious norms of their ancestors.

The Apache and Navajo that now inhabit the balance of the lands along the Mogollon Rim and the Colorado Plateau came shortly after the demise of the Anasazi and Mogollon cultures, approximately 1300 A.D. Anthropologists contend that these Athabascan peoples migrated to the Southwest from Canada and our northern regions. The Navajo were livestock managers and semi-nomadic. The Apache were a loose knit culture of diverse tribes who roamed the entire Southwest and northern Mexico at will. Tribes would use an area, passing through, and might not return to the same location for several years.

Gila Cliff Dwellings of the Mimbres culture near Silver City, NM. Photo by USFS, Gila National Forest

Apache have always been known as accomplished hunters and skilled warriors. Sometime after Francisco Vasquez de Coronado's expedition in 1580, and several subsequent Spanish explorations, the Apache obtained a limited number of horses and quickly became "shadows of the forests." Even afoot, the Apache were able to travel unbelievable distances in a short time, under the cover of canyon, forest and night. They were also the original "guerilla warfare" special forces when it came to conflicts with invading white settlers, prospectors, and heavily laden army forces who moved with more precision than speed.

The Apaches roamed these lands for more than 500 years, until the influx of European-Anglo settlers, ranchers, prospectors and farmers disrupted their way of life beginning about 1860.

When the Apaches began raiding settlements in an attempt to repel those whom they perceived as invaders and a threat to their way of life, the United States Army began an all out campaign to remove all of the southwestern Native Americans from their ancestral lands. Tribes were sequestered on reservations and forced to take on "white man's" ways of living in one place and making a living by farming. Conditions were squalid and counter to all the Apaches knew and believed.

After years of breaking out of bondage from the San Carlos Reservation and going on raids of retribution, Geronimo and his band of warriors finally surrendered to General Nelson Miles in September of 1886, and the Apache life of free-spirited wandering ended. Another era passed. [1.c] A change of significance that the mountain knew!

*   *   *   *   *

White Mountain Apache lore claims that the Creator placed them specifically in the White Mountains and that their ancestors — "Ndee" guided them in all the ways necessary to live well. That would refer, it seems, to the Ancient Ones. After the U.S. gained control of New Mexico and Arizona in the War with Mexico of 1848, several leaders of the White Mountain Apaches, including Escapa (known as Miguel to the Army) traveled to Santa Fe and met with U.S. authorities to explore avenues of cooperation and co-existence.

In July 1869, Army Major John Green led an expedition into the White River area and entered Escapa's village to discover it adorned with white flags waving from every hut and pole in a gesture of non-aggression. That resulted in what was one of the few peaceable exchanges of the era. In May of 1870, the Army built a fort that was to become Ft. Apache, which was occupied by Cavalry troops until 1923, when it was turned over to the Bureau of Indian Affairs.

The White Mountain Apache were allowed to live in peace and retain their tribal hunting rights, including possession of weapons. They also kept the freedom to move about the 1.67 million acre reservation, live where they wished and continue practices of farming, gathering and ceremonies basic to their religion and way of life.

In 1871, General George Crook enlisted the help of the White Mountain Apaches as scouts in his efforts to quell rebellion and resistance by Geronimo and other bands of Chiricahua Apaches. These scouts served with distinction until the unit was retired from service at Ft. Huachuca in 1947. [1.d]

My friend, Edgar Perry, is a White Mountain Apache. He is a well-respected educator and historian who has shared much with me over the years, since the "Big Fire" of June 2002. In the early 1950's, Edgar fought fire as a young man on the White Mountain Apache Reservation. He was also instrumental in working with the Wycliffe Bible Foundation in building the 36-letter Apache alphabet and translating the Bible to Apache.

He now teaches the Apache language at Northland Pioneer Community College. Edgar has given me permission to share his interpretation of the Apache outlook on life and their analysis of the four elements that make up Apache Earth. Much of what follows is from my notes, but from Edgar's Apache spirit and sharp mind. (Note: It is given in first person, as Edgar shared it). Thanks so much for sharing, Edgar. [1.e]

*   *   *   *   *

Diagram of the sphere of the Earth with the other three Anasazi elements, Rain, Wind, and Fire.
Sketch by Duane Swanson.

Much like the Greeks and the Ancient Ones, the Apaches had no periodic chart with 100 + elements, as we do today in our "modern" world. Their world is made up of only four elements… Earth, Wind, Rain and Fire. Everything comes from Mother Earth and the other three elements intertwine so as to affect life on a daily basis. Living well means doing well, in all things.

To an Apache, respect is primary and must be given to all things, plant, animal and human. There is no separation between culture/religion and nature. Everything is to be initiated with prayers, which start in the east and progress clockwise to the south, west and north. Also, prayers are offered to the heavens and to the ground beneath our feet, because all things come from the Earth.

The actions of political and religious leaders affect natural events such as rainfall or drought, crop success or failure, hunting success or dearth, and even whether interaction with other communities will result in beneficial trade and coexistence or enmity and warfare. Gods are considered distant family and only certain individuals are empowered to commune directly with them. Further, droughts, epidemics and crop or hunting successes or failure are not random events, but rather orchestrated by the gods and often reflect the results of positive or negative actions of the community as a whole.

Everything in the Apache culture demands respect. The elements are a starting place. If we respect them, they will give us a good life and daily events will be positive and beneficial. If not, then we will suffer the consequences when the elements strike us in various ways to get our attention and eventually our compliance (or sadly, our destruction). Mother Earth, as the first element, is ever-present, and while she watches over us, she also requires our attention, respect and worship.

The second element – "Wind"

As a primary element, Wind brings good things, even when it blows hard, for then it is cleansing the area blown. When it whispers softly, Wind brings clouds and promise of moisture for crops. Wind is the means for pollination of plants, for scattering of seeds and bringing good fortune to the ones who respect it and each other. Wind stirs the world in ways that only the gods understand.

The third element – "Rain"

Rain is of two types. Soft rains are feminine and nurturing. Her rains replenish and restore. These rains also provide collected water for the birds and small animals. The soft, soaking rains are the rains that cause crops to flourish. It is considered prudent to take shelter under large trees when we have a soft soaking rain, much as a child would seek shelter and comfort by being close to a parent.

Hard rains are masculine and thunderstorms accompanied by lightning are evidence of braves on the warpath. Lightning and thunder are angry warriors, yelling, shooting, and chasing the enemy. Lightning bolts are thrown at the enemy and often hit the ground and of course we know that it is not a good idea to take cover under large trees in such a storm, as we might be struck by lightning as well. If an Apache sees a lightning strike, he will be still and observant, listening for the message from the gods.

The fourth and final element – "Fire"

Apaches must speak softly and pray to "Fire" every day. Fire is a means of survival. It is the means by which we prepare food and stay warm. Fire is used in each and every ceremony that Apaches adhere to, even today. Fire gives us charcoal with which we draw and write. Fire provides sacred ashes to be worn on the forehead when one's kin pass away in order to keep ghosts at bay. Ashes are also a key ingredient in tanning deer and elk hides to be used for ceremonial clothing and pouches.

Edgar told me that his parents always cooked outside in respect and deference to fire, and would offer prayers and blessings to Fire and Mother Earth while preparing the food. They maintained that food prepared outside incorporated all the elements, was better for you and even tasted better than meals prepared inside.

The simple act of starting a fire is an experience to be done gently, reverently and carefully. Fire is very important in every young girl's puberty rites, where Sunrise girls light the fire, but a young man must tend it and keep it going for the days of ceremony, until its conclusion. There are still Apaches who do not let fire go out in their household, so that there is no interruption in the blessings that fire brings a family and their home.

The Apaches live close to the land and understand the importance and use of fire in their everyday life. There is some historical support that they may have used fire more than we think. Anthropogenic fire, as Pyne calls it, may have had as much influence as lightning in the last 1,000 years or so. For example, when they left an area, the Apache often set fire to vegetation, so that when they returned in a few years, there would be tender and succulent grass and browse for their animals and for wildlife that they could hunt more easily.

Fire was used in warfare. If the enemy approached from downwind, fire could be used as an offensive tool run towards the enemy or as a smokescreen for them to escape. Fire was even used in hunting to drive animals to cliffs or waiting hunters.

The treaty with the United States in 1870 confined the White Mountain Apache to their reservation lands only. In essence, sequestering all the Southwest Indians to tribal lands or removing them from the area removed a major source of fire on the lands to the north, east and west.

How did we get Fire?? There is an Apache legend that poses an interesting answer to that question:

"Long ago, animals and trees talked to each other, but there was no fire (ko').

Fox (Ba') was most clever and he tried to think of a way to create fire for the world to use. One day, he decided to visit the Geese (te-tl), whose cry he wished to learn and imitate. The geese promised to teach Fox their cry, but only if he would fly with them. They contrived a way to attach wings to Fox's body and cautioned him to never open his eyes while flying or he would instantly fall.

Whenever the Geese rose in flight, Fox also flew with them and practiced their cry, but always with his eyes closed, listening for the cries of the geese and then flying in that direction. On one such

6

adventure, darkness descended suddenly, just as they flew over the village of the fireflies (ko-na-tcic-a).

In mid-flight, the glare from the flickering fireflies caused Fox to forget and open his eyes. Instantly, his wings collapsed! His fall was uncontrollable and he landed within the high-walled area of the firefly village, where a fire burned constantly, brightly in the center of the compound. At that time, this was the only fire in the entire world.

Two very kind fireflies came to help Fox, who in turn, gave each of them a necklace of Juniper berries (katl-te-i-tse) as a gesture of thanks and friendship.

Fox hoped to persuade the two friendly fireflies to tell him how he could find a way over the wall to the outside, so that he could return to his home. They led him to a Cedar tree, which they explained would bend down upon command and catapult him over the wall to the outside, if he so desired.

That evening, Fox found the spring where the fireflies obtained their water. There, also, Fox discovered colored earth, which, when mixed with water, made paint. He decided to give himself a new coat of white. Upon returning to the Fireflies' village, Fox suggested that all the fireflies join in a festival of dance and Fox would produce the music.

All the fireflies agreed that a festival with dancing would be fun and they gathered wood and built up a great fire. Secretly, Fox tied a piece of Cedar bark to his tail. Then he made the first drum ever constructed and beat it to a quick rhythm, while singing for the dancing fireflies. Gradually as the fireflies danced, Fox moved ever closer to the fire.

Fox pretended to tire from beating the drum. He gave it to some fireflies and instructed them as to the method of beating and singing. They began to help make the music with the drumbeat and chanting. Fox quickly thrust his tail into the fire, lighting the bark, while exclaiming, "It is too warm for me here. I must find a cooler place." And so Fox left the fire.

Straight to the Cedar tree Fox ran, calling, "Bend down to me, my Cedar tree, bend down now!"

Down bent the Cedar tree for Fox to catch hold, and then it lifted him up and carried him far over the wall, before setting him down. Fox ran as fast as he could, on and on, with the fireflies in hot pursuit. As Fox ran, brush and woods on either side of the trail were ignited from the sparks dropping from the still burning bark tied to his tail.

Fox finally grew too tired to run any more. Along came Hawk (i-tsarl-tsu-i) who took the burning bark and carried it up into the night sky and gave it to Brown Crane (tsi-nes-tso-l). Brown Crane flew southward, scattering fire and sparks everywhere he went. This is how fire first spread over the earth.

The Fireflies continued chasing Fox all the way to his burrow, into which he dove. The fireflies declared to Fox, "Forever after, Wily Fox, your punishment for stealing our fire will be that you will never make use of it for yourself and when a fire starts, it will chase you as we have!" [1.f]

For the Apache Nation, this too was the initiation of their use of fire. Soon, they learned to cook their food with fire and keep their wickiups warm with coals, and to use the fire for ceremonies, festivals and dances. Apache people are close to the land and worship Mother Earth. They are attuned to fire as a major element of life… and so it continues today.

Edgar also told me that in the old days, "Apache were always careful with fire. Old ones instructed the young to speak softly and give blessings to the fire, so that it will continue to cook our food and keep us warm. Young ones were warned that if they kicked the fire or swore at it, that it would get them back sometime in the future, and burn them. Fire does not forget."

Once sequestered on their government appointed reservation, the Apache people were no longer able to manage fire on the lands of the broader Southwest. But the records of the ancient ones and the Apache can still be found on the land and in the fire scars of the trees. In the too near future, one young Apache would use fire in a wrong way and would kick and curse it. And fire, like the mountain, does not forget!

CH. 2: RECIPE FOR DISASTER

"As long as people have lived here, they have shaped this land's fire regimes."
Stephen J. Pyne, <u>Smokechasing</u>

Anglo European settlers began entering Arizona in the 1860s and '70s. They brought different ways of life to the land of the Ancient Ones and different, even from the historical Apache and Navajo ways of life. Fertile lands were commercially farmed and waters were diverted for irrigation. Forests were logged for the necessary raw materials to build the railroads and houses and towns. These newcomers grazed livestock to produce meat and hides, which included horses, cattle, sheep and goats. In many areas, there appeared to the newcomers to be a "sea of grass" as they entered the country with their livestock. First sheep, and then cattle… too many animals were grazed for too long, use that could not be sustained.

Lands were overgrazed and meadows denuded, forcing herders to take their animals farther out from their settlements. The hungry newcomer-critters had to eat any vegetation available, often down to the roots. By removing the fine fuels of grass and low browse, the "fire starter" and continuous carpet of fuel for Mother Nature's lightning ignitions, the occasional fires of Native Americans were not just interrupted, but in many cases stopped.

Lightning, Mother Nature's fire starter has worked for eons.
Photo by National Interagency Fire Center.

The cycle of slow moving, low intensity fires every four to seven years in southwestern Ponderosa Pine forests, consistent for eons and having functioned flawlessly to clean the forest floor, thin the "too many seedlings" and give the "coup de gras" to old, infirm or diseased trees, that fire cycle was lost and has not recurred since Anglo settlement.

Left: Light burn in a prescribed fire application.
Photo by Ecological Restoration Institute of Northern Arizona University.
Right: Light to medium intensity prescribed burn. Photo by E.R.I.-N.A.U.

Mother Nature had swept the forest floor often, and now her broom had been taken away. [2.a]

Mother Nature uses fire as a broom to periodically clean the "forest floor."
Sketch by Duane Swanson.

This process of change wasn't immediate, but as settlers concentrated due to the early threat of Native American retaliation, they formed communities of much greater density than the land had previously endured. From the towns and settlements, the spread of livestock continued across most of the west, the natural fire cycle was changed for all but a few islands of land mass that resisted settlement, due to steep ground, difficult weather, inaccessibility, or the area simply was not suitable for livestock grazing, such as extensive lava flows, and the steep-walled Grand Canyon.

Reports from early travelers illustrated the appearance of the Ponderosa Pine forests before Anglo-European settlement. Mr. E. F. Beale's 1858 report of travels in Northern Arizona was quoted:

Left: Sketch of Mt. Trumball on the Kaibab Plateau by H. H. Nichols in 1870 as he accompanied John Wesley Powell in exploration of the Grand Canyon. Used by permission from E.R.I.-N.A.U.
Right: Photo of Mt. Trumball in 1994 from the same spot and perspective as the sketch of Mr. H. H. Nichols in 1870. Notice the drastic change in tree density and loss of meadow in the photo compared to the sketch.
Photo by E.R.I.-N.A.U.

- "We came to a glorious forest of lofty pines, through which we traveled ten miles. The country was beautifully undulating, and although we usually associate the idea of barrenness with the pine regions, it was not so in this instance. Every foot being covered with the finest grass and beautiful, broad grassy vales extending in every direction. The forest was perfectly open and unencumbered with brush wood, so that the traveling was excellent." [2.b]

- Historian D. F. Cooper concluded in 1960 that, "The overwhelming impression one gets from the older Indians and white pioneers of the Arizona pine forests is that the entire forests were once, much more open and park-like than they are today." [2.c]

*   *   *   *   *

Long time Forest Service researcher Jack Dieterich of Alpine, Arizona has been looking at the situation of changing forests for more than six decades. He concludes that natural fire frequency was interrupted by:

1. Domestic livestock grazing, especially trampling and overgrazing in the 1880's and 1890's.
2. Construction of roads and trails broke up the natural continuity of fuels and prevented low intensity, slow moving fires from continuing across landscapes. The roads essentially formed firebreaks that prevented uninterrupted spread of slow moving, low intensity fires.
3. Active fire suppression around communities and west wide after 1910, reduced the number of fires that grew

Photo of a mature ponderosa pine stand thinned to 60 square feet basal area, meaning that this stand will sustain fire without any crown damage and is close to what Mother Nature would manage to.
Photo by Ron Moody

10

large for more than 70 years.

4. and… that a direct result of the interruption of periodic fire is the propagation of overgrown and overstocked forests and the accumulation of pine litter, logs and flammable debris on the forest floor. [2.d]

"Doghair Pine" estimated at more than 1,200 trees per acre. Photo by Jim Paxon.

*   *   *   *   *

I am just an ol' firefighter and professional forester, but I have spent the last 37 years observing nature at work and drawing my own conclusions. Arizona is truly blessed with having three sons, who each lead the world of fire in their own specialty. I call all three of these fine men "friends" and hopefully colleagues, each having come from a fire environment and sharing some history. Here are a few most summarized and paraphrased thoughts from each that may help understand our situation prior to the Rodeo-Chediski Fire.

My good friend, Dr. Wally Covington, in Flagstaff, has spent his career investigating changes in forests and documenting conditions prior to Anglo-European settlement. Dr. Covington is the world's foremost authority in restorative ecology and his focus has been Ponderosa Pine ecosystems.

In 1994, Covington and other forest scientists estimated that there were, at best, only 15 to 20 years remaining, during which forest managers might remediate the overcrowding problem in Ponderosa pine forests, before large tracts succumbed to crown fires, large scale insect outbreaks, or mortality from competition. [2.e]

Dr. Covington is Regents Professor of Northern Arizona University's Ecological Restoration Institute. E.R.I. is involved in research and restoration ecology to assess conditions (historical and present day) of forests and woodlands across the western U.S.

There is a distinct difference in the mission of E.R.I. as compared to any other forestry or land management institution. E.R.I deals with the "applications side" of science for practitioners. They condense and summarize volumes of research and put it into language that ground level agency personnel, residents, government officials and others can understand. Then they use Mother Nature's classroom, the great outdoors as the laboratory in applying that science and examining the results.

Left: Study plot in Gus Pearson Natural Research Area "before treatment." Photo by E.R.I.-N.A.U.

Right: Same photo point after a forest health thinning emulating pre-European settlement period (prior to 1870) in Northern Arizona. Photo by E.R.I.-N.A.U.

E.R.I. also is working in a practical sense in the restoration ecology area. Knowing what the forests were in pre-Anglo settlement times is valuable information, but only as a benchmark from which to form goals for modern forests of tomorrow, based on health, security, reduction of climax fire risk, funding limits, and social expectations. E.R.I. is working with state governments and federal agencies in determining costs and priorities for implementation of programs in fuels reduction and community wildfire protection plans. There are continuing workshops and programs to share their findings with the public. [2.f]

The Ecological Restoration Institute has been documenting change in our forests from pre-European settlement times. We have recently witnessed a series of fires increasing in severity, damage and size since Dr. Covington's warnings. Just since 1990, fires with a size in excess of 20,000 acres in Arizona are:

- 1990—Dude Fire burned 28,400 acres and 56 homes. Six firefighters died.
- 1993—Piety Complex burned 24,850 acres on state lands in southeastern Arizona.
- 1994—Perkins Complex burned 25,946 acres, including McDowell Mountain, north of Scottsdale.

- 1994--The Rattlesnake Fire burned 27,500 acres on the Coronado National Forest.
- April 1996 — Lone Fire burned 61,370 acres on the Tonto N.F. up towards Roosevelt Reservoir in Sonoran Desert and woodland fuel types. 40,000 acres of desert burned in one day.
- 1996—Bridger Complex burned 53,570 acres on both sides of the Grand Canyon.
- 2002—Ryan Fire burned 38,000+ acres west of Sierra Vista and across Ft. Huachuca in early May. Very fast moving fire in light fuels.
- 2002—Bullock Fire burned 30,563 acres from the San Pedro River to the crest on the north side of Mt. Lemmon.
- 2002—Rodeo-Chediski Fire burned 468,638 acres, 465 homes, 6 businesses and many outbuildings. The White Mountain Apache Reservation and Sitgreaves National Forest burned.
- 2003—Aspen Fire burned 84,750 acres across Mt. Lemmon, including the town of Summerhaven. 320 homes were lost.
- 2003—Kinishba Fire burned 24,734 acres in and around town of Whiteriver on the White Mountain Apache Reservation.
- 2004—Nuttal Complex burned 29,400 acres around the top of Mt. Graham and the U. of A. telescopes.
- 2004—Willow Fire burned 119,500 acres to the west and south of Payson. Approximately ½ the fire was in desert chaparral fuel types.
- 2005—Cave Creek Complex burned 248,310 acres above town of Cave Creek and to the Verde River, again southwest of Payson. It is the largest single fire in Sonoran desert type in recorded history. [2.g]

Sketch by Duane Swanson depicting damage of "mega fires" on the forest.

As we have witnessed fires drastically increasing in size and severity in only the last few years, the fear is that the trend will continue and fires will grow more widespread and more destructive. Now, Dr. Covington does not believe we have until 2015 or 2020. He believes that we are NOW, TODAY at the critical juncture of the major loss of many of our older forests in the Ponderosa Pine type.

Theory is that the forests that come back after "mega fires" may well be changed, "desert-ified" and much less desirable, ecologically. Soils from these mega-fires can be damaged long term and caused extensive erosion. Watersheds provide us the water by which we live; yet many may well be dramatically damaged and less productive due to climax or "mega fires" of the near future. [2.h]

To emphasize the change from pre-1900 natural, fire-maintained forests to higher risk "fire absent" forests of today, the accompanying photos are of the same research photo point in the Fort Valley Experimental Forest, to the west of Flagstaff.

Gus Pierson was the forester in charge in 1908, when the Chief of the Forest Service designated this area as the very first research station. Gus managed and documented conditions in the research area from 1908 to 1944. What a great record and legacy that we can now continue to use and learn from. [2.i]

Left: Ft. Valley Photo Point taken in 1909. Photo courtesy of E.R.I.-N.A.U.

Same photo point taken in 1941. Photo courtesy of E.R.I.-N.A.U.

Right: photo point taken in 1990. Photo courtesy of E.R.I.-N.A.U.

Photo 1 (left) shows the plot as it was in 1909. Note the logs on the ground and total lack of stumps. Most trees are large and mature, and the forest is open, much like that described by E. F. Beale in 1858. The reference point is the crooked limb on the upper, right side of the tree in the middle of the frame.

- Photo 2 (center) is the same location in 1941. There was documented a bumper seedcatch about 1919, and in an extremely good moisture regime, both summer and winter, for approximately five years, establishing a dense carpet of seedlings. The crooked limb is still distinguishable, but is shown slightly more to the right. In comparing the two photos, a picture of change in only 26 years is more than ominous… it is drastic!

- Photo 3 (right) is the same location about 1990. The 1919 era seedlings are now young poles and small sawtimber-sized trees, with the big mature trees still in the background and even additional seedlings and brush evident in the foreground. Researchers at N.A.U. have estimated this photo point to have 1,200 trees per acre. Only with serious study can the crooked limb be found in the upper center of the photo. Fire in any forest stand like this could be a disaster in even the most mundane and low intensity burning conditions. You can imagine fire here under explosive conditions like the Rodeo-Chediski. Some areas were this dense or even more so, where the R-C was to burn. As a result of the change in fire-deprived forests with fuels stacked on the stump, fire is no longer a "treatment option" of this stand without extensive cutting and removal of dead and live fuel. Mother Nature may use fire here, but only to replace "the junk" and start over.

The graphic changes in only 81 years of this one plot are very dramatic and it is hard to argue with the ground, or in this case, photos that shows change in the concentration of trees, over time. The site has gone from less than 40 trees per acres to more than 1,200. There has been no fire occurrence documented since 1876 at this site. There was some grazing before the Research Area was set aside, then it was fenced and protected from domestic and wild grazing ungulates.

Again, fire regimes were radically interrupted when settlement and livestock grazing patterns

15

changed most all of the Ponderosa Pine forests across Arizona and the west. Unfortunately, we no longer have this plot to compare, as it was thinned about 1995, to prevent outside fire from racing across and destroying the stands of trees in the Research Area.

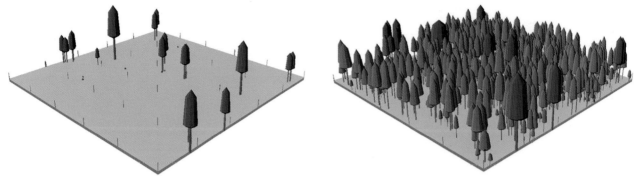

Left: Graphic visualization of plot measurements taken by Theodore Woolsey, Forester at Ft. Valley, Plot S1A. in 1909 shows only 24 trees. Graphic by E.R.I.-N.A.U.
Right: Same plot visualization from measurements taken by E.R.I. in 1997 shows 670 trees. Graphic by E.R.I.-N.A.U.

Also, shown in this E.R.I. graphic visualization, which summarizes research initiated by Forester Theodore Woolsey and is continued today by the Ecological Restoration Institute. It shows another research plot in the Gus Pierson Natural Research Area. Note the change from 24 trees per acre in 1909 to 670 trees in 1997. The exclusion of fire makes a huge statement verified by both these research plot examples (and many others across the west). There are more trees than the land or water resources can support. That is why we are seeing major pine beetle outbreaks, death of trees from disease and drought and of course, great fires.

I have used the analogy of the trees as soda straws and the land as a "punch bowl." There are simply too many straws in the punch bowl and the land is running out of "punch" or moisture. Mother Nature can only stand our best intentioned, mismanagement of stacking fiber,

Too many trees are like too many straws in the punchbowl. Sketch by Duane Swanson.

fuel and unused energy on the stump before she says "Stand back, kids, I am going to clean up this mess... I just cannot stand it anymore!"... as she was about to in the Rodeo-Chediski. She will only allow the exclusion of fire for a short term and then the fires will be radical and destructive.

*   *   *   *   *

I first met Dr. Tom Swetnam on the Black Range Ranger District of the Gila National Forest about 1988. Dr. Swetnam is the Director of the Laboratory for Tree Ring Research at the University of Arizona in Tucson. He is the professor of Dendro-chronology or the study of tree growth rings and fire scars.

We met on that backwoods New Mexico, National Forest district, where I was the new District Ranger, and Dr. Swetnam was doing tree ring and fire scar research. I got a quick education in his tools and methodology and have continued to follow his findings since. He and I have also become good friends. Much of his work echoes that of E.R.I. and Dr. Covington, but from a different perspective… that of examining the recorded "journals" of passing time and fire occurrence in the annual tree rings of literally millions of Ponderosa Pine tree samples.

Basically, Dr. Tom explained that, if a surface fire burns close to and around a tree, it may damage that tree. If it does, it is somewhat analogous to a human receiving a cut or deep burn. The tree has an epidermis (skin) called bark. Ponderosa Pine bark is very resistant to fire. Mature trees (old cinnamon-barked "punkins") have 2" to 5" thick protective bark plates, down low to the ground where most surface fires put heat against the tree. A young pine tree, however, has much thinner bark and is more susceptible to damage from fire.

The protected live, green bark (phloem and cambium) is similar to our venous and arterial, vascular tissues that carry water up and photo-synthetically manufactured sugar down to the roots. When the live bark is invaded by intense heat, it "bleeds" sap and makes a wound. If the burn is deep enough, the wound makes a "cat-face" that will seep and mark the scar with an interior, black notch in that year's annual ring.

Left: Light prescribed fire on the Black Range Ranger District-Gila National Forest in New Mexico. Note the "catface" on the tree burning in the upper right of the photo. Photo by Jim Paxon

Right: Catface shown close up. Photo by Jim Paxon

The tree will continue to grow new wood and bark and attempt to cover over the wound as in a "fire scar." However, when the next fire came along, there would often be exposed wood and very flammable resin residue (or pitch) that would burn again and mark the latest fire in that year's green bark, from which comes the next scar in a subsequent annual ring.

Basically, the tree becomes a journal, from which researchers can cut a horizontal wedge close to the stump, read the annual growth rings and examine where and when fires occurred. Earliest years are in the center and latest years are at the outside of the tree's circumference. Then, researchers can match one sample's annual rings to those of other samples and tell us when the fire burned, how large, how severe it was and what the intervals were between fires in that area. From the width of the annual rings, we can even discern how moist or dry a spring or summer was in the years preceding the fire.

Left: Horizontal wedge cut from a fire scarred or catfaced tree and fire scars dated by Laboratory for Tree Ring Research, University of Arizona. Photo courtesy of Laboratory of Tree Ring Research, U.of A.

Left: Forester showing a fire scar in Northern Arizona. Photo by E.R.I.-N.A.U.

Right: Horizontal wedge showing fire history in detail on a frequently burned site. Note there are no fire scars after 1900 until 1978. Photo by E.R.I.-N.A.U.

Shown above is a cross section from a tree that was taken from Black Mountain Lookout on my old district. There is a consistent pattern that fires burned in Ponderosa Pine forests every four to seven years in New Mexico and Arizona, up until the time of settlement by white men, which is confirmed by this sample. Then, from about 1890, there were few fires that burned regionally and the natural fire cycle was interrupted.

Note that the last fire recorded at this particular tree was 1899... and no others occurred prior to its demise in 1951. That is a change from fires every four to seven years to no fires for 52 years plus and beyond, as the journal was closed in 1951 when this tree died! There are no fires recorded at this site on the south side of Black Mountain prior to 1992, which is 93 years. There has been a staffed lookout at this site since the late 1920's and records of fires detected are consistent. [2.j]

For another perspective, the other two photos show a similar cat-face, showing fire damage and a wedge showing fire scars by year from E.R.I.'s Fort Valley Experiment Station.

*   *   *   *   *

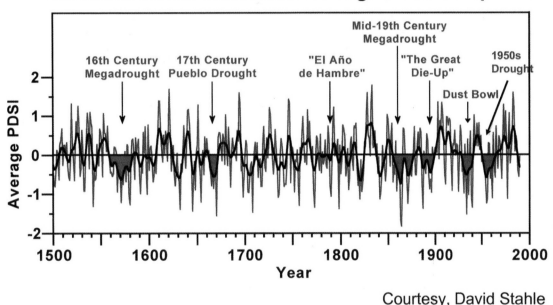

Selected North American Drought Catastrophies

Courtesy, David Stahle

Drought Disasters of the Southwest using Palmer Drought Severity Index by David Stahl. Used by permission of Laboratory for Tree Ring Research, University of Arizona

Dr. Swetnam's Laboratory of Tree Ring Research at University of Arizona also delves into history of precipitation and moisture regimes in these same mountain climes where Ponderosa Pines reside. The chart at left shows drought disasters in North America using the Palmer Drought Severity Index. The PDSI system uses temperature and precipitation over many years to determine how wet or dry a period might be.

The PDSI is measured at a local geographic level and is excellent for examining conditions for a specific area. "0" is normal (again, over long term), so the peaks above the line show dryness and below, wet periods. Anything **0.4 and lower is extreme drought.** Note the 12th year of drought that we are experiencing in the southwest is 0.6 and still rising. [2.k]

The mid-1990s to present drought follows the extraordinary decadal wet period of the mid-1970s to early 1990s.

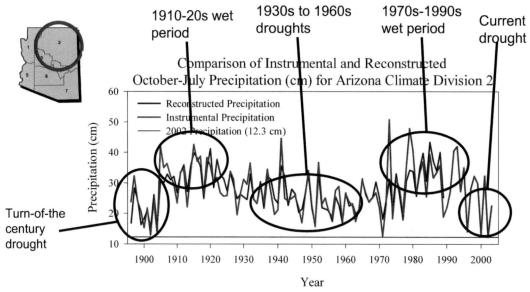

Courtesy of Kurt Kipfmueller, Univ. Arizona Laboratory of Tree-Ring Research. From Ni et al., 2002

Wet and Dry Periods of the 20th Century by Kipfmueller.
Used by permission of Laboratory for Tree Ring Research, University of Arizona

Kipfmueller's chart above shows moisture occurrence by decades in recent history for northeastern Arizona. Note the lows in the most recent years. Lastly, the chart below displays moisture regimes at Lee's Ferry on the Colorado River (note that 1840, 1910 and 1990 are all about the same—the wettest years in recorded history).

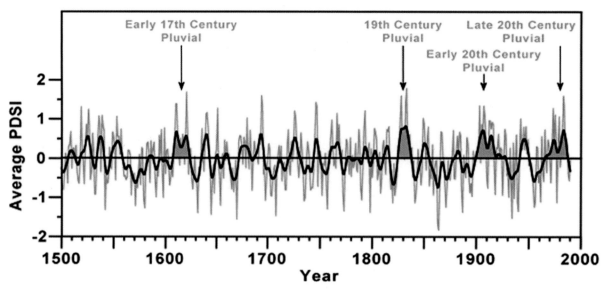

Pluvials (wet periods) at Lee's Ferry on the Colorado River from 1500 to 2000.
Swetnam, Laboratory for Tree Ring Research, University of Arizona.

All of these just indicate that we are in the midst of the most severe drought that has occurred since the cliff dwelling Anasazi and Mogollon societies' demise about 1300 A.D. We are not out of the drought and when we will return to normal (whatever that is) moisture is a crystal-ball guess. Dr. Swetnam really feels that we have a few more years before we begin to see a change in both our summer and winter wet periods.

*   *   *   *   *

Finally, Dr. Stephen J. Pyne is America's Fire Historian. He is Professor of American Studies at Arizona State University and has written thirteen books on fire. He worked his way through college and graduate school as a firefighter at Grand Canyon National Park. As a former supervisor of the 40 person North Rim Longshots, his experience in fighting fire and observing fire behavior repeatedly, up close, gives him credibility.

Dr. Pyne has traveled the world and examined not only fire histories, but also the histories of the people who shaped the land with fire. He refers to "natural fire" as "First Fire" and those by ancient and indigenous peoples as "Second Fire" or "anthropogenic fire." Dr. Pyne, in _Smokechasing_, postulates, "However much researchers (especially Americans) might long for a pristine fire ecology, uncontaminated by humanity… it does not exist in any meaningful form. The geography of fire on Earth looks as it does because modern humans have held fire as a species monopoly since our origins." [2.l]

He has examined many crisis events of large, destructive fires from a historical view and how those events affect current fire and land management. In his book, _The Year of the Fires_, which covers the events circa August 20, 1910, when fires burned approximately three million acres of National Forests in only two days and 85 people died, 78 of them firefighters. Dr. Pyne shares with us that six towns burned, five on the Montana side and Wallace, Idaho.

Existing lightning fires from a 400-mile-long lightning bust in late July were affected by passage of a dry cold front with winds of at least 70 miles per hour. Fires near the St. Joe and the Coeur d'Alene National Forests literally blew up, "grew legs" and ran hard, all the way to Canada. An estimated 8 billion board feet of timber was destroyed. Snags from the fires are still visible at Moon Pass.

Rain and snow followed the dry cold front on August 23rd and stopped the advance of the many headed flame front. [2.m] Those fires put the pall of wood smoke in Chicago, Boston and New York City and deposited ash in Greenland.

In 1911, Congress passed the Weeks Act, which gave the State Foresters authority to spend federal grants on fire prevention. The fledgling Forest Service also began an all out campaign to suppress wildfires. Rangers and Supervisors who survived the Big Burn quickly advanced into positions of authority in the Forest Service. To the man, they swore to never experience the same loss of life or forest.

Aggressive suppression worked at keeping fire activity and damage minimal in the forests of the west for three quarters of a century. Now we are fighting to keep communities safe and forests functioning… and losing the battle. Due to the absence of periodic fire for so long, Mother Nature is wreaking havoc in attempting to restore some balance to the "fuels" situation in our wildlands.

We must understand that to keep fire from functioning naturally, periodically in our forests is to delay the inevitable. After the long-term absence of low intensity fire, the fires that do occur, from whatever ignition source, will be climax, damaging and deadly.

In his analysis of the Rodeo and Chediski Fires, Dr. Pyne compared fire conditions to a recipe for a perfect firestorm—or if you are a poker player… it was a Royal Flush of conditions:

1. June 18th, two days short of "Summer Solstice." The longest day of the year with almost 15 hours of direct sunlight, not counting dawn and dusk… and in the hottest time of year. Fuels, live and dead, were pre heated more than any other day. On south facing slopes, trees would

receive the most direct sunlight and would be "super dried," which enabled hotter and faster burning conditions.

2. Any fire below the Mogollon Rim would be in very steep canyons with flumes, chutes and chimneys, where even light breezes would be accelerated into strong winds. A fire that escaped control in Initial Attack would gain energy and momentum that would make it impossible to catch. The steep slopes would pose great hazards to firefighters with no escape routes and few safety zones available, so crews would have to work further away from the flames in an indirect attack.

3. A century-plus of accumulated fuels was waiting for recycling, but Mother Nature had been denied the ability to burn excesses in slow moving, low intensity fires. Mother Nature could only stand so much energy stored "on the stump," until she had to release that energy by removing debris, reducing competing trees and restoring some balance to the fuels equation. Fire was and is her primary tool.

4. Prevailing winds that would push any fire uphill on pre-dried slopes... winds that on this day would be 25+ miles per hour by mid-morning. Red Flag warnings were posted for several days during the period of the two fires, which cause firefighters the greatest concerns in being able to stop growth and slow the forward progress of fires.

5. The ignitions, first by Leonard Gregg (in his anger) at the Cibeque Rodeo Grounds, and second by Valinda Jo Elliot (in a desperate attempt to attract attention and be rescued) above Chediski Farms, completed the flush and would "win the pot" of Arizona's largest and most destructive wildfire. Dr. Pyne mused that the source of the ignitions was irrelevant and was the only card left to draw the "Royal Flush." It could have happened by another method or source, but the end result was truly inevitable. Mr. Gregg and Ms. Elliot were just the catalyst that set two more multi-headed monsters in motion. [2.n]

There is one more wildcard in this fire-risk card game, which is that of homes and cabins built in the forest. In 1953, when Show Low incorporated, there were less than 2,200 people in the town. The only buildings scattered across the forest, outside of towns, were ranches, Forest Service guard cabins and lookouts. After World War II, people discovered the joys of nature and the charm of the White Mountains.

As Phoenix and the Salt River Valley grew to metropolitan status, so did visits to the forests. Many old homesteads inside the boundaries of the Sitgreaves National Forest have been subdivided and sold off in small parcels. So many of those drawn to the forests and mountains built a cabin in these woods, their dream getaway. When the Rodeo-Chediski Fire burned, Show Low had a population of approximately 8,500 residents.

Today (2006) Show Low has more than 10,500 residents, which is a 20% increase in only 4 years. What a change from the sleepy little town of the '50s! For comparison, Navajo County had 29,446 residents in 1950, 101,615 residents in 2002 and a population of 108,432 in 2005. [2.o]

Many of these newcomers to the White Mountains sought the serenity and solitude of the forest and have bought or built a cabin or home in the White Mountains, not wanting to be in an "organized" community with traffic, street lights and urban stress. Some residents came to the White Mountains from the valley desert to live in "green" and escape 110-plus-degree heat in the summer. Most all of them "loved" their trees. Some even name their trees and care for them with irrigation and fertilizer.

Left: Guaje Peak Trail in Los Alamos, New Mexico before the Cerro Grande Fire of 2000.
Photo by U.S.F.S., Santa Fe National Forest

Right: Same point on Guaje Peak Trail after the Cerro Grande Fire.
Photo by U.S.F.S., Santa Fe National Forest

Few of the new residents understood that the forest that they came to live in was not a natural forest, and one that Mother Nature was working relentlessly to change.

Many of these same newcomers also brought urban ways and urban expectations with them. Some thought logging was "ugly!"... that smoke from prescribed fire was obnoxious... that there should not be any livestock manure fouling public hiking trails... these woods should be preserved as they are.

I have heard some folks say that they did not want to thin their trees, because they did not want to see their neighbor 200 feet away. Others have said that the denser and darker, the better... as this was their refuge from "the City"! So many just did not understand the mountain and what Mother Nature was desperately trying to convey to them. They built wooden structures in areas where natural fire and anthropogenic fire, once common, have been removed for more than 120 years.

When you examine the structure of wooden based buildings, and separate the emotion and sentimentality of ownership, they are simply an additional and extremely flammable fuel source. Structures are just concentrated "fodder" for a hungry, fire-breathing monster, or as many firefighters refer to them—"fuel depots."

Wildfire pays no attention to jurisdictional boundaries, nor for what kind of fuel is available to burn. Mother Nature was and still is bound and determined that fire will be back on the ground in a big way in the White Mountains. This "wildcard" of added fuels of houses and wood-framed structures would play in a big way in the ensuing fire.

Indefensible House due to fuels and trees adjacent. Photo by E.R.I.-N.A.U.

*   *   *   *   *

Ed Collins is the District Ranger of the Lakeside Ranger District on the Apache-Sitgreaves National Forest. His district is headquartered in Pinetop-Lakeside and the district is roughly split in two by U.S. Highway 60. Ed was promoted to District Ranger in 1987, so he had 15 years of on-the-ground experience when the Rodeo-Chediski Fire burned. When interviewed, Ed's face showed sadness and fatigue when I asked him what immediate emotion did the mention of the fire bring up?

He replied with a sigh, "Sadness at all the loss and destruction. Sadness for my neighbors and my two employees who lost homes." And finally, "Sadness, because if the Forest Service had been allowed to manage the forest, the fire would not have been as intense and damaging!"

Ed witnessed some disturbing changes over time that he strongly feels helped set the stage for the Rodeo-Chediski Fire. [2.p] In summary format, they are:

- 1990s was a decade of public protest and lawsuits over management, more of logging and prescribed burning than all other activities.
- 1997, Southwest Forest Industries began conversion of the paper mill at Abitibi to use recycled cardboard, due to the shortage of timber sales and available raw materials within a 150-mile radius of the paper mill.
- 1999, Abitibi Paper Mill ceased using any roundwood (logs) for paper.
- Environmental constraints for the Mexican Spotted Owl Recovery Plan and Northern Goshawk Habitat Guidelines (both extensions of the Threatened and Endangered Species Act of 1973) severely limited actions of thinning and prescribed burning, but these "limits" forced on managers did not take into account the frequent fire regime of southwestern pine forests. They were more tailored for Northern Rockies habitats with much more moisture. (Note: A classic example of forcing constraints on managers, counter to what Mother Nature would have us do.).
- New residents protested the prolonged smoke of prescribed fires, especially since they moved to the mountain to escape valley smog and enjoy clear blue mountain skies.
- When the Lakeside Ranger District executed prescribed burns, public calls to Arizona Department of Environmental Quality often shut burns down.

- 1994-95, residents of Timberland Acres and White Mountain Environmental Coalition appealed the Cold Bath and Fence Tank Timber Sales on the basis of disturbance to soils and degradation of visuals on Juniper Ridge. Both of these sales were intended to cut small diameter trees and reduce fuel loading south of Timberland Acres and Pinedale.
- Local Arizona Game and Fish managers strongly objected to the 1996 Lon's Timber Sale south of Pinedale. It was a multi product sale that included both small diameter trees and occasional large trees over 16" diameter. Again, the objective of the sale was reduction of fuels and forest health thinning.
- Studies of the 1996 Cottonwood Fire revealed that extended drought was negatively affecting burn survival of mature ponderosa pines. Anything over 1/3 crown scorch and 25% root zone scorch was proving fatal to even large pre-settlement pines. Usually, large trees would withstand 2/3 crown-scorch and up to 50% root zone scorch, but that was in times when there was a moisture reserve in the tree and the ground.

* * * * *

In March 1992, the two Southwest Type I Incident Management Teams held their pre-season team meeting in the White Mountains. As part of our meeting, we had a "sand table exercise" or simulation of fire coming into Show Low from the Reservation. The Forest Service, B.I.A. and White Mountain Apache Tribe, as well as all of the local fire and law enforcement agencies and the city governments were involved.

The path of the simulated fire came up Corduroy Canyon, crossed U.S. Highway 60 and roared up Forestdale Canyon into Wagon Wheel. Then the fire fanned out and burned north and east through Show Low and across Porter Mountain. We dealt with evacuations, triage of injured and strategies/tactics where we might stop the fire. Even as a simulation, that was an emotional exercise for us. Fire coming into the communities from the southwest was ominous.

* * * * *

Log landing and loader. Photo by E.R.I.-N.A.U.

Log truck loaded with pine logs, destined for a sawmill. Photo by Doc Smith.

Old Man Mountain has stood since time began. His hair of forest and meadow has covered his head and face for all that time. Through all the ages, since forests have grown on the faces of mountains, Mother Nature has given Old Man Mountain an occasional trim and a shave, with fire as the razor.

After about 1890, the primary grooming and cleansing tool of periodic fire had been changed and/or removed. Mother Nature's only recourse now is a much hotter and more radically changing fire. She must put away the razor of periodic fire and use heavy-duty clippers of climax fire that will remove most of the "beard." That most often means starting over on that site, since a climax fire removes much of the vegetation and soils are changed from heat damage and severe erosion. Neither the Mountain nor Mother Nature agrees with this kind of management philosophy.

The mountain knew… and waited… patiently. Harsh lessons were to come from a stern schoolmaster, Mother Nature. Change was on its way for the White Mountains.

Sketch by Duane Swanson.

CH. 3: FIREFIGHTERS

"For no man has greater love than this… that he lay down his life for his fellow man"
~ Jesus, Gospel of John 15:13

Fire is the decomposition of organic material by rapid oxidation and the release of heat. The fire triangle shows fuel at the base and heat and oxygen as the other two legs or elements. All firefighting involves removing one of the three elements, resulting in combustion no longer able to be sustained (the fire goes out).

Fire Triangle. Diagram by National Interagency Fire Center.

Without over-simplification, Class A fires involve the organic materials found in paper, woodpiles, stick-framed houses, log cabins, forests and woodlands and anything "organic." Most fires are of this type. The other classes involve petroleum distillates and flammable liquids (Class B), electrical fires (Class C) and burning metals (Class D).

There are two principal types or divisions of firefighters, structural and wildland.

*   *   *   *   *

Structural firefighters have been putting out house fires ever since humans have lived in communities. It is amazing to look back in history and realize that even in ancient Rome, there were both paid and slave firefighters in the 1st century. They were the first career firefighters whose "retirement system" was usually realized by succumbing to extreme conditions, while fighting a fire.

Ben Franklin is credited with advancing organized firefighting into paid "fire brigades" which were trained and equipped to fight structural fires in Philadelphia, Pennsylvania. In the 1700's, horses pulled manual pump and hose wagons (primitive engines) to a blaze. Pumps were operated by several men pushing and pulling levers to create a vacuum and draft water. Ponds or water wagons were pumped to supply water to a nozzle on the end of a leather hose and "firemen" extinguished the blaze.

In rural or less developed areas, volunteer bucket brigades passed pails or buckets from the water source to the burning structure in hopes of saving it, or if not, then limiting the spread of fire so that adjacent buildings were saved from damage or destruction. Even though the tools and practices of structural firefighting have evolved with new technology and progress, the elements of structural firefighting have remained basically the same.

For whatever reason, when a fire starts in a house, or building, the fireman's job is to contain the fire to that structure and try to limit the damage. We still use pumped-water to extinguish the fire, although now we mix it with liquid soap and a myriad of chemicals to make foam and extend the wetting properties of just plain ol' water.

We have sophisticated engines and ladder trucks that have both self-contained water tanks and large volume mechanical pumps attached to large diameter hoses connected to municipal water system fire hydrants.

Firefighters wear protective gear and self-contained breathing apparatus (SCBA's or air packs) that enable them to enter burning buildings and attack the fire right at the source of flame. New generation turnouts are the safest ever made, able to protect firefighters from temperatures in excess of 1,000 degrees for short periods. An SCBA contains up to one hour of air and has an alarm to alert the user when air reaches critical volume. In the typical "box fire," the structural firefighter responds to an alarm, attacks the fire and contains it. Then all burning materials are extinguished. Salvage and overhaul operations are completed to minimize damage.

Tools and hoses are backhauled to the station. Fire engines are cleaned, hoses washed, dried and put back on engines. Tools and supplies are restocked, air packs filled and protective "turnouts" are put back into ready condition, and the firemen await the next alarm, while training, exercising and completing job lists at the station.

The "box" that is on fire, usually stays in one place while being attacked by fire and defended by firemen applying water, unless it is falling down. Most urban-suburban "box firefights" are started and finished within one shift. These are everyone's "white hat" professionals whose lives and careers are dedicated to helping people and protecting life and property.

The automatic response of firemen that culminates in searching for people inside a burning box, under rapidly deteriorating situations, sometimes results in the ultimate sacrifice... and firefighters are killed. From those early Roman times to the medieval knights of crusades, who provided the basis for the Maltese Cross as a symbol of firefighters, comes the fireman's creed of protection and service. It remains constant. It is a rare individual indeed who, even though equipped and trained, *willingly* rushes into a burning building when everyone else is running out! Sadly, even with all the advances in technology and training, firefighter deaths have increased annually over the past 30 years. [3.a]

Today in metropolitan Phoenix, we need only look to Alan Brunacini as Chief Emeritus of Phoenix Fire Department. He spent 48 years in that department and 28 of those as Chief. His philosophies of structural firefighter duties and responsibilities are simple:

- Take care of Mrs. Smith! If she is having a "bad day," it is our job to make her day better, whether her problem is her husband having a heart attack, the cat stuck in the tree or her kitchen is ablaze. We are to care for her, treat her with lots of "nice" and use our knowledge, training and tools to accomplish the job at hand in an efficient and timely manner.
- Another axiom that Chief Bruno preaches is "Don't hurt the troops!" Everyone needs to go home at the end of shift, happy and whole. [3.b]

These few simple axioms wrap management and command in a compact package that in practice, is often difficult to deliver. When difficulties arise, Bruno encourages us to take a deep breath and go back to basics.

*   *   *   *   *

Wildland firefighters, in an organized sense, are a relatively new breed. They have been tasked with battling forest fires as new agencies were formed to manage public lands.

Long before organized firefighters, the cavalry fought fires in Yellowstone in the 1880s, while they were still patrolling for Indian warriors off reservations. Later, in May 1900, a survey crew battled a blaze on Mt. Lemmon as documented by Dr. Tom Swetnam. [3.c]

Beginning in 1905, the fledgling Forest Service delegated authority for detecting and stopping wildfires to District Rangers in charge of geographic areas of National Forests called Ranger Districts. Rangers most often enlisted pickup or temporary firefighters from logging camps, railroad crews, ranches or even a local jail's temporary occupants (from too much celebration in a local watering hole). The Forest Service was the only non-military entity to be able to "impress" or draft workers for fires, although that authority has long since passed from the laws.

Tools were primitive, sometimes limited to shovels, hoes and axes used to cut a path or to dig fireline. At times, even tree boughs were cut to swat out flames in light grassy fuels. Snags and larger trees that had to be cut were felled with two-man crosscut saws, known as "misery whips." Men who fought fire were outdoorsmen, used to harsh environments and primitive ways. Those who looked to the skies for both work and a paycheck have become known as "smokechasers" or those who were "chasing the dragon."

Firecamps had cooks and mess tents, usually close to the fire. Sleeping facilities most often were the hard, cold ground and what an individual had to lay on and cover up with. As we do today, the earliest wildland firefighters "lived in the dirt" and pretty much carried their needs for the day with them.

Old Time Firefighter. Photo by National Interagency Fire Center.

Oldtime firefighters, as shown in photo came to the job as they were, in dungarees, wool shirts, slouch hats, and with a knowledge of the woods and living on the land, as documented by Dr. Stephen Pyne in his book, *Year of the Fires*. [3.d] What really makes wildland firefighting so different from structural firefighting is:

- There is no burning box to attack. Rather, the fire moves and is ever changing, as pushed by wind and pulled by fuels and topography.
- Therefore the firefighters must also move. They must carry all their tools and supplies on their backs and use tools as they go, to chase and stop the wildfire.
- Few wildfires, even the small ones, are one-shift fires. Some even burn for months on end, until summer monsoons or fall snows quench them. The wildland firefighter must have a marathon approach to firefighting. Endurance and patience are keys to success.
- Water on a wildland fire is precious. A firefighter carries home on his/her back and works 10-12 hours of arduous labor, hiking steep slopes. The inclination or the ability of carrying water for other than drinking is just not possible, as firefighters consume about one quart per hour of work

on a fireline. Even wildland fire engines carry only 200 to 500 gallons of water that is used sparingly. Refills are either from nurse tankers or stock ponds and lakes that may be an hour or more from the fire.

- Wildland firefighters will not (or should never) enter burning buildings, unless as a last resort when there are lives at risk. Nomex fire clothes and equipment that we wear/carry are meant to work close to low intensity flames of no more than four feet high and not on fires that are "up and running!" The heavy, protective turnouts and air-packs that structural firefighters wear are not meant for moving over mountains and through forests, and the air-pack's air supply is limited to an hour or less. If a wildfire threatens cabins and other buildings, structural firefighters are called in to assist and protect those improvements. Even then, most structural battles with wildland fire are defensive, since the wildfires come against the building from the outside.

Another good friend, Chief Roger Mineer of Lakeside Fire Department, up here in the White Mountains, spent 27 years with Casa Grande, Arizona Fire Department, retired and moved to Lakeside in 1982. Shortly after moving here, he became the Chief of the Lakeside Fire Department and a community in the middle, with Show Low to the north and Pinetop to the south.

Roger has been on huge "box fires" in warehouses, apartment complexes and discount stores, oil and gasoline storage facilities, hazardous materials spills, colossal vehicle and train wrecks… to say he is experienced is an understatement. Since becoming Chief of Lakeside Fire, he has also been on a several wildland assignments, but they were small and mirrored his fire service experience.

The primary fireground strategy amounted to "hit 'em hard, keep 'em small, put 'em out and return to station!" Only a few of the larger incidents lasted more than a couple of hours, on scene. Roger also embodies the command philosophy of take charge, make decisions, and **if** you need more firefighters and equipment, sound another alarm. Hook up to hydrants and drown the fire.

Wildland fire, especially the Rodeo-Chediski (R-C) Fire, has left him in awe and given him pause for reflection. He was so used to attacking fire, all out. Being forced to wait on the fire to burn to a point that it could be engaged, and then playing by the conditions and fire intensity that Mother Nature dictated, was a totally different approach. His entire department felt helpless, reduced to standing and watching, without any mitigating actions that they could implement.

Before the R-C, Roger had never paid much attention to fuel moisture, relative humidity, high temperature, forecast winds, etc., because a structural fire is about "drowning" the fire in the box and then cleaning up. But he does now, because those elements affect not only how the fire will burn, but also how the firefighters will be able to attack it. He also understands that the structural strategy of "if the fire gets bigger, just call more engine companies and hook up another hydrant to deliver more water" does not apply to wildland firefighting. Strategy and tactics and being at the right place at the right time are keys to wildland firefighting success… that and command patience. Today's young I.C.'s think strategy and tactics. Old I.C.'s think logistics and timing. [3.e]

*   *   *   *   *

Today's wildland firefighter is a modern marvel of technology and training. Dr. Stephen Pyne compares them to extreme sports athletes. [3.f] Many career firefighters pursue extreme sports in their off time. They are mostly outdoors and adventure oriented, physically fit, dedicated and always ready for a challenge.

Figure 3.3[3.g] shows a firefighter with the basic equipment required of the job. The Nomex clothing is light, however, the aramid fibers protect flesh and skin from radiant heat, allowing firefighters to work immediately adjacent to creeping flames less than four feet high. Fire pants are usually green and built with utility pockets on the legs like military "BDU's." Shirts are high visibility yellow and have Velcro closures on the sleeves and collar, that when closed, help keep out heat and ash.

Battle gear for the wildland firefight

Firefighter
Nina Walker, BLM

Smokejumper
Scott Hunnicutt, BLM

Helmet: motorcycle type with metal screen for face protection

Hard hat

Fusees: flares for igniting backfires

Main parachute: 375-square-foot "ram-air" chute

Rip cord: drogue release handle pulls out main chute

Fire shirt: flame-resistant Nomex material

Parachute harness

Portable radio/harness

Jumpsuit: heavily padded, fireproof Kevlar; for all-terrain jumping

Reserve handle: deploys reserve chute

Reserve parachute

7-26-93 CRAMER
B-011R

Pulaski: basic fire-fighting tool has ax/hoe combination

Flight gloves: fireproof gloves for use in aircraft and during jump

Leather work gloves

Fire shelter: basically a foil tent

Flame-resistant pants: Nomex material

PG bag: personal gear bag carries food, water, fire shelter, safety goggles, other supplies; converts to backpack for fire-line work

Leg pockets: contains 150 feet of rope for rappelling in case of tree landing

Jump boots: logger type for fire-line work

GARY MOSS

JULY 1993

Modern Firefighter. Photo by Sunset Magazine, July 1993. Used with permission.

31

Nomex material will not sustain flame. Fire can cause shirts and pants to smolder and eventually ignite, but as soon as the source of flame is removed, the fire will snuff. Gloves, goggles, hardhats and head shrouds all provide additional protection from the rigors of digging fireline close to flames.

Footwear is the foundation of today's firefighters. Heavy, lug-soled leather boots that lace up and are at least 8" high are mandated by safety regulation. "Whites Boots" have been the firefighters' standard for a century. There are now many cloned derivatives of which several are excellent footwear. Good boots will withstand the hard use of mountain work and the severe environment of fires. A new pair of firefighting boots often costs more than $300. Breaking in a pair of new boots is best accomplished by filling each boot with hot water while on your feet, lacing them tight, and walking them dry. Then you oil them, once they have entirely dried, and they are ready for action.

Hopefully, break-in does not have to occur on a fire. Moleskin and bandaids are in every firefighter's pack to take care of blisters and sores on one's feet. Sore feet can put a firefighter out of commission and even make them a liability to the rest of the crew.

The typical wildland firefighter also is burdened with a daypack that includes at least two meals, six to eight quarts of water, first aid kit, poncho or light jacket, parachute cord, fusees (road flares specifically for burning out line), the ever-present fire shelter (pup tent looking shelter of layered aluminum, fiberglass and silica cloth, designed to protect the firefighter when conditions become too intense to escape and survival would not be possible without the shelter), two way radio in a chest pack along with cell phone, handheld GPS, signaling mirror and either a belt weather kit or pocket electrical weather instrument.

When in an initial attack situation, firefighters will often work for 24 hours straight, with no more than a few rest breaks and time for a quick snack or meal. In extended attack situations, firefighters are limited to 16 hours on shift, so they may get much-needed rest and recuperation to continue on for however many days are necessary to stop a wildfire's spread and limit the destruction it might cause.

Wildland fires move through the woodlands and forests… so then must also the firefighters. That is why all the gear and supplies for the shift are carried on the individual's back. Also, wildland firefighters must be "marathon oriented," since even small fires must be chased until stopped and worked until quelled/quenched. Large fires have been known to burn for weeks or even months.

Endurance is a key ingredient of the wildland firefighter's makeup and one reason that women firefighters have done well. For example, the Rodeo-Chediski Fire started on June 18th and 20th. It was not contained until July 7th and was not controlled until September 7th. Firefighters were present and working during the entire time that smoke was seen on the fire.

Southwestern Firefighters face amazing variation in temperatures on a fire. Daytime temperatures may be close to 100 degrees and yet near freezing at night. Working next to flames elevates the temperature even more. Extreme perspiration can also cause heat exhaustion, even if the temperatures are cool. Frontline firefighters must be in shape and able to handle these wide variations in temperature.

Night is a firefighter's friend. It is a joke among smokechasers that their "best work is done in the dark." With the aid of headlights and light from the fire, firefighters can work closer to the fire at night, due to cooler temperatures, higher humidity and no sun pre-heating the fuel. The toughest part of working night shifts is trying to get rest and sleep in camps where the daytime activity is compounded with airplane and helicopter traffic. Finding shade to stay out of the hot summer sun is also a challenge and requires good planning, including the strategic placement of overhead tarps. Enclosed tents don't work well due to the stifling heat and lack of air movement.

*   *   *   *   *

There many types and flavors of firefighter jobs in wildland firefighting. The following describes the most important distinctions:

- Engine crews consist of three firefighters on Type 6 Engines, which are basically one ton 4x4 pickups with 200 gallon water tanks, 300-400 gallon per minute pumps, one or two hardline hose reels, and assorted cotton/rubber hoses and fittings. Many Type 6 Engines are being built with Compressed Air Foam Systems (CAFS) added to the pump/tank combination, that stretch the water four to five times what plain water alone will cover. The engine crew can lay hose to a specific area so that water can be pumped to attack flames, or use their hardline reel if the engine is close to the fire.

Type 6 Wildland Fire Engine.
Photo by B.I.A.-Ft. Apache Fire.

- Type 3 Engines are all wheel drive, but bigger and more like structural engines with bigger tanks (500 gallon), bigger pumps (700 gpm) and usually a crew of five.

- Helitack crews work on the ground setting up landing zones, coordinating troop transport to and from a fire and doing initial attack. Initial Attack by helitack crews is also standard procedure on small fires. Some helitack crews are "rappel" certified and can drop from a hovering helicopter down a rope to cut and prepare a helispot (or landing zone) or perform initial attack on a fire in areas that are too thick to land reasonably near the fire.

- Smokejumpers are considered by many to be the elite or "Green Berets" of firefighting. Some non-smokejumpers will tease a smokejumper about being a "lawn dart," but it is all in good fun. Firefighters often have something of a self-deprecating and macabre sense of humor. Each specialty has its own

Type 3 Wildland Fire Engine.
Photo by Phoenix Fire Dept.

name, such as engine slugs, no-shots, grunts, dirt-diggers, etc. Shown in photo on page 31 is the additional equipment required to get a smokejumper out of the plane and down to the fire. Once they hit the ground, they become much like any other firefighter with the similar equipment. However, they are responsible for their jump gear, and if they are not picked up, they will have to hike out with as much as 100 lbs on their backs.

- Handcrews are 20-person crews and are either Type II (casual or regular agency crews) or Type I (Hotshot crews). Each is detailed below.

*   *   *   *   *

Southwestern Forest Firefighters (SWFFF crews) have a long and proud history. These special crews are made up of trained and equipped individuals working through a sponsoring agency such as Fort Apache. They are also known as "Type II Crews." Twenty individuals from a Native American nation or local rural area answer the call through dispatch when a fire emergency occurs and hand crews have been ordered. Each crew has a crew boss and three squad bosses. The crew boss and squad bosses have more experience and additional training, which is why they are the supervisors of the other 16 firefighters on the crew.

All crewmembers must have successfully completed basic 40-hour fire training and then pass physical fitness tests and standards. Each crew member is equipped with P.P.E. (personal protective equipment) – fire pants and shirts, hard hats, gloves, goggles, fire shelters, etc. – and their line packs carry water (4-6 quarts), lunches, jackets, first aid kits, parachute cord, headlights and flashlights, and anything else that they might need during their shift on the fireline.

This 30-40 pound pack, including the day's food and water, stays on their back for the duration of their work on the fireline. Each firefighter must also have a personal "red bag" or duffle type bag that they must then pack with clothes, toiletries and personal items for a two-week stay out on one or more fires. Both line pack and personal gear bag together must not exceed 65 pounds and must enable each firefighter to exist for a minimum of two weeks.

One of the marks of a professional wildland firefighter is that he/she is prepared to "live in the dirt" without complaint, near the fire and often in the smoke, 24/7 for the two weeks of any assignment.

These termed "casual hire" firefighters are often farmers, ranchers, loggers, carpenters, housewives and independent small business people who are able to drop everything and answer the call when a fire poses a threat to communities and/or resources. Many of these men and women make a substantial part of their living as a "call when needed" or "casual hire" firefighter. Once the fire emergency they are working on is over, their crew will either be transported to the next fire or returned home to continue their normal lives and await their next fire callout.

As mentioned earlier, SWFFF crews or Southwestern Forest Firefighters have a long and valiant history that began in 1948. The first organized Native American crew that worked on fires off their home nation's lands came from the Mescalero Apache Tribe.

The Mescalero Reservation, located in the pine-covered Sacramento Mountains of South-Central New Mexico and is bounded on the north and south by the Lincoln National Forest. These Native American firefighters were known as the Mescalero Redhats, for their red painted hardhats, most adorned with Apache symbols of tradition and protection. The Redhats had a well-earned reputation as tough, experienced firefighters with legendary endurance and the ability to work steep ground in heavy fuels. All of our Southwestern Indian nation crews carry that same proud tradition and are well known for their endurance and excellent fire fighting skills.

Today, crews are dispatched to fire assignments from rural communities and Indian nations all across the United States. During emergencies and drought periods there may be hundreds of 20-person crews made up of these "emergency hired" firefighters working on small and large fires (as well as other emergencies) all across the nation. When the emergency is over and the fire controlled, these crews return home and resume their normal lives.

Recently, policy was changed so that the "casual hire" crews could continue to work on a fire after it had been declared "contained." There is always "crew work" in rehabilitation and recovery efforts. SWFFF crews are ideal for this work due to their skill, work ethic, patience and endurance.

*   *   *   *   *

Interagency Hotshot Crews, also known as Type I Crews, or just "hotshots" to the media, are the "special forces" of the firefighting community. Each crew is a multi-skilled and experienced unit of elite firefighters. Like other hand crews, Hotshots are a 20-person crew. Unlike other crews, they are self-contained and extremely mobile. Most crews have two large all-wheel-drive crew carriers, called "Crummies" and a utility type 4x4 pickup that the Superintendent drives.

Hot Shot Crew Buggies or Crummies.
Photo by Dewayne Saxton.

Each Crummy carries tools, food, water, chainsaws, personal packs and gear for ten crewmembers. The crew is expected to respond immediately to a fire dispatch and be self-sustained for 48 hours on the fireline. These men and women are trained, disciplined and experienced. They work together for up to ten months a year and are the first to be called to a raging wildland fire. Teamwork and performance are the trademarks of a Hotshot crew.

Ft. Apache Hotshots. Photo by B.I.A.-Ft. Apache Fire.

There are now 93 Hotshot crews nationwide. They come from every federal land management agency with fire responsibility (66 crews are Forest Service, 12 are from the Bureau of Land Management, nine are from the Bureau of Indian Affairs, two are from the National Park Service and three are State crews, and only one, Granite Mountain from Prescott, Arizona is a Municipal Hotshot Crew). When not working on fires, these crews are in training and maintain a rigorous physical fitness regimen.

Hotshots are also tasked with special projects and assist with prescribed burns that require technical firing and line holding actions. A Hotshot crew is expected to build 50% more fireline per hour than a Type II crew, under the same conditions. Most often, when operations require burnouts to secure firelines, Hotshot crews conduct the firing operations and assist in holding the line to prevent slopovers, fire that crosses the wrong side of the line and/or escapes and spreads uncontrollably.

When fireline construction is on steep ground and in dangerous conditions, Hotshots are called upon to build line in a safe and efficient manner. More than 20 Hotshot crews worked on the Rodeo-Chediski Fire.

Cartoon from Arizona Daily Star, June 7, 2002.

35

*   *   *   *   *

Fire shelters are a wildland firefighter's "safety blanket" and means to escape heat and flames that get too close, too intense, too fast. Generally, when a shelter has to be deployed, the situation is dire and some primary indicators of change in fire behavior have been overlooked or the warning system of communications has broken down. Modern shelters have been in use since about 1970, but they were not the first fire shelter.

On October 29, 1805, a prairie fire ran "with great fury" and overtook a camp of Indians, killing two, while injuring several others. An ingenious mother took advantage of a green buffalo hide and placed her son on the ground, covering him with the green hide. After the flame front had passed, the boy was retrieved unscathed, protected by the fresh hide that kept the grass from burning where it covered the infant. [3.h] The first documented fire shelter!

Fire shelters have been mandatory for being on the fireline since 1977 and have been responsible for saving more than 1,000 firefighter's lives. Deploying a fire shelter is the last option, and used only when all other options have been exhausted. [3.i] Today's fire shelter is a combination of layered aluminum, fiberglass and a silica cloth. Second generation fire shelters were pointed on top and long on two sides with closed ends and flaps that fold underneath to lie on and hold the shelter down in turbulent winds. It looked like a shiny one-person pup tent with closed ends. The newest shelters are more like an expanded mummy bag than a tent. They are rounded on all sides, much easier to enter and to hold down in turbulent winds experienced in a blowup situation. The new shelters are twice as thick as the second generation shelters. They are better able to reduce the heat inside to approximately 20% of what the heat outside would be.

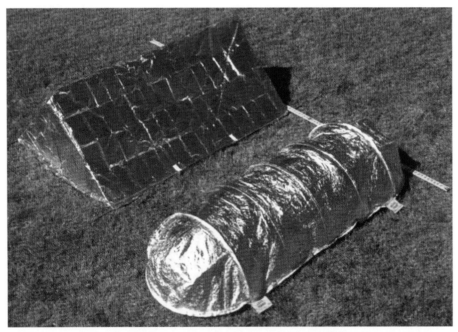

Comparison of old and new fire shelters.
Photo by U.S.F.S. Missoula Equipment and Development Center.

Many enjoy dry saunas of 150 to 180 degrees, but anything hotter gets rather uncomfortable. Sustained temperatures of over 200 degrees Fahrenheit are unbearable and will damage mouth, throat and lung tissues, and can cause first and second-degree skin burns. Therefore, firefighters must find a place that is clear of ground fuels and as far away from trees and larger dead fuels as possible, so the duration of the fire visit affecting the shelter is shortest and least intense possible.

Outside temperatures over 1,000 to 1,200 degrees become fatal in short order. Such was the case on the Dude Fire near Payson in June of 1990. Members of the Perryville Prison Crew and their crew boss, David LaTour, were caught in Walkmore Canyon, north of Payson, when the fire blew up. Six members

36

of the crew deployed shelters in a very narrow part of the canyon with trees all around… and perished. Five other crewmen and LaTour deployed a short ways down canyon in an area that was more open and fuels were much less dense… and survived. Just a few feet made the difference in survival. [3.j]

*   *   *   *   *

Firefighting is dangerous business, whether it is structural or wildland. Since 1910, when records of organized wildland firefighting began, a total of 952 firefighters have lost their lives, the latest being the five members of Engine 57 on the Esperanza Fire in California, in October, 2006. Almost one-half of those deaths are attributed to "burnovers," when a fast moving fire overtakes the firefighters who cannot escape.

The age of "mega fires" mandates that fire teams and land managers look closely at firefighter safety, as well as the safety of the public. A disturbing trend shows that 312 deaths on wildland fire duty have occurred since 1990 for a sickening average of 20 deaths per year. The 60 years previous to 1990, deaths by fire averaged slightly more than 9 per year, still unacceptable.

1994 stands out as our worst year since 1910 for firefighter fatalities, when 38 men and women died, including the 14 who perished in burnovers on the South Canyon Fire in Colorado. [3.k] The trend toward mega fires that move so very fast and burn so hot have altered the decision making processes for land managers and for incident commanders. All firefighters, operations overhead and incident commanders are as dedicated to protecting life and property. We simply will not knowingly put firefighters in harm's way. Let it be said and understood, once again, *there are no trees, acres nor houses worth a single firefighter's life.* Below is the "Code of Conduct for Fire Suppression" that came from intense evaluation of firefighters' mindsets after South Canyon. It was implemented in 1995 by then Chief of the Forest Service, Jack Ward Thomas.

CODE OF CONDUCT FOR FIRE SUPPRESSION

- *Firefighter safety comes first on every fire, every time!*
- *The 10 Standard Fire Orders are firm! We don't break them! We don't bend them!*
- *Every firefighter has the right to know that his/her assignments are safe!*
- *Every fireline supervisor, every fire manager and every administrator has the responsibility to confirm that safe practices are known and observed.*

---

*   *   *   *   *

Firefighting is based on teamwork, skills, trust in and care for your crew, and good leadership based on the right kind of experience. Fires at the local level are fun and rewarding. "Smokechasing" is where most firefighters gain experience and get their foot in the door to a wonderful career. Young people out of high school and/or going to college can apply to be on a fire crew as a seasonal worker for one of the federal land management agencies or a state fire organization.

Many are on engine crews or suppression squads. Some may work on helitack crews that work directly with a specific contract helicopter, and others are on Hotshot crews.

After basic training in fire behavior, fire fighting, safety, chainsaw operations, driving and such, rookies are yoked to more experienced, seasoned veterans. Smoke reports from lookouts, air patrols (or sometimes the public) send resources to the location of a fire, through a dispatch system.

Arizona has the highest incidence of lightning caused fires in the U.S. [3.l] Lightning storms may or may not come with moisture. Sometimes, the fire is a lone snag (standing dead tree) or just low intensity fire creeping in the duff (pine needles and dried grass). The snag must be cut down and the fire put out. If the fire is creeping, line must be dug around it to contain or stop the spread of the fire. Then all the burning materials inside the line must be put out.

Most of these are short duration fires of one to several days, depending on the final size and how many firefighters work on it. The fire crewmembers, working on the fireline, tend to feed off each other, building teamwork and teaching the rookies the ropes.

One of the most enjoyable aspects of firefighting comes from "hotlining" a fire that is trying to get away. A crew boss will lead the way with a chainsaw operator to clear trees and brush in the direction the fire is burning. Then five to six Pulaskis (a combination tool that's part axe and part trenching mattock, built by Ed Pulaski, Ranger on the Big Burn in Wallace, Idaho in 1910), will cut and grub a "scratch line." Another five or six each of fire shovels and Mcleods (another combination tool with a 12" wide hoe on side and a rake on the other) will clean the line down to mineral soil.

Once the head of the fire is "hooked" and it is no longer growing, the crew will go back on both flanks and complete a scratch line all the way around the perimeter of the fire. When finished, the fireline looks like a freshly cut hiking trail, only it just goes around the fire. Hotlining requires rapid progress and the "bump up method" is used. Instead of individuals attempting to dig and complete sections of line by themselves, all but the sawyer with the chainsaw will "hit a lick and take a step!" If the crew is more than ten individuals, work goes quickly.

Diagram: Parts of a Wildfire by National Interagency Fire Center.

In the event that you catch up to the person in front of you, just call out "Bump!" and they will take two or three steps forward, without "hitting a lick" and pass the "bump" up the line to the lead digger. That way there is room for you to swing your tool safely and the crew is able to move on up the line faster.

The rear of the line dictates how fast the crew moves and every person shares in the labor. The result is a 24" to 48" wide fireline or trail that is void of all burnable material. Even surface roots are cut to keep fire from creeping across the line. Often times, no rest breaks will be taken until the head of the fire is "hooked" or cut off and the fire is slowed down and no longer growing at the front. Then the crew will complete the line around the flanks and to the heel or starting point of the fire, always to the satisfaction of the "Super!"

More than 99% of all wildfires are caught in this kind of direct, local, initial attack. In 2002, there were 88,415 fires nationwide, of which only 615 fires escaped initial attack and became large fires (more than 100 acres).

Sawyer sharpening the chain on his saw. Photo by Ken Palmrose.

That is a tribute to all the ground-pounding, dirt-digging firefighters' dedication and super-human efforts.

Slightly less than 100 large fires grew "huge" and that number was responsible for 6.9 million acres burned and almost $1 billion spent in suppression. Colorado, Oregon and Arizona all three, recorded their largest fires in more than a century. One million acres burned between the Florence-Biscuit Fire in Oregon and the Rodeo-Chediski Fire in Arizona. That is one-seventh of the acreage burned in 2002, on just two fires. [3.m]

Firefighters mopping up a log deck. Photo by U.S.F.S., Apache-Sitgreaves National Forest.

Firefighters came from near and far to help out, and stayed until the job was done. Photo by Phoenix Fire Department.

CH. 4: INCIDENT COMMAND – THE SYSTEM

"It generally takes about twenty years to get twenty years experience."
Doc Smith, Type I Incident Commander & Forester (Ret.)

Several events in the 1960s and 70s led to significant changes in the way we fight fires. In November 1966, the El Cariso Hotshots were building fireline in a steep, brushy canyon on the Loop Fire in the Angeles National Forest, when fire raced 2200 feet uphill in less than one minute, with temperatures approaching 2500 degrees. Fire caught the crew in dense brush. They had very little warning and no chance to get away. Fire shelters were not in use, at that time.

Ten members of the crew perished on the Loop Fire that day. Two other members succumbed to burn injuries in the following days. *Most* of the nineteen members who survived were critically burned and remained hospitalized for some time. A total of 12 El Cariso Hotshots lost their lives in a single tragic event.

The Loop Fire only burned 2,870 acres, but the loss of life serves as a reminder that fire fighting is a hazardous profession and that Mother Nature is most unforgiving in the way fire can burn through any particular piece of ground. She does not recognize political boundaries nor will she make accommodations for anything or anybody on the ground, be it home, person, or animal. Fires will simply burn as fast and furious as conditions allow.

Also, in 1966, the Forest Service and Bureau of Land Management Fire Centers in Boise were consolidated into the Boise Interagency Fire Center. The National Weather Service co-located there and assisted fire managers by providing immediate fire weather forecasting for the Great Basin and Intermountain areas. In the early 1970s, the National Park Service, the Bureau of Indian Affairs and the U.S. Fish and Wildlife Service joined the center. The name was changed to the National Interagency Fire Center. State Foresters nationwide became involved and placed representatives at the center.

In September 1970, the Laguna Fire burned in San Diego County, in much the same path as the 2003 Cedar Fire. Eight firefighters died. In the fall of 1970, during a 13-day period, 16 lives were lost to fire and more than 700 structures burned in a series of fires that consumed a total of 1.5 million acres, all in California. Federal, state and local fire agencies cooperated as best they could, but differences were great and problems proved insurmountable in dealing with fast moving, multiple fires. There was no common command system. Structural firefighters, the State of California, the B.L.M and the Forest Service all had distinctly different fire terms and tactics.

Firefighters from different agencies were on the same fire and could not talk to each other on their agency radios. There were disagreements and discussions on the wildfire scene as to who was in charge and how fires would be fought, especially when jurisdictional boundaries were crossed. When the Santa Ana winds stilled and fall rains quenched the fires, an interagency group of leaders formed FIRESCOPE, which stands for "Firefighting Resources in California Organized for Potential Emergencies." It included all the agencies with responsibility for fire prevention and fire suppression in Southern California.

In 1971, Congress funded FIRESCOPE's efforts with Forest Service and B.L.M. participation to devise a system to "coordinate interagency action and allocate suppression resources in dynamic, multiple fire situations." [4.a]

In 1973, the members of FIRESCOPE tested two new approaches to fire fighting coordination by multiple agencies:

1. The Incident Command System (ICS) changed from the old "Large Fire Organization," which had been in use by the Forest Service since 1911. ICS works on a span of control that increases resources and overhead as the fire escalates. It requires standardized positions that mandate uniform training and experience for all of the positions from basic firefighter to the Incident Commander (old Fire Boss). It established a system of enumerating and identifying equipment,

crews, aircraft, engines and dozers by type and capability, with Type I being the biggest, most experienced and highest level. Finally, ICS established uniform terminology that is applied to fire suppression, nationwide. All positions require minimum training, experience and certification. The higher the position, the more training and experience required. An individual certified in a certain position would be qualified in that position, whether he/she were dispatched to California, Arizona, Alaska, Florida, etc.

2. The Multi-Agency Coordination System (MACS) was designed and formed to ensure all agencies in California would be represented at the State level in planning and coordination. When a fire burned across several jurisdictions, there would be a system to keep command fluid and continuous and eliminate "turf wars" over who was in charge.

Some of the spin-offs of FIRESCOPE included routine interaction and meetings between the various fire agencies to plan for catastrophic fires as well as multiple fire situations. Communication systems began to incorporate mutual aid radio frequencies so that on-the-ground forces from numerous agencies could communicate with each other. Fire teams that had been unique to each agency and extremely duplicative, began to merge and work together in geographic areas. Local cooperation and familiarity provided better and faster response to emergency situations, which in turn provided much enhanced protection to wildlands, communities and the public.

In 1974, The National Wildfire Coordinating Group (NWCG) was chartered to coordinate fire management programs for all the Federal and state agencies. NWCG's primary role was to develop nationally common standards, practices and training. Interagency coordination was required and all land management and fire agencies, including State Foresters, were included.

In 1977, the new ICS was tested on the 117,700-acre Marble Cone Fire between Santa Barbara and Monterey. The fire burned most of the Ventana Wilderness. Not only was ICS used, but also multiple fire teams working on the same fire with an umbrella or oversight system, known as "Area Command" were tested. The focus was orderly, timely coordination between the four Type I Teams and allocation of scarce resources, like hotshot crews, and air resources, such as air tankers and helicopters. The ICS worked as hoped and even better than expected. Refinements and minor changes have continued to be implemented over the years.

By 1982, the ICS was in use nationwide. All of the FIRESCOPE documentation was transferred to the National Interagency Fire Center in Boise, Idaho, where the National Wildfire Coordinating Group (NWCG) continues to revise and refine standards in terminology, training and organization. Now, we know FIRESCOPE as NIIMS, the National Interagency Incident Management System. Additionally, ICS has evolved to an "all risk" management system that provides efficient and coordinated management of a wide range of hazardous and emergency situations, such as floods, earthquakes, hurricanes, chemical spills, and aircraft crashes.

ICS and Type I Incident Management Teams were used during Hurricane Andrew in 1992 in both Florida and Louisiana. Four Type I Incident Management Teams went to New York and the Pentagon after 9/11. Hurricanes Katrina and Rita, both in 2005, utilized Type I and Type II teams for logistics and handling of supplies from various caches and supply depots. ICS and Incident Management Teams were even used during the debris and personnel recovery efforts after the Columbia Space Shuttle disaster in February 2003 in East Texas and Louisiana.

ICS has been well tested and deemed "all incident, all hazard," although the primary use continues to be fire suppression. In today's world, the Department of Homeland Security has adopted ICS as the standardized incident organizational structure for the management of all incidents. Simply stated, DHS sees this as one of the most important 'best practices' that has been incorporated into the National Incident Management System (NIMS). The Incident Command System (ICS), is recognized as **the** standard, on-scene, all-hazards incident management system already in use by firefighters, hazardous materials teams, rescuers and emergency medical teams.

*   *   *   *   *

The Incident Command System is a modern marvel in that it is easy to learn and it works. For the purpose of wildfire discussion, it begins with the Initial Attack of a wildfire. Whether the initial attack resources are ground (engines, crews or bulldozers), or airborne (smoke jumpers, helitack, air attack, lead planes or air tankers), the first resources that arrive on the scene (usually on the ground) determine who's in charge. The leader of that group becomes the Initial Attack Incident Commander.

One qualified individual is referred to by the fire's name and "I.C." (for example: Rodeo I.C.). He or she would be "carded" or certified as a Type V or Type IV Incident Commander. If the fire escapes Initial Attack, it changes into Extended Attack. As additional resources arrive and the complexity of the fire increases, a qualified Type III I.C. would be assigned and the organization would grow as needed to include Operations, Safety, Plans, Logistics, Finance and possibly Information.

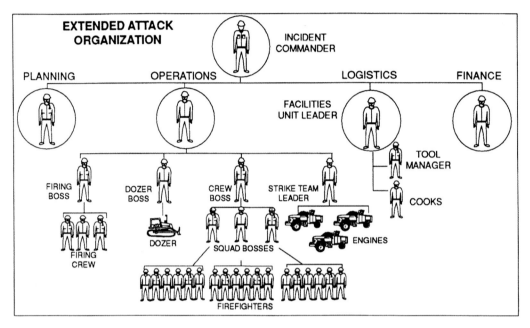

Extended Attack Organization from the Fireline Handbook by National Interagency Fire Center.

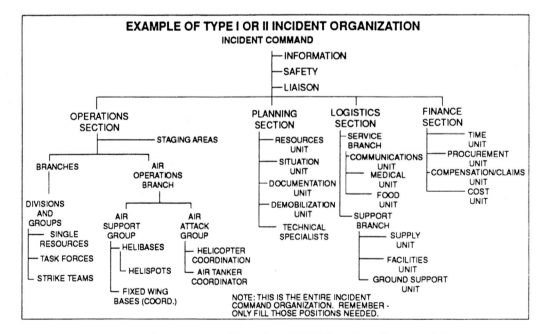

Type I Team Organization Chart from I-200 Incident Command Course
by National Wildfire Coordinating Group.

When Extended Attack is unable to "catch" the fire and/or the complexity increases to include more risk and a greater possibility of property damage or serious injury, a Type II Team might be brought in. That is usually a local or area team of qualified individuals from a rapid response area (usually within the state). The team receives a ***delegation of authority*** from the land management agency administrator(s), with jurisdictional responsibility over the lands where the fire is burning. ***The delegation actually gives the team the authority to manage and suspends the agency's authority for the actions on that incident.*** In that authorization, objectives are included for the management of the fire, such as:

1. "Protect Life and Safety of the public and of firefighters.
2. Protect homes and developed areas.
3. Minimize damage to an area that might include endangered wildlife or plant species.
4. Keep retardant out of streams, so that fish-kill will not occur.
5. Keep fire away from the proximity of communities or electronic sites, etc.
6. Others that apply to the unique situation of where and how the fire is burning and special management considerations, such as
7. Examine cost-effective, as well as environmentally friendly, suppression tactics and strategies

The Type II team formulates strategies and tactics to meet the objectives and stop the growth of the fire at the minimum size, damage and cost possible. They order resources as needed to accomplish the task at hand. All of the individuals on a Type II team must be trained, experienced and qualified at the Type II level for the position they occupy. Trainees must also serve at least two assignments as a trainee or apprentice. For each position, there is a task book that must be successfully completed and kept in records for future reference, along with annual experience to keep one's qualifications current.

Much the same is true for Type I Teams, except they must receive additional training in their area of expertise and as a team. Type I Teams are more experienced in critical incidents, such as complex and potentially catastrophic fires and fire threats to communities and infrastructure.

There are only 16 Type I Teams in the nation and each team takes its turn on a national two-week rotation to respond anywhere in the nation for any kind of incident assignment. **When a Type I Team is called, the situation is already a disaster.** There is no way that any team can undo the disaster, but they are adept at working to make the disaster the least damaging and least harmful that it can be through aggressive action.

Information Officer Jim Paxon at a media briefing in Show Low on the Rodeo-Chediski Fire.
Photo by USFS, Apache-Sitgreaves National Forest.

Besides the span of control, Type I teams are expert at logistics and coordination. A Type I Team can set up an instant city of approximately 1,500 firefighters and support staff in less than 36 hours. That includes catering to feed and supply firefighters, showers, portable toilets and laundry facilities for sanitation, fuel, oil and mechanical support, command and plans office facilities, reproduction and mapping services, even security and law enforcement. Logistics allows the Operations and Air Operations Chiefs to devote maximum efforts to suppressing the fire.

Information is the ICS position that I have worked in since 1989. There are four areas of responsibility for Information Officers on a Type I Team:

- Information is part of the Command and General Staff and works directly with the Incident Commander and the liaison officers from the agencies to formulate strategies and tactics for managing information on the fire and assist in building shift plans for each morning and evening shift on the fireline.

- Information handles all news releases, briefings and the coordination with news media. Trips for media to the fireline are coordinated by Information to **secure** approval from Operations and Safety.
- News and coordination with communities, evacuation centers, and the public at large, are also the responsibility of the Information function. Community meetings are utilized to give and get information to and from locals.
- Lastly, when on a fire, crews and resources working on the firelines are most often separated from the outside world and especially "home"! The Information function provides updates to the firefighters by newspapers, bulletin boards, camp newsletters and briefings. There is also a concerted effort to send information back home to the firefighters' base and let their families and loved ones stay abreast of developments at the incident.

Sunset through the fire on the Rodeo-Chediski Fire. Photo by Varnell Gatewood.

CH. 5: BEFORE THE MONSTER AWOKE

"So great a forest is set aflame by such a small fire." James 3:5

The magnitude of fire has changed dramatically in my 34 years in the Forest Service. Below are some brief remembrances from my first fire in 1969 to the Rodeo Chediski Fire in '02. The purpose of including these thumbnail sketches of my fire experience is to help you understand how fire has changed and just how put out with our "best intentioned mismanagement" Mother Nature is.

I went to my first wildland fire in 1969. As I recall, it was approximately 200 acres. Two bulldozers, each pulling a triple-disc plow went around the perimeter of the fire as close to the flames as the dozer operator could safely travel. This dozer-pulled plow would cut through flammable leaf litter, grass and brush on the ground and even knock over trees in the way and sever roots that a fire might utilize to creep across the fire line. The plowed line was cut down to non-combustible mineral soil, which also served as a walking path as well as a fire line.

Several crews walked along the line, dug short stretches of handline through rocky areas where the dozer's plow could not go and kept fire from crossing the fire line. The fire line separated fuel from the fire, except where the dozer was not able to get right against the edge of the burning forest. When the dozer was 100 feet or more from the fire an "indirect line" was built, which had to be burned out to be effective in stopping the fire. It is an old firefighter adage that "the only safe line is a black line."

Some of the more qualified fire individuals used drip torches. These were cylindrical metal cans with a wand and a burning wick on the end used to burn out the area between the dozer line and the fire. A drip torch drips a combination of diesel and gasoline fuel onto the burning wick, which drips the blazing mixture on the grass, brush and ground. With it, the firefighters would burn to the inside of the dozer or hand-dug line, back into the fire, robbing the fire of fuel and stopping its forward advance.

Finally, we spent three days mopping up and extinguishing all burning trees, logs and stumps inside the perimeter of the fire line. I remember that the burned timber was marked and logged that summer and approximately one million board feet of timber was sold off that one burned area. To a young forestry student on his first fire, this was a "big one!"

Igniter using a "driptorch" to burn out from a fireline.
Photo by Phoenix Fire Dept.

*　　*　　*　　*　　*

My first permanent position was as a Post Sale Forester in the Piney Woods of East Texas, which are wonderful, productive timberlands. After a timber sale on the National Forest lands had been cut, merchandisable timber removed and the sale closed, my effort was focused on getting the land where trees had been cut back into production. That involved measuring boundaries, determining acres, protecting streams and critical wildlife habitat, and putting together and then administering contracts for clearing cull trees and piling logging slash and debris by bulldozer.

We burned dozer piles and debris followed by machine or hand planting of pine seedlings, thus beginning the next generation of forests. Much time was spent monitoring fire behavior, when we were burning piles of slash and timber debris. The objective was to keep the fire from getting out of control, but it was also most educational and gave me time to really observe fire behavior, close up, much like watching approaching thunderstorms in West Texas, when I was younger. Monitoring of conditions appropriate to consume the slash and not burn so hot as to damage soil or get out of control was part of the job that I enjoyed the most. From then on, I looked forward to assignments in fire management and going to wildfires.

During the 1970s, in the Forest Service, everyone went to fires. If you were physically fit and able, you were expected to fight fire. We did not have dedicated fulltime firefighters on many of the districts, like we do now, so... if there was a fire, you dropped what you were doing and went to help out. As did most of us, I went to several fires each year, locally as well as outside our home area.

Critical fire seasons occur around the nation almost every year. Resources from all over the U.S. are dispatched to help out when a particular geographic area is experiencing fires that exceed their local capability. For example, fire season in the Southern U. S. peaks in February, March and April and then again in October/ November if it is a dry fall. In the Southwest, major fire danger is usually May to mid July. The Northern Rockies most often face the threat of major fires from mid-June through August or into September, as do Washington and Oregon. California is a place where major fires can occur from March to Thanksgiving. If it isn't raining in California, there seems to be the threat of major wildfires.

I moved to Cloudcroft, New Mexico in January of 1974 as a presale forester on the Lincoln National Forest. There, I was in charge of a marking crew and helped lay out timber sales and road systems for harvesting timber.

Easter weekend of 1974, a youngster started a campfire, just like he had seen his Dad do. Only it was in 40 mile per hour spring winds. The Spring Fire traveled nine miles in only three hours in a Ponderosa Pine forest near the little towns of Weed and Sacramento, New Mexico. I worked on the Spring Fire for almost two weeks. Our hose lays froze at night, it was so cold. Then for the next three months, my crew and I marked burned timber to be sold as salvage.

In June, we went to the Molina Basin Fire on the east flank of Mt. Lemmon and the Haystack Fire out in the Coronado badlands. They were my first fires in Arizona, with the Haystack growing by leaps and bounds every day until it reached 21,000 acres. New benchmarks for the "big one!"

*   *   *   *   *

In 1976, I moved to Ruidoso, New Mexico. When old Smokey Bear died in the Washington Zoo in November 1977, I was privileged to drive the Old Man home, accompanied by the District Ranger, Ray Page and Paul Jones, the District Fire Management Officer. Paul had actually worked on the fire in the Capitan Mountains in May 1950, where firefighters rescued a baby bear cub that had survived the fire, but was badly burned. That little bear cub went on to become the national symbol of wildfire prevention.

Now there is a State Park in Capitan and a ten-foot diameter boulder from the fire covers and marks his grave. At the time of his death, Smokey was the most widely known persona in the entire world, second only to Jesus Christ. Smokey was the product of a very aggressive public relations campaign that changed forever the way the public views fire danger and the need for fire prevention.

*   *   *   *   *

The Marble Cone, My First "Mega Fire," 1977

In 1977, I was in charge of a 20-man hand crew from Mora, New Mexico that was a "call when needed" or casual crew of firefighters organized under the Southwestern Forest Firefighters. They were trained and equipped and when called, they assembled, were transported and worked under the supervision of a Forest Service leader, until the emergency was over. The crew would then either go to the next fire or return home.

These crews come from small communities, Indian Nations and other areas where their "home job" allowed them time to be away on fires. Many of these firefighters worked in farming, logging, construction or other outdoor work. They were typically in good physical shape and used to the rigors

46

of arduous physical labor. Many of them had great fire experience, even though not having worked as "regular" federal land management employees. So it is today.

This dispatch was to the Marble Cone Fire that burned between Monterey and Santa Barbara, California. The fire pretty much consumed the Ventana Wilderness, occurring just a few weeks after John Denver hiked it and wrote a song about it. We were there for three weeks and worked on the Northwest flank of the fire, above Carmel, California's municipal water storage lake. The canyons were full of poison oak and poison sumac, some of it more than one inch in diameter and ten feet tall. Cutting and digging fireline in it took a severe toll on my crew.

I was assigned as the Crew Liaison Officer (C.L.O.), for the 20-man Mora crew. During the next three weeks, nine of my crew were taken to a hospital emergency room and then sent home. These men reacted to the Poison Oak and Sumac so much that for many of them, their eyes swelled shut and weeping blisters broke out on their skin, even while using "gallons" of Calamine Lotion (or so it seemed). Two of the nine affected had to receive additional treatment for respiratory problems, as the spores of the poison plants were transported in the smoke of the fire, infecting their throats, bronchial tubes and lungs. Seems there is no "poison anything" in Mora, New Mexico and they had no natural resistance nor antibodies to resist the itchy malady.

When the Marble Cone Fire finally laid down, it had burned 117,000 acres and was a disaster of great magnitude. More than 2,000 firefighters had worked at quelling this monster. It actually burned down to the beaches of the Pacific Ocean, where it simply ran out of fuel. Many of the old time fire dawgs wiped the soot off their brows and said "Whew, we never have and we probably never will see anything like that again!" They were wrong. Another benchmark, set higher with each event.

*   *   *   *   *

I was the District Ranger of the Taylor River Ranger District in Gunnison Colorado in 1985. We had a prescribed burn in cooperation with the Colorado Division of Wildlife to benefit the Bighorn Sheep Habitat on the Taylor River. This sheep herd needed large openings in their traditional paths of altitudinal migration from winter range on the Gunnison River to their summer range above 13,000 feet elevation near Taylor Peak and back down in the fall. If predators approached, the sheep's survival depended on seeing the intruder and having the opportunity to run, leap and climb rock walls to escape.

Their traditional migration routes had grown in with trees, due to the lack of fire, thus the Bighorn Sheep herd had quit using these migration routes. Another problem was that dung beds where the sheep would bed down had become so deep and polluted that Bighorn Sheep were being infected with parasitic worms that could kill them, also a result of the lack of fire.

Due to their altitudinal migration routes having been interrupted, the survival of the Taylor River Bighorn Sheep herd was at risk. Our plan was to burn the travel ways and the bedding grounds and allow fire to run uphill until it hit existing snow banks, which were at timberline. We got national publicity when helicopters using a helitorch started the burn. Two national environmental correspondents, Roger Caras of ABC and Roger O'Neil from NBC, were on site with their cameramen in June when we lit the first fires. They both did stories for the national daily television news programs. The June 14th evening news with Peter Jennings on ABC even showed Smokey Bear with a flame thrower as the lead-in to the story.

The burns went well and the dung beds burned like barbeque coals. The travel ways were opened up, but required several more burns to complete the project. This burn project was a direct benefit to wildlife, but showed the need for prescribed fire as one of the primary tools in our bag to manage the lands. We had no other way to treat the problem on these steep slopes above the Gunnison River. Fire had to be considered in all our management activities.

Views toward fire were changing from "put 'em all out" to an element of ecosystem management that our wildlands could not exist without. Researchers and practitioners identified fire as an effective tool to accomplish management objectives, in keeping with the needs of the land. Nowhere was this idea more hotly debated across the country than after the big fires of 1988.

*   *   *   *   *

Yellowstone Fires of 1988

In 1988, I moved to Truth or Consequences, New Mexico as the District Ranger on the Black Range Ranger District of the Gila National Forest. I was to remain there until my retirement in January 2003. After many busy fire seasons and a trend toward more intense and destructive fires, a change in national fire management philosophy occurred.

The thought was that perhaps we should not be aggressively putting all these fires out. After all, research showed that before Anglo-European settlement of the west, fires burned naturally, more often, but with much less intensity than the mega fires that were occurring more and more. Typical for land management agencies, national changes in fire policy that began in the late 1970's, took several years to implement and get down to the ground level. The National Park Service pioneered returning fire to a more natural role in ecosystem management and began their transition in the late 1960's.

In the summer of 1988, lightning had started several fires in and around Yellowstone National Park. Many of them were allowed to burn in a slowly advancing fire front that cleaned the forest floor and reduced fuels, emulating Mother Nature. All went well, until a severe hot, dry period and a delay in the normal monsoon rains caused many of the fires to change character and burn in ecologically climactic fire behavior with extreme rates of spread and tree-killing crown fires.

In late July and August, these fires gobbled up thousands of acres per day in Yellowstone and the five National Forests that surround the park. The park was evacuated and many thousands of firefighters from all over the nation concentrated efforts in Montana, Idaho and Wyoming, for more than six weeks. The fires ravaged 1.2 million acres, threatened Old Faithful, and the Knotty Pine Lodge. Many buildings in the park burned and many houses and buildings were lost on private lands in the surrounding National Forests. Early snows in September finally quenched the fires, thank goodness.

The "old fire dawgs" were scratching their heads and wondering what we might see next. The fire community began to talk about "mega fires" with unheralded fire behavior and rates of spread that were off the charts and almost beyond comprehension. Universities and federal fire research centers accelerated their search for answers to protect forests and communities from these anomalous fires. This new benchmark, so far beyond what we knew and understood, disturbed all in the fire community.

Jack Dieterich had worked with the Forest Service Rocky Mountain Experiment Station at Northern Arizona University for several decades. As early as 1961, he predicted catastrophic fires in southwestern forests based on the exclusion of natural fire and a dangerous accumulation of fuels from too many trees. [5.a] The Yellowstone Fires caused us to regroup and consider the fuels situation nationwide. New and much more constrictive policies were issued. No longer would fires be allowed to burn naturally without a written fire management plan and a prescription that detailed fuel conditions and fuel moisture, objectives and allowable burning conditions such as temperatures, humidity and winds.

Fire managers were required to examine forecasts, including the anticipated passage of storms or wind events and to make plans for the inevitable "what if…?" Managers had to endure much more oversight from above. If the prescription limits were exceeded, then suppression action to limit fire growth and damage had to be initiated. When the prescriptions were exceeded, the fire actually changed from a "wildland fire use" emulating Mother Nature to a designated wildfire with an aggressive suppression effort. Plans also required having the qualified resources available and on site to suppress the fire, if it "went over the hill."

After 20 days on assignment in Yellowstone, I was beat and feeling pretty puny for more than a month with a bad cold and bronchitis. It was hard to find personal achievements and victories in working on one of five fires that burned a collective total of 1.2 million acres. But we had saved a 20,000+ square foot log lodge on the Clover Mist Fire, belonging to the Quaker food corporation.

At 42 years of age, I was getting kind of "long in the tooth" to be chasing teens and "twenty-something" youngsters around the mountains. My Forest Supervisor, Steve Kelly, suggested that I

48

pursue the route of Information Officer. He got me enrolled in a national information officer course in Reno, Nevada. He even joked that "I was getting sort of old and fat, but that I talked pretty good and had good ground experience to apply to fire situations."

The rest is history, as I have been on Type II and Type I Incident Management Teams since 1989. I also spent the next 15 + wonderful years on the Black Range Ranger District of the Gila National Forest. Although I still went to fires on the ground at the local District and Forest level, my main fire job out of the local area became that of Lead Information Officer and Spokesman on fire management teams.

Fire Information is a critical job that becomes more important as the fires escalate and threaten communities. "Info" serves two main purposes. First is to give timely, concise and accurate information on the fire and how firefighters are attacking it. Second is simply to make "order out of chaos." When communities are threatened and have to evacuate, or there are injuries and God forbid, fatalities on the fireline or in the public, then the Information function has to explain what happened and why and most importantly, what *we* are doing to make the situation better. Often, on a particular incident, the lead information officer will become the "face of the fire" that the public will associate with and depend on.

Information Officer Jim Paxon at Information Center in Show Low on Rodeo-Chediski Fire. Photo by White Mountain Independent News.

*   *   *   *   *

The Dude Fire—Firefighter Fatalities and L.C.E.S

In 1990, my team and all firefighters on the Dude Fire were to be challenged, physically and emotionally. Walt Shaw's Southwest Type I Team arrived on the fire north of Payson, Arizona on June 25th. It had started by lightning several days before. Arizona was in a severe drought, live trees were as dry as they could be and still be alive. Dead logs on the forest floor were less than 5% moisture and the fire was spreading uncontrollably.

Our team was assuming control of the fire from a local Type II Team and the transition took place around noon. June 26, 1990 was one of Arizona's hottest days ever recorded. Sky Harbor Airport had to shut down all landings and takeoffs for several hours when the temperature reached 122 degrees Fahrenheit. The F.A.A. did not have air density calculation charts to determine safe aircraft payloads for temperatures that exceeded 120 degrees. It was 104 degrees on the fireline at 6,500 feet elevation.

In the early afternoon, a cumulus thunderstorm cloud passed over the fire in Dude Canyon and climbed the Mogollon Rim. The thunderstorm merged with the smoke column, building a huge plume, which with the updraft of heat, rose to well over 30,000 feet. Then the top of the column cooled and collapsed. The 70 + mile per hour winds from the microbursts from the thunderstorm and smoke column collapse caused the fire to blowup and burn 3,000 acres in less than 30 minutes.

At approximately 2:00 p.m., the Perryville Prison Inmate Fire Crew was building fire line in Walk More Canyon just below Bonita Estates, a rural housing subdivision. When the fire blew up, many crews retreated to safety zones, but the Perryville Crew was caught in the canyon. They deployed their fire shelters, but temperatures were too intense for firefighters to withstand the heat.

The shelter reduces heat by 80%, so 1,000 degrees outside, reduced to 200 degrees inside, gives firefighters the chance to survive. However, over a period of time, temperatures in excess of 200 degrees Fahrenheit inside a shelter are simply not survivable. The investigation showed that temperatures were closer to 2,000 degrees at the fatality site. The fire was so hot that wooden tool handles burned right out of the metal eyes in the tool heads.

Dave Latour discussing events of entrapment and burnover that resulted in six fatalities on the 1990 Dude Fire near Payson. Photo by U.S.F.S., Tonto National Forest.

Five inmate firefighters and one warden died. Five other inmate firefighters and their crew boss, David Latour, were just down canyon. They deployed their shelters where the fire and the intense heat were cooler and the location a bit more open. Lesser amounts of fuel and lower fire intensity at their location resulted in the survival of these six firefighters. Just a few feet made the difference between death and survival.

Survivors told of being in their fire shelters for 45 minutes, until the firestorm passed, before they were able to exit as rescuers approached. The fire howled and winds blew much like being in a hurricane or tornado. Two of those who died just could not take the intense heat and the fire's fury. They got up and ran with their shelters wrapped around them. They each collapsed a short ways down Walk More Canyon, having breathed super-heated air, instantly cauterizing their airways.

Above the canyon, forty-seven homes burned in Bonita Estates and the cars that remained simply melted. It was an inferno, close up. Immediately, the Dude Fire became a national news story. The loss of firefighters is always a tragedy. The heart of the collective fire family, the Town of Payson, State of Arizona and the entire nation reached out in sympathy. The fire eventually consumed 24,174 acres and 63 homes burned, including western author Zane Grey's historic cabin.

Left: Site of two of the six fatalities in Walk More Canyon on the 1990 Dude Fire.
Photo by U.S.F.S., Tonto National Forest.
Right: Memorial to the six firefighters lost on the Dude Fire, at the entrance of Bonita Estates Subdivision.
Photo by U.S.F.S., Tonto National Forest.

Interest in the investigation and what could be done to avoid a future loss like this was intense among all who experienced the blowup. Paul Gleason, then Oregon's Zig Zag HotShot Crew Superintendent was one of the first rescuers to the fatality site and administered aid to the injured.

Gleason, who had a passion for firefighter safety, later formulated a simple system to guard against situations that have killed firefighters. It was adopted as "L.C.E.S." which stands for Lookouts, Communication, Escape Routes and Safety Zones. Changes were made in the timing and coordination of command transfer from one team to another team, so there would be no transition in the middle of any shift on the line. Communications were improved and procedures were reinforced.

Fire crews began to be briefed on "situational awareness" and both how and when to leave an assignment and go to a safety zone, where they would not have to deploy shelters. Emphasis was put into training on the need to always be "heads up" so as to go home at the end of the fire. Use of "people lookouts," crew members, posted on high points, who were fire experienced and would be able to tell when trouble was brewing, became standard operations.

Every firefighter was taught that fire shelters were only to be used as a last resort. When a fire shelter had to be used, training emphasized how to choose the best site and how to stay in the shelter even when Hell is raining down around you. The message was serious and given to each and every firefighter. The end result is that lives have been saved since the Dude Fire tragedy.

The Dude Fire changed lives and changed the way we look at all firefighters. Those inmate firefighters made some mistakes and bad choices and were repaying society by their prison terms. They were also giving something back to society in a positive contribution.

Curtis Springfield had only two weeks to parole. He planned to seek work on a fire crew when he got out. James Denny (39) said in an interview on the Houghton Fire, only a month earlier, that he had been in trouble with the law since he was nine years old. This was the first thing that he had ever done that was of a positive nature and he was proud of it. Sandra Bachman was the warden who was proud of getting her firefighter training and actually getting out with "her crew" on a "hotline" fire assignment. She had become engaged just shortly before being called to the Dude Fire.

They each died as firefighters and are remembered as such. Working a fatality incident as an information officer or spokesman is the most difficult thing I have ever done; yet it is also one of the most rewarding efforts one can imagine. My staff and I worked at telling the story and the human side of the five inmates and the one warden who died protecting life and property. Each of those who died was someone's son or daughter, husband, wife, brother, sister, friend or loved one. Each and every one of them had a history on this earth that was unique and interesting. A memorial has been erected at the entrance to Bonita Estates. If you hike up Walk More Canyon, there are six simple crosses made of metal fence posts welded together at the site that each of the six took their last breath. May we remember.

During the battle of the Dude Fire, the Town of Payson knew what we were up against. They could easily view the smoke columns and plumes up close, just to the north of their community. Knowing the seriousness of the situation and the tragedy that unfolded, the community began a yellow ribbon tribute to firefighters. Every pole, every sign, every house and building flew yellow ribbons in tribute to those who lost their lives and those who continued to fight the fire.

The townspeople also wanted to demonstrate their gratitude for those working the fire and came up with a unique "pie campaign!" Many civic groups and individuals began making pies and the Red Cross delivered them to all the fire camps every afternoon. Because of the complexity and far-flung boundaries of the Dude Fire, there were four fire camps, each with a Type I Incident Management Team. Pies were put out on tables in the mess tents at every meal.

They just kept coming, day after day, until the fire was totally contained on July 14th. It lifted our spirits and demonstrated to us that the community was behind us and rooting for us. And most importantly, it was their way of paying tribute to the six who died, doing their job… as firefighters. The goodness that came out of those Payson folks was like getting to the top of the mountain, just as the sun rose.

That assignment was tough and left all of our fire teams drained. It also prepared us for things to come. Wildfires were changing and becoming more dangerous, less predictable and certainly more challenging.

*   *   *   *   *

Back Home on the Black Range

Fire was just part of the job for me as a professional forester. In my home job as the District Ranger, I worked on the Black Range Ranger District for a little over 15 years. My district straddled the Continental Divide and contained roughly one-half of the Aldo Leopold Wilderness and part of the Gila Wilderness. It was a very remote and untamed area of isolated ranches and steep mountain country that Apaches had freely roamed in Geronimo's time. Because the country was so remote and undeveloped, we were able to have an aggressive prescribed fire program, as did most of the Gila National Forest.

In ten years, the Black Range District burned over 140,000 acres using prescribed fires, and lightning ignited managed fire use fires. Following Mother Nature's lead, these were low intensity, slow moving, beneficial fires that thinned patches of "way too many pines" and made new grass and browse for wildlife and livestock.

Some of our fires were meant to restore watersheds that had been too long choked by brush and trees, resulting in perennial waters drying up. After the burns, many seeps and springs returned and streams flowed for longer periods after snowmelt and summer rains. Most importantly, fuel loads were reduced so that the chance of climactic, forest-destroying wildfires was remote.

Ted Turner of CNN fame, owns the Ladder Ranch, adjacent to the Forest. He held the grazing permits on approximately 170,000 acres of forest below or east of the Continental Divide. He was a major contributor of both money and people for planning and implementing prescribed burns to reduce fuels, benefit wildlife and restore productivity of watersheds. Cooperation with the Ladder Ranch continues today as a partnership where the land is the primary beneficiary.

The Black Range was great country to be out in. I will remember forever splendid times horseback, checking trails, looking at projects, riding with grazing permittees and taking pack trips. My district contained portions of both the Aldo Leopold and Gila wildernesses. The Gila was the first wilderness set aside in the nation in 1924. It was impossible to ride across either wilderness area in just one day. Pack trips with a mule carrying our home and groceries on his back, was just a normal way of life.

If we had VIP's or we were doing functional reviews with some of the Forest staff or Regional Office folks, why... we might be out most of a week. You just cannot imagine how many stars you can see on a cloudless night at 10,000 feet elevation, or the number of shooting stars that fall from the sky. Counting shooting stars is much better than counting sheep, as a means to slumber. Days were filled with sunshine and blue sky, and even being out in the occasional monsoon rain or spring snowstorm was a delight.

Jim Paxon on Drummer Boy on the Continental Divide, Gila National Forest in New Mexico.
Photo by Shane Shannon.

This picture of me horseback shows my old friend, Drummer Boy carrying me along the Continental Divide Trail of my District on the Gila National Forest in New Mexico. This photo was taken December 4, 2002, just one month before I retired. I bought Drummer Boy in 1984 as a two-year-old Missouri Foxtrotter. I broke him to saddle and he has carried me literally thousands of miles across many National Forests. I have even ridden him through and around prescribed fires and Managed Fire Use fires. I always took care to not put us in close proximity to flames so that his feet and legs would not get hot. He never showed any skittishness or fear of fire or smoke.

Fire Season 2002

Fire season started in a big way for the southwest area in 2002, which includes Arizona, New Mexico and West Texas. Larry Humphrey's Southwest Type I Incident Management Team's (my team) first fire assignment of the year was the Middle Fire on the Wilderness and Reserve Ranger Districts of the Gila National Forest on April 3, 2002. The Middle Fire ran quickly, driven by wind, and burned more than 40,000 acres in a narrow "v" pattern. It gained 20,000 acres on the second day, with gentle breezes, but not gale-force winds. Hump's Team was only on it for four days before God and a spring snowstorm put it out. Such an early, large and fast moving fire convinced all fire and supervisory folks that it was going to be a very long and difficult fire season.

The next fire assignment was on April 30th. This was the Ryan Fire, west of Sierra Vista, Arizona. The Ryan Fire burned 38,000+ acres, which was very aggressive and unusual for as early in the season as it was. It burned in the Sonoran Desert, which had chaparral and woodland fuel types. In the winter of 2001/02, the lower elevation portions of Arizona, including the Coronado National Forest, received virtually no moisture. All of the grass and much of the brush was dry and dead, and the live trees were so dry as to be at the point of mortality.

Due to the drought and record-breaking high spring temperatures, even those lower areas with relatively less fuel loading (grasslands that had been grazed), burned with fierce intensity. One hundred foot flames were observed that many considered amazing, given the light fuel loading.

On May 23, 2002, our team was dispatched to Oracle, Arizona for the Bullock Fire. This was a person-caused ignition in the San Pedro River drainage on the north side of Mt. Lemmon. This was our third dispatch of the year and it still wasn't even "high fire season," yet. With this much "practice," the team was really working well together. On the Bullock Fire, Operations were split into two branches or commands. The northern branch of Operations battled the fire to the East of Oracle and to the South of the San Pedro River. The southern branch worked the Santa Catalina Highway on the crest of Mt. Lemmon, up to the mountain town of Summerhaven, preparing for the fire to come, as it advanced uphill from the San Pedro River to the top of the Santa Catalina Mountains.

My shop, the Information function, also had two distinctly different publics to serve: 1) The Oracle townsfolk, San Pedro River ranchers and recreationists, and 2) As the fire progressed, the City of Tucson, Mt. Lemmon summer homeowners, and the Summerhaven folks. My Deputy Information Officer, Chadeen Palmer worked the north end and I went to the Santa Catalina Ranger Station at the entrance to Sabino Canyon, where we set up an information center. Local information officers on the Coronado Forest did a great job of helping us to get information out in a timely manner.

The north side of Mt. Lemmon and the Santa Catalina crest is comprised of long sloping ridges that run northward, broken by deep canyons, as the mountains descend to the San Pedro River. Though the dominant winds blow from the southwest, the crest of the Catalinas shields and deflects those winds, and reduces their direct effect at ground level. The Bullock Fire burned uphill, against the dominant southwest winds with the aid of squirrelly, erratic canyon winds and the preheating of the summer sun, which heats and dries fuels on the slopes, causing air to rise up those broken canyons.

As the fire approached the top of Mt. Lemmon and the Catalina Highway, the paved road was used as a firebreak and primary supply route. Gravel pits and large parking areas were used as dip sites for helicopter operations. Pumpkins (large open top bladders fed by nurse tanker trucks) were located for easy helicopter access.

The ridge-top access was very important in reducing flight time for helicopters working the ridge and attempting to protect hundreds of summer homes scattered along the ridge, in the town of Summerhaven, as well as Mt. Bigelow's multi-million dollar electronic site. As fire approached the ridge, multiple helicopters joined in dousing hotspots, reducing the speed with which the fire approached the highway, and constructed firelines on the north side of the Santa Catalina Highway. Heavy air tankers worked the flanks in country too steep to put firefighters close to the fire without escape routes and safety zones.

Everyone on Mt. Lemmon and in Summerhaven was evacuated as crews, engines and aircraft made a hard stand on the highway and prepared for burnouts as the fire approached the Santa Catalina Highway. Areas with cabins were prepared for fire to come against them by emergency thinning, cutting and hauling of fuel debris in dump trucks, which reduced the risk to houses and cabins. Sprinkler systems were set up to work off 2-3,000 gallon "foldatanks," which were supplied with water from nurse tankers. Hose lays with site-made sprinklers were fed with gasoline-powered pumps, drawing water out of the foldatanks. That way, some protection was afforded structures, even if the fire forced our firefighters to retreat to safety zones.

If firefighters were forced to withdraw, pumps would be turned on, sprinkling the cabins, until the foldatanks were emptied. Engine and hand crews worked around twenty most-at-risk structures to complete this preparatory work.

To the west, the focus was on Mt. Bigelow. If the fire overran the electronic sites, key radio, television and microwave communications would have been shut down, such as FAA's Tucson International Airport, FBI, Border Patrol, Arizona Department of Public Safety, Tucson Fire and Police, telephone microwave sites, television repeaters, and others.

Our firelines on top held, and the fire burned right to the Catalina Highway and to the north edge of the small Mt. Lemmon Ski Area. The retardant line also held on the north side of Mt. Bigelow and to the east, above General Crook Campground. Effective work by both air tankers and heavy helicopters supported crews on the ground and contributed in a major way to the success of the ground firefighters.

This broken, steep and heavily forested area presented unique challenges to firefighters. The communities and electronic sites in the fire's path compounded that complexity. When the fire was contained in mid–June, it had burned 30,563 acres. More than 1150 firefighters worked its perimeter, and it cost almost $13 million to suppress. The City of Tucson and travelers on Interstate 10 had a ringside seat for over three weeks.

We held two public meetings in Tucson, one attended by 600 people at Catalina High School. There, I used a PowerPoint photo presentation to explain the dire fuels situation and how fortunate the mountain cabins and communities were… this time! I encouraged all those folks to support Firewise and to thin, prune and remove dead vegetation before Mother Nature did it for them with the next fire.

District Ranger Ron Senn warned Tucsonians that the same fire conditions with an ignition on the south side of Mt. Lemmon would have a very different outcome. When fire came from the south, I just hoped that we would not lose people and would be able to get everyone safely evacuated. That proved true when in 2003, the Aspen Fire, started by smokers in Sabino Canyon on June 17th, ravaged Mt. Lemmon and burned 300 + plus homes in Summerhaven, almost a year to the day after our prophetic meeting.

Our team finished a fourteen-day assignment, closed out and transitioned to a Type II team on June 6th. We were home on June 7th, the Bullock Fire recent history… but lots of paperwork, letters and unanswered phone calls on my Forest Service desk back in Truth or Consequences, New Mexico.

Just one day after my sweetheart, Debbie and I got married, I received a phone call from Gila Dispatch about 2:00 p.m. on June 17th, sending Hump's Team to another fire. The fire north of Cuba was called "BMG" for the gas field location. With the sixth year of drought and very little winter snow, this fire had the chance to spread in a big way.

The Santa Fe National Forest was very concerned with the explosive forest conditions, communities in the path of the fire and with public issues. The possibility of additional natural gas line ruptures was on everyone's mind, especially since the cause of this fire was under investigation. For that reason, they had requested the Type I Team, while their local resources worked on the fire.

The natural gas in the transmission line had been shut off and we were tasked to contain the fire in the forest surrounding the gas-line break. Initial attack crews from the Santa Fe National Forest and local fire departments did an excellent job. Our team had a relatively easy time and after only 48 hours, we were relieved from that fire and demobilized, but not released from duty.

*   *   *   *   *

The Rodeo Fire

The members of Humphrey's Team were to meet at a hotel in Albuquerque near where the Southwest Coordination Center is located. It is common practice that once a team is dispatched to a fire and finishes the task in just a few days, that team may be held over and staged, in a "civilized location," in case they are needed to respond immediately to another fire. It takes from 12 to 24 hours to mobilize the 40 + people on a Type I Team from their home base and transport them to a fire. Having a team strategically positioned, assembled, and ready can often make a full day's difference in responding to a blowing and going fire.

In the Southwest, we have a team policy of individuals driving to a fire so they can bring not only their rig, but also personal equipment, laptop computers, etc. and each member is then ready to live out of their vehicle for that assignment. In the southwest, driving is often as quick as flying, due to the time it takes getting in and out of airports, checking luggage and equipment, renting a vehicle, etc. Most all our agency vehicles have programmable radio communications and emergency equipment, which are key elements to safety and operations on a fire.

Before we even reached the hotel in Albuquerque, we were rerouted to a new fire below Show Low, Arizona on the White Mountain Apache Reservation. That fire was named "Rodeo" and we were to meet at the Ft. Apache Tribal Forestry Headquarters in Whiteriver at 2100 hours (9:00 p.m.) for a briefing with Ben Nuvamsa, B.I.A. Superintendent at Ft. Apache, John Bedell, the Supervisor of the Apache-Sitgreaves National Forest and other officials.

As we drove on I-40 West toward Holbrook, the pall and smell of smoke changed from an occasional wisp to a fog by the time we reached the Arizona border. When we turned south at Holbrook on Highway 77, the smoke was so dense that all vehicles were driving with their headlights on, even though the sun had not set. As we drove through Show Low to the briefing, we could see the glow of flames to the southwest.

Before we got to the briefing, all of us knew that this Rodeo Fire was going to be a real challenge. Little did we know that the "monster" had already reared his ugly head… and we were about to do battle with him. The monster had awakened!

CH. 6: IGNITION – AND THE DEVIL DANCED!!

"Let he who is without sin cast the first stone." Jesus (John 8:7)

When I look back at the things that have recently affected our lives, especially the Rodeo-Chediski Fire, I look at the people who understood those events and took part in a major piece of history that was written in just two weeks. It is a history that Arizona will remember for a long, long time. I have paused to consider the people and their contributions to this saga and how their actions affected the outcomes.

While Arizona and the world watched and waited, people's lives and the very existence of twelve White Mountain communities hung in the balance of the actions of those "on the scene!" We must go back just a little and give you some background information that I hope you will digest and use in reading the rest of this tale of the many-headed dragon that attacked the forests and communities of the White Mountains.

*   *   *   *   *

In August 2001, Larry Humphrey's Type I Incident Management Team was dispatched to the "Moose Fire" on the north side of Glacier National Park. There, in one burn period, on September 1, 2001, more than 27,000 acres burned in a plume dominated fire run, the most dangerous of all fire types. Plume dominated fires build their own weather when the smoke, unburned gases from vaporized trees and heat rise vertically. Fire whorls (unattached flames in the sky) several thousand feet high are common.

Eventually, as the hot smoke rises, the column will cool off, ice out and form a big anvil shaped thundercloud on top. Then, the lifted air cools, moisture forms droplets and the column will no longer support the weight of the cooled smoke particles and moisture droplets. The column collapses from the top down through the inside, much like a runaway elevator plummeting unchecked down an elevator shaft.

Rodeo fire column from Show Low Airport, evening June 22nd. Photo by Arizona DPS-Highway Patrol

A "tattletale" is when the fire becomes eerily quiet and there is a slight mist or light rain. Experienced firefighters know that all Hell is about to break loose and it is time to get as far away from the fire as possible, because it will run in every direction.

At ground level, winds can be more than gale force in all directions. The closest example to consider is much like standing on a stepladder and pouring a five-gallon bucket of water out, all at once. You would see how the water splashes violently and spreads in all directions.

Fire reacts in a similar fashion, although the scale of force is millions times more. The Moose Fire's plume dominated run was in Lodgepole Pine on undulating foothills. There was no wind influencing fire conditions, yet the fire "got legs" and ran across Big Creek on the Flathead National Forest and into the north side of Glacier Park at more than 7,000 acres per hour. Flames of 500' to 1,000' and rates of spread of five miles per hour or more were common at the fire front, although the flanks burned outwardly almost as fast.

The fire grew in three directions with no opportunity to stop its progress. As our Operations Section Chief, Roy Hall quipped, "It was a bleacher day!" Firefighters were withdrawn to safe zones until the flame front either passed or subsided. Only then were they able to continue building fire line closer to the fire, in a safe environment. The Moose Fire was our most recent "up close" witnessing of the power of a plume dominated blaze for Hump's Team.

Many of us were on the same Incident Management Team, commanded by Walt Shaw in June of 1990, when we saw another plume dominated blowup on the Dude Fire, which killed six firefighters and burned 47 homes in little more than one hour.

*　　*　　*　　*　　*

In March of 2002, George Leech, Assistant Fire Management Officer at Ft. Apache Fire gave a talk during the White Mountain Zone's Annual Fire Refresher Training. His discussion centered on his concerns and predictions for "Fire Season 2002." George, a widely respected trainer and fire manager, related that even this early in the fire season, "the hair is standing up on the back of my neck with considerable dread of what the fire season might bring." [6.a]

As a trained expert in fire behavior in the Incident Command System, George knew full well the potential for an extremely bad fire year. FBAN is the acronym for George's fire behavior analyst credentials. FBAN's have extensive experience and training in predicting how fires will burn and spread under measured conditions.

George is also a very experienced Type II Incident Commander and a Type I Operations Section Chief. He actually grew up in Whiteriver and fought fire there during summers as a college student. He has worked in three regions with the Bureau of Indian Affairs. George spent the last 23 years of his career in fire management at Ft. Apache, so he has seen many fire seasons in all kinds of conditions, including extreme. Here are some bullets from that talk:

- E.R.C or Energy Release Component is an index based on the average of the last three days of the estimated energy that would be released at the flame front, or the hottest part of the fire. Daily changes in the E.R.C.'s are displayed in charts, based on changes in moisture content of various fuel types: grasses, shrubs, standing trees, logging slash, dense chaparral, etc. E.R.C.'s also include the rate of heat released from the fuels that are burning and the duration of the flame at a particular point. ERC charts are compared to averages and maximums experienced from 1975 to 2000 and indicate a theoretical 100%.
- The 90th percentile indicates a "Very High" fire danger and need for increased preparedness. The 97th percentile indicates an "Extreme" fire danger and the highest need to have resources ready to respond. The ERC.s for March 1st exceeded the 97th percentile, giving a frightening warning that the White Mountains were already in "Extreme" fire danger, when it typically would have been "Low."

The stage had been set for what many fire experts and resource managers predicted to be one of the worst and most active fire seasons in Arizona and the Southwest in more than the last century.

George continued to share his observations with:

- Charts for the Energy Release Component are at never before seen highs, breaking the previous high of 1977 by a wide margin.

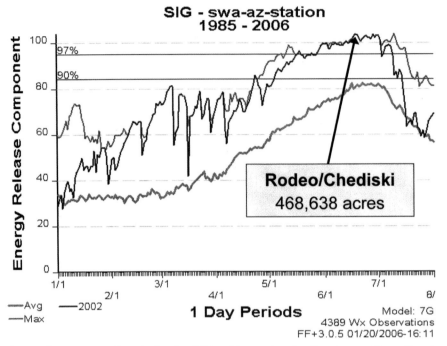

Energy Release Component Graph for the White Mountains by Southwest Coordination Center. Note: June 18th was over 100% when Rodeo Fire was ignited.

- National Drought Monitoring shows Arizona to be experiencing the two driest winters in the last 107 years.
- The southwest had been in a drought since 1995.

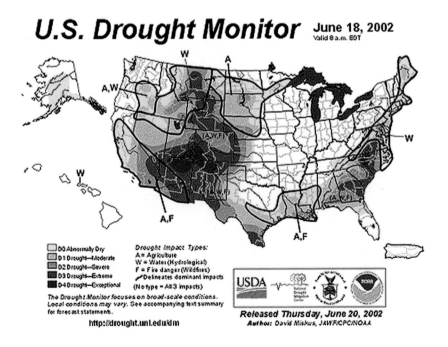

Drought Map for June 2002 prepared by National Oceanographic and Atmospheric Administration.

- Precipitation is less than 25% of normal for the last 1.5 years with no snow pack at all, this last winter.
- Stream flows are less than 30% of a 50-year average.
- With absolutely no snow, fuel moistures of the 1,000 hr. fuels (logs on the forest floor greater than 3") are below 10% when they should be 20-22%. For comparison, kiln dried wood in a lumber yard is approximately 12% to 14% moisture when it is shipped to the lumberyard.
- Initial Attack on small fires in January and February exhibited a fire intensity and rate of spread that was more typical of June fire conditions. There were many more winter and early spring fires than normal, due to the lack of snow and extremely dry conditions.
- Firefighters should expect very hot burning fires that display erratic burning behavior.
- Expect long range spotting with very little winds. Lofted embers and firebrands will land "hot," creating new fires.
- Expect significant torching and crowning with moderate (or less) ladder fuels and only light winds. (Fire will burn into the tops of trees and race through forest stands more easily than when normal winter moisture has been received. The dryness of live trees will actually promote fire in the treetops and the extreme spread of fire).
- Heat and dryness of fuels will contribute to extremely long flame lengths and very high rates of spread. Firefighters will have to fall back and use more "indirect line" construction and burnouts.
- Such high ERC's have never before been recorded in the White Mountains. The stage was set for the most active fire season in Arizona and other areas of the Southwest in more than the last century.

Rodeo Fire from Cibeque, June 19th. Photo by Varnell Gatewood.

George then gave the group some anticipated actions to keep in mind for fires:

Safety

Main Safety Page | Home

The 10 Standard Fire Orders were developed in 1957 by a task force studying ways to prevent firefighter injuries and fatalities. Shortly after the Standard Fire Orders were incorporated into firefighter training, the 18 Situations That Shout Watch Out were developed. These 18 situations are more specific and cautionary than the Standard Fire Orders and described situations that expand the 10 points of the Fire Orders. If firefighters follow the 10 Standard Fire Orders and are alerted to the 18 Watch Out Situations, much of the risk of firefighting can be reduced.

10 STANDARD FIRE ORDERS

The NWCG Parent Group just approved the revision of the Ten Standard Fire Orders in accordance with their original arrangement. The original arrangement of the Orders are logically organized to be implemented systematically and applied to all fire situations.

Fire Behavior

1. Keep informed on fire weather conditions and forecasts.
2. Know what your fire is doing at all times.
3. Base all actions on current and expected behavior of the fire.

Fireline Safety
4. Identify escape routes and make them known.
5. Post lookouts when there is possible danger.
6. Be alert. Keep calm. Think clearly. Act decisively.

Organizational Control
7. Maintain prompt communications with your forces, your supervisor and adjoining forces.
8. Give clear instructions and insure they are understood.
9. Maintain control of your forces at all times.

If 1-9 are considered, then...
10. Fight fire agressively, having provided for safety first.

The 10 Standard Fire Orders are firm. We Don't Break Them; We Don't Bend Them. All firefighters have a Right to a Safe Assignment.

18 WATCH OUT SITUATIONS
1. Fire not scouted and sized up.
2. In country not seen in daylight.
3. Safety zones and escape routes not identified.
4. Unfamiliar with weather and local factors influencing fire behavior
5. Uninformed on strategy, tactics, and hazards.
6. Instructions and assignments not clear.
7. No communication link between crewmembers and supervisors.
8. Constructing line without safe anchor point.
9. Building line downhill with fire below.
10. Attempting frontal assault on fire.
11. Unburned fuel between you and the fire.
12. Cannot see main fire, not in contact with anyone who can.
13. On a hillside where rolling material can ignite fuel below.
14. Weather gets hotter and drier.
15. Wind increases and/or changes direction.
16. Getting frequent spot fires across line.
17. Terrain or fuels make escape to safety zones difficult.
18. Feel like taking a nap near fireline.

Standard Fire Orders from National Interagency Fire Center
Eighteen Situations that Shout "Watch Out!" from National Interagency Fire Center

- Follow all safety precautions and use the 10 Standard Fire Orders and the 18 Situation that Shout WATCH OUT!"
- Use L.C.E.S system (Lookouts, Communications, Escape Routes and Safety Zones) and have escape routes and safety zones shared with every single firefighter and anyone else assigned near the fire.
- Have current weather forecasts and request spot weather updates, as needed, when on a fire.
- Bump up your initial orders for Incident Commanders to a higher level than the initial size up of the fire indicates. Fires will escalate faster than expected, especially if Initial Attack does not contain them.
- Go heavy on resources. If you need two of anything, order three or even four.
- Use aerial retardant early and often to assist firefighters on the ground.
- Request, no demand, Air Attack to be the Safety and "Eyes in the Sky" to keep track of fire conditions and changes and most of all as an "early warning" device to get firefighters out if conditions turn for the worse.
- Do not be afraid to pull out if things get "too hot, too quick!"
- Time will be short to react to changing conditions. All firefighters must keep one eye up, communicate with others and be ready to move quickly to Safe Zones.

*   *   *   *   *

Frank Hayes is the District Ranger of the Clifton Ranger District on the Apache-Sitgreaves National Forest. Frank was also one of the Air Attack Group Supervisors on Larry Humphrey's Type I National Incident Management Team. Frank, with a long history in fire suppression, is also a regional expert in the application of prescribed fire on the ground. He is on the Board of Gran Quivera, a coalition of environmentalists and users of the land that seek "wise use" and conservation of southwestern lands.

In January and February of 2002, the Clifton Ranger District was involved in prescribed burning to reduce fuels for wildfires, improve wildlife and livestock forage and browse, and improve watershed conditions. During blacklining (burning boundaries of planned burn areas in less than optimum conditions to give defensible borders and stop growth of prescribed fires) of a Pinyon-Juniper burn, even though conditions were within the limits set by prescription and a burn plan, the fire managers noticed extreme burning conditions, including torching of isolated Ponderosa Pine trees. This torching occurred even though there were no ladder fuels to take fire into tree crowns.

Fire crept through grass and pine needles and then flames would climb the trunks of trees. The bark and sap deposits on the trunks would literally explode into the upper tree limbs and branches. Those trees torched and flung embers without ANY wind. Where embers landed, spot fires immediately ignited and began to spread. The blacklining was completed, but the actual burning of the prescribed fire projects was deferred until moisture and fuel conditions improved, much later in the summer after monsoons began.

At an April Apache-Sitgreaves Forest Leadership Team meeting in Springerville, Frank displayed the results of his prescribed burning observations for the other Rangers and Forest Staff to consider. He stated that in his opinion, Fire Season 2002 would be worse than 2000, the year that Los Alamos burned. The rest of the leadership team was somewhat skeptical, as they had not experienced what Frank's district had. However, he sounded the clarion. The "dragon" was rousing from a deep slumber, in a foul mood and with a ravenous appetite. [6.b]

In mid April, Humphrey's Type I Incident Management Team was dispatched to an early fire on the Gila National Forest (the Middle Fire) that burned 40,000 acres in cool weather conditions and was then quenched by a two-day spring snowstorm. Frank was one of the "Air Attacks" on that fire and flew with Gila veteran Air Attack, Steve Blest. The two discussed three major elements, while observing the Middle Fire from the air:

1. The fire's flame front ran so fast that it was impossible to map. Fuels were light, mostly grass with pockets of brush and timber only in the draws. Winds were not excessive. However, the fire ran as if it were pushed by much harder winds than were actually experienced. Temperatures were still cool, so the extreme rate of spread was a function of extremely dry moisture readings in both dead and live fuels. If temperatures had been 10 to 15 degrees warmer, both Blest and Hayes doubted that we would have caught the fire until it exited the forest in the grasslands of the San Augustine Plains some ten miles to the north.

2. Heavy air tankers had to run maximum coverage levels to stop creep of the fire through the vegetation of the area that the tankers "painted" or dumped on. The level of retardant drops was the same as normally used in heavy brush or even light timber forests. Usually, a spring fire would require less than half the amount of retardant coverage utilized to stop the spread of fire on the flanks, due to cooler temperatures and residual snow (of which there was neither). There were no air tankers on active duty at that time. However, four were called up early and stayed on contract for the duration of the season.

3. This fire ran hard and firefighters found it to be unstoppable, until snow pretty much quenched it. Very unusual conditions for as early and as cool as it was and this was early spring. Another reminder that it was to be a very scary spring and summer.

*   *   *   *   *

The White Mountains are unusual in that the makeup of the communities demonstrates wide ethnic diversity, excellent community cooperation and neighborly co-existence. Fire season 2002 would see many players in the upcoming battles, some who were unlikely and unwilling participants in a drama that would be played out before the world.

One such player in this unscripted drama was Leonard Gregg, a White Mountain Apache. He was born in 1971 in Whiteriver and was given up for adoption shortly after birth. Leonard was very likely born with "F.A.S." (fetal alcohol syndrome), a condition caused by a pregnant mother's use of alcohol, which damages the brain and limits cognitive skills and reasoning in her unborn baby

Leonard struggled through the 9th grade, when he dropped out. He depended very much on his stepmother and stepbrother, Wilson to help him with direction and simple decisions.

Leonard was known as a shy, gentle soul — not a troublemaker. However, even as a child, Leonard was known to have a fascination with fire. On the morning of June 18, 2002, Leonard was reported to have had an argument with his stepmother and stormed out of their house in Cibeque, a small logging community on the White Mountain Apache Reservation. The sawmill in Cibeque was the major industry in the area. Most of the residents were involved in either logging or working at the sawmill that produced lumber.

Leonard was unable to keep a steady job, but he had advanced through the basic firefighter training the Bureau of Indian Affairs Forestry and Fire staff put on each year. Leonard and many others, who have been trained, have passed the physical fitness test, were then issued personal protective equipment and packs and could be called up and put to work whenever fire conditions were severe.

At times crews were organized and sent out of their home area to fight large fires that require extensive people-power to dig fire lines, mop-up and do other "non-hotline" fire duties, as well as do fire rehabilitation work. This is the only way that Leonard had to make money and he was broke. Leonard needed money to support his girlfriend and her five children. *Fire employment was really the only means he had to make money.*

Sadly, those afflicted with F.A.S. often do things in reaction or on impulse, without considering long-term effects or the bigger picture. They may have an idea of right or wrong, but any decisions made by them are limited in scope and understanding. They exhibit naïve ways and often seek resolution of their issues in immediate, graphic action. Such it was for Leonard on June 18th. [6.c] The results of his actions would impact the residents on the reservation and in the high country above the Mogollon Rim… for the next several generations!

The first fire allegedly lit in anger by Leonard Gregg was named the Pina Fire, within the village limits of Cibeque, next to Cibeque Creek. Structural firefighters and two forestry engines from Ft. Apache Fire responded to this blaze at approximately 10:30 a.m. Ft. Apache Fire Helicopter, H-355 also made water drops to help the firefighters on the ground.

A structural engine from Cibeque also responded, since the fire was in the community. Firefighters were able to contain the Pina Fire at 10 acres and the two Forestry engines mopped the fire up, totally extinguishing any burning materials, while the structural engines and firemen returned to their station, by about 3:00 p.m. It was only providence that the first fire was lit near the creek, which ran water and there was some "green!"

At approximately 4:11 p.m., Cibeque fireman Gary Thompson looked out the window of the fire station and saw a definite smoke plume to the north. The only development in that direction was the Cibeque Rodeo Grounds. Gary called Ft. Apache dispatch to report the fire. B.I.A. policy restricts structural firefighters from leaving their district of responsibility, in this case, the community of Cibeque. Their responsibility, equipment and training is for structure protection, not wildland firefighting. The large fire engine that they drive would not have easily maneuvered up to the rodeo grounds. [6.d]

At about the same time, Chediski Lookout also spotted the plume of smoke and called in the location to Ft. Apache dispatch. Shortly after, Limestone Lookout confirmed the smoke and gave an azimuth (compass reading) to cross reference the location. With two lookouts giving azimuth readings (direction in degrees such as North is "0" and South is "180"), the location of the smoke could be plotted (triangulated on maps) to a point closer than 10 acres. Since the fire was plotted near the Cibeque Rodeo Grounds, it was named the "Rodeo Fire."

Before the fire was reported, Leonard Gregg had told a neighbor that he was soon to be called to a fire and he needed to get ready for the call to go and help fight it. Leonard was one of the first "casual firefighters" to be called up and put to work.

With just one match, the dragon opened one eye and yawned. Before firefighters could get to the Cibeque Rodeo Grounds, the dragon was fully awake, in a rather bad mood at being deprived exercise for so many decades and he was ravenously hungry. He took a deep breath and exhaled fire and fury. It was now his time and he would be in control. This was a fire as had not been seen on the reservation, in its 133-year history.

The following is a summary from the Ft. Apache Fire Dispatch Log in 24 hour or military time (0001 hrs. is one minute after midnight all the way around to 2359 for 11:59 p.m. It avoids the confusion of a.m. or p.m. in telling and communicating time) for June 18 and 19, 2002:

June 18th, Tuesday

- 1611--New Fire reported by both Cibeque F.D. and Chediski L.O.
- 1613—Location confirmed by Limestone L.O.
- 1614—Gentry & Promontory Lookouts confirmed and crossed for location.
- 1614—Launched Single Engine Air Tanker (S.E.A.T.), lead plane and Helicopter H-355.

Air Tractor Single Engine Air Tanker (S.E.A.T.) at Cibeque Airstrip.
Photo by White Mountain Independent News.

- 1616—Dispatched nurse tanker, two engines and two crews (Leonard Gregg was one of the first called). All confirmed, "Enroute." Two engines and the nurse tanker proceeded from the Pina Fire only four miles from the Rodeo Fire.
- 1617—Chediski L.O. reports thick black smoke column.
- 1622—Apache-Sitgreaves National Forest Air Attack 39-Quebec (Jerry Beddow) requested and

enroute. Fire is showing erratic behavior on the southwest slope and is crowning and torching in the brush and Pinyon-Juniper.

- 1623 — First SEAT dropped retardant. Indicated it would "Load and Return" as the fire was spreading quickly. Beddow/39-Quebec would be taking off from Springerville Airport with a 20-minute flight time to the fire. Dispatch confirmed more retardant needed.
- 1624 — First firefighters on scene. Estimated fire at 15 acres in grass, brush and small trees. Varnell Gatewood is Initial Attack I. C. (Incident Commander—in charge of all resources and people attacking the fire).
- 1626 — Apache-Sitgreaves National Forest Air Attack 39-Quebec (Jerry Beddow) *confirmed* enroute. Fire is showing erratic behavior on the southwest slope and is crowning and torching in the brush and Pinon-Juniper.

Rodeo Fire close up on afternoon of June 18th. Photo by Varnell Gatewood.

- 1633 — Fire has moved to west slope of drainage. Now estimated at 30-40 acres. Crowning and running w/ estimated 70' flames. Spotting 1/8 mile in front of flames. No heavy (Type I) airtankers available. Will keep using two S.E.A.T.'s (Single Engined Air Tankers—look like crop dusters but "spread" retardant) and have asked for S.E.A.T from San Carlos Reservation to the south.
- 1638 — 20-person crew enroute from Pinedale.
- 1643 — Two D-6 Bulldozers ordered. Overhead (to command extended attack) ordered. George Leech in Helicopter H-355 will serve as Operations Section Chief. Varnell Gatewood is to remain as I.C. on the ground. He will coordinate with George in Helicopter H-355.
- 1655—4 heavy airtankers ordered from Southwest Coordination. Center in Albuquerque. Fire is moving away from Cibeque. Estimated at 75 acres and spotting ¼ mile in front of flames.
- 1700—One SEAT enroute from Springerville.

64

- 1704—3 SEAT's, 4-20 person crews, Air Attack, 2 brush trucks, 2 engines, Helitack & 3 dozers enroute or on scene.
- 1718—Fire estimated at 100+ acres. Call for Type II Incident Management Team and additional resources.

Rodeo Fire at 1730 hrs. on June 18th. Photo by Varnell Gatewood.

Fire climbing Cibeque Ridge at 1730 hrs. on June 18th. Photo by Jerry Beddow.

- 1720—Fire crosses Cibeque Ridge Road. Fire flanking to east and west on Cibeque Ridge. Fire intensity too hot to staff with ground resources, dozers to work flanks as soon as they arrive.

- 1746—39-Quebec reports that a spot fire has reached the top of Cibeque Ridge.
- 1800—I.C. Gatewood, Ops. Leech and Fire Staff Butler make decision to switch to Extended Attack mode and call on more resources of crews and dozers.
- 1819—Two heavy airtankers enroute from Albuquerque. Will get only one drop each, due to late time of day.

Fire topping out on Cibeque Ridge at about 1830 hrs. on June 18th. Photo by Paul Bead.

Right: Fire across Cibeque Ridge at dusk on June 18th. Photo by Paul Bead.

- 2001—39-Quebec requested 3 Heavy Air Tankers and lead plane for 0700 tomorrow.
- 2016—Eight 20 person crews ordered.

- 2230—Kvale's S.E. Arizona Type II Team confirmed and enroute.
- 2300—Fire over the top of Cibeque Ridge and headed toward Carrizo Creek. Head of fire estimated to be 1.5 miles wide.

By 1830 hours (6:30 p.m.), the Rodeo was putting up a very visible plume and there was also quite a bit of drift smoke to the east and north of Cibeque. White Mountain Zone Dispatch received over 400 calls reporting the smoke. All of the fire and police departments and 911 Dispatch were overloaded with reports of the smoke. Many of them gave the wrong location as out to the east of Show Low or even east of Heber-Overgaard. Firefighters and fire departments spent an inordinate amount of time checking out false alarms. That people were alarmed and concerned, and "reacted" is an understatement.

Deuce of Clubs in Show Low looking west in the afternoon of June 18th.
Photo by Corrine Ruiz, White Mountain Independent News.

Shortly after 4:00 p.m. George Leech (the Assistant Fire Management Officer at Ft. Apache Fire for Bureau of Indian Affairs) was at a Pinetop Fire District Board meeting when he had received a phone call informing him of a new fire at the Cibeque Rodeo Grounds. George left the meeting, and proceeded down Highway 60 to Foresdale where he met Helicopter 355 and began to recon the Rodeo Fire.

Once the Rodeo Fire put up a large smoke plume and began its march to the north, Chief Paul Watson of Pinetop Fire and Tom Beddow, Fire Staff for the Forest Service, went to Whiteriver and met with Ken Butler, Fire Management Officer before dark on the 18th. Paul offered any of his engines and firefighters that could be used. [6.e] Ken responded that the B.I.A. could not use fire engines on the fire. They needed crews and dozers. Tom Beddow suggested that Chief Watson and some of the local fire departments go to Pinedale and Linden and begin to triage houses with Linden and Pinedale-Clay Springs Fire Departments. He would send Forest Service resources to the Mogollon Rim on Forest Road 300 to prepare for a burnout if the fire got away from initial attack.

Chief Roger Mineer of Lakeside Fire met George Leech, who was in charge of Operations on the Rodeo Fire, at the Cibeque Ridge vantage point close to midnight. There, he remarked at how extensive and how hot the fire was burning. While there, Roger and George saw several pinyon and juniper trees burst into flame ahead of a rapidly moving flame front.

Chief Mineer echoed Chief Watson's offer to dispatch Lakeside's engines and equipment. Both fire departments had the one-ton pickup, Type 6 4 x 4 wildland fire engines and the larger Type 3 engines. Show Low and Linden Fire Departments were also ready to lend assistance. George explained that this was not an "engine show" as the few roads in the area were very steep and the fire was not moving along those roads that would facilitate engine operations. This was a "dirt diggers" show. [6.f]

Ken Butler sincerely felt that the Ft. Apache Fire forces would catch the Rodeo Fire that night, when the temperatures cooled down and the humidity rose.

Earlier in the evening, Show Low Mayor Gene Kelly presided over a City Council meeting, which began at 7:00 p.m. Mayor Kelly had been elected only two weeks prior in a special election. The City Council took a break and went to the front porch of City Hall to look at the smoke plume of a new fire on the White Mountain Apache Reservation. What they saw caused alarm. Mayor Kelly expressed frustration and apprehension with the severe conditions and the possibility of fire coming toward Show Low. [6.g]

June 19th, Wednesday

- 0009—Night winds picked up from the South. Winds began to fan fire on the east side. Fire moved rapidly toward Carrizo Creek with 100'+ flames.

Fire across Cibeque Ridge from Cibeque Ridge Road about midnight on June 18th. Photo by George Leech.

- 0200-- George advised Ft. Apache Fire Staff, Ken Butler of the gravity of the situation. Ken called Navajo County Sheriff's Office and the chiefs of the Rim Fire Protection Group to advise them that this fire is not going to stop and they should prepare communities in the path of the fire's advance.

Night winds fan the fire. Photo by Paul Bead.

- 0630—All available crews are assigned to Carrizo Creek to flank the fire and slow the advance to the east and north. Nearly 300 firefighters and four dozers were working on the ground. 3 SEAT's launched and dropped continuously on the head of the fire, without slowing the fire's advance any at all.

Fire approaching Carrizo Creek from the south at 0900 hrs. Photo by Jerry Beddow.

- 0809—4th S.E.A.T in from Springerville dropped—load and return requested as fast as it could cycle. S.E.A.T.'s are working out of Cibeque Airstrip with a portable retardant mix base.
- 1000—Early morning winds push fire across Carrizo Creek. All crews pulled off line and to safety zones. Fire runs hard up slope toward Jumpoff Ridge in heavy brush. Fire is crowning on all four sides. 400' flames on north side, as fire is 1.5 to 2 miles wide and spotting 1.5 miles in front of flames.

Fire crosses Carrizo Creek at 1000 hrs. Photo by Jerry Beddow.

- 1110—Order for a Type I Team through White Mountain Dispatch in Springerville was placed with Southwest Coordination Center in Albuquerque.
- 1115—Humphrey's Type I Team assigned and enroute from Albuquerque.
- 1254—Winds in excess of 35 knots (a Red Flag Warning from National Weather Service) cause shutdown of the use of all aircraft, for safety reasons.
- 1342—Fire is approx. 3 miles south of Rim Road 300.

*Rodeo Fire under the smoke and below the Mogollon Rim in the afternoon of June 19th.
Photo by Jerry Beddow.*

- 1421—Fire entering McCleve Canyon and Mud Canyon. Estimated to be 19,200 acres and growing rapidly.
- 1440—Rodeo Fire has five separate smoke columns or plumes with extreme-plus fire behavior. It has become a "Plume Dominated" fire.

Flying over Highway 60 south of Show Low looking west at the five plumes of the Rodeo Fire at 1600 hrs on June 19th. Photo by Jerry Beddow.

Fire mid-way up Jumpoff Canyon below the Mogollon Rim. Photo by Jerry Beddow.

- 1529—Fire is topping "Jump Off" Canyon and spreading north.

Fire tops the Mogollon Rim at 1732 hr. with 300' flames on a six-mile wide flame front. As fire leaps up the chutes and narrow canyons of the Mogollon Rim, approximately 10,000 acres burns in only 15 minutes. Photo by Jerry Beddow.

- 1643—Evacuation Order requested for Linden, Pinedale, Timberland Acres and Clay Springs through Navajo County Sheriff Gary Butler. Hwy 260 is closed west of Show Low and east of Heber-Overgaard.
- 1724—Fire is in Turkey Canyon and at the top of Skunk Canyon and Jump Off Canyon.
- 1732—Fire crosses Rim Road 300 on 6-mile wide fire front. 300' to 1,000' flame lengths, extreme, intense burning conditions and very fast-changing, dangerous fire behavior.
- 1853—Fire estimated at 48,000 acres plus.
- 2100—Humphrey's team *receives line officer briefing* and will assume command of the Rodeo Fire at 0600 on June 20, 2002. Team will set up camp at Show Low High School.
- 2400—Fire estimated to be 53,000 acres and moving fast, even though it is midnight. Fire has developed its own weather and there is no moisture recovery due to little increased humidity at night. Fire burns as if it were the middle of the day.

In the dark of midnight, fire burns as bright as day. Photo by Varnell Gatewood.

*　　*　　*　　*　　*

Gary Holdcroft, a contract courier, had been in Cibeque about noon, to pick up medical samples that were to be sent to a Valley laboratory for analysis. He was also a volunteer fireman with the Linden Fire Department. Gary owns a home and lives just to the north of the fire station in Linden, which is to the west of Show Low on Highway 260. Gary took his collected samples and put them on the afternoon flight to Phoenix at the Show Low Airport.

Looking to the south, he saw a building smoke column that disturbed him. His training and recent weekly fire meetings had *made* him aware of the dangerous fire conditions in the White Mountains.

Gary even called Ft. Apache Fire Dispatch to report the smoke plume. He was told that fire resources were on the scene and that action was being taken on the fire.

From his house in Linden, before dark, Gary noticed the smoke column continuing to grow and darken. Gary "… noticed what appeared to be snow, wafting down from the sky. It was actually quite pretty, but I knew what it was. Ash… one large piece was in the shape of an oak leaf… the fire was burning with enough intensity to send this bit of ash over twenty air miles to the north"… to his front yard.

Rodeo Fire from Linden Fire Department in the afternoon of June 19th. Photo by Dewayne Saxton.

With a sense of dread, Gary and his wife began to pack valuables into their cars for a possible evacuation. His gut told him that this action was not just a precaution. [6.h]

*   *   *   *   *

Officials of Ft. Apache Fire have received considerable criticism for not stopping the Rodeo Fire when it was small. Some observers felt that more resources should have been but on the fire, quicker. Ft. Apache Fire threw just about everything they had at this fire. This was a fire season that had been predicted by Forest Service researcher, Jack Dieterech, some 40 years prior and Dr. Wally Covington only eight years prior. There are some things that need to be remembered/considered:

- The first two S.E.A.T.'s dropped a load of retardant each on the head of the fire only 12 minutes after it was reported. The fire was not slowed at all, in fact the retardant vaporized before hitting the ground. Conditions were more than extreme.
- Two fire engines, a nurse tanker, two 10-person crews and an Initial Attack I.C. were on scene only 13 minutes after the fire was reported.
- The fire had already grown to 15 acres when the first firefighters arrived.

- I.C Varnell Gatewood asked White Mountain Dispatch for as many as 8 heavy airtankers. He got two initially. Each had 1.5 hours flight time from Albuquerque and Silver City. They only dropped one load, as dusk was approaching and aircraft cannot fly over a fire at night, by federal regulation.
- Three bulldozers were ordered, but two hours were required to transport the first two to the fire. The third arrived several hours later.
- Ft. Apache pulled all available hand crews into the firefight.
- Four 20-person crews arrived close to midnight and were immediately rested so they could begin work in the Carrizo Creek area at daylight.
- At midnight, George Leech, Operations Section Chief for I.C. Gatewood, estimated the fire to be larger than 2,000 acres.
- The fire simply beat the firefighters to Carrizo Creek and that was the "last stand" before fire began its climb up the Mogollon Rim.

From 1000 hours (10:00 a.m.) on June 19th, when fire ran across Carrizo Creek and began its march up to the Mogollon Rim, to the time it breached the Rim at 1732 hrs. (5:32 p.m.), the Rodeo Fire burned in "blowup conditions." It changed from the awakening dragon to a multi-headed monster, roaring and spewing flame as it grew by leaps and bounds.

It consumed everything from the ground litter, pine straw, grass and brush to most all of the standing trees, burning them to stumps, with virtually no green left behind. As the flame front climbed an individual canyon, the walls of the canyon served as a chimney, compressing the fire's energy and accelerating up the chimney.

When it reached the top of the canyon, the flames moved faster than an elk can run and with enough power to uproot mature trees and toss them like matchsticks.

The Ft. Apache Fire organization had fought major fires in recent years that had threatened escaping the reservation… and they had been able to stop them. Ken Butler, Ft. Apache Fire Management Officer did relate that they were throwing all of their resources at this fire and that they would call the Rim Fire Protection Group (comprised of the area fire departments who had jurisdiction along the Mogollon Rim), if he felt they needed additional help. The problem with their confidence was that this was not a "normal" fire season, nor was this fire anything near "normal," even in its infancy.

The nighttime temperatures on the fire never cooled and the humidity never rose. The Rodeo fire actually burned more aggressively during the night than it had during the daylight. Afterwards when asked about not using the resources of Pinetop, Lakeside and Show Low, early on, F.M.O. Butler is said to have shrugged and admitted that it may have been a bad decision, but the resources did not fit the need or more simply, that fire engines were not what were needed. They could not get to where the fire was burning.

In retrospect, once the Rodeo Fire escaped initial attack, there truly was no catching it, no matter what was thrown at it. After only an hour and a few minutes, the Rodeo Fire had grown to more than 100 acres and was crowning and running. By that time, it simply was not "catchable!!" After analysis of dispatch logs, review of summaries/personal logs and interviewing those in charge of the fire efforts at suppression, I feel strongly that Ft. Apache reacted professionally and efficiently. One only has to utilize Dr. Pyne's analogy of the Royal Flush of fire conditions, discussed in Chapter 2. The land and forests were just awaiting an ignition to awaken the monster.

The monster was certainly awake and moving with a ravenous appetite as fire came up over the Mogollon Rim in a spectacular display of Ma Nature's raw power with 300 foot, 2000 degree + flames. The monster had flexed his might and now was running in many directions, seeking anything that burns to satisfy his ravenous appetite. Ken Butler was quoted as saying, without humor or sarcasm, "The Rodeo Fire fight was sort of like Humpty Dumpty, with all the King's horses and all the King's men…!" [6.i] Arizona history was in the making.

The face of the Monster captured in the Rodeo Fire's smoke column, taken late afternoon of June 19th from White Mountain Lakes, about 16 miles from the fire. Photo by Jean Burr.

CH. 7: LOST & DESPERATE

"There is no right way to do a wrong thing." ~ Poppa Garrett

She was not familiar with the Mountain and she had not "studied" the ways of life in the school of Mother Nature. She was from the Valley and accustomed to universal cell phone service, traffic lights, sidewalks, malls and the immediate benefits of emergency management services, such as fire, police and E.M.T.'s. There, she lived in a civilized, sheltered environment. Mother Nature was prepared to give the young woman a lesson in basic survival.

It was June 17th. She was Valinda Jo Elliott, a 31-year-old woman who left Phoenix at about 9:00 a.m. with her boss, Ransford Olmsted, to service arcade and vending machines in Young, Arizona. She was about to enroll in Mother Nature's school of reality.

Due to the extreme fire season, warnings were up everywhere. The Tonto National Forest was closed and the Apache-Sitgreaves National Forest was in total fire restrictions. White Mountain Apache Tribe had warnings and closure signs and barricades up on every road access entering the reservation. Either Olmsted and Elliot ignored the warnings or they chose to go a different route to avoid the restrictions.

Restrictions Sign. Photo by USFS, Apache-Sitgreaves National Forest.

They missed the turnoff to Young on the south side of Roosevelt Lake and continued on to the Salt River Canyon, where Mr. Olmsted bought a map at the White Mountain Apache Trading Post and asked for directions to Young through Cibeque. For some reason, he did not buy gas. Just out of Cibeque, the pair again made a wrong turn, taking Apache Route 12-A instead of State Route 12.

Elliott had gotten cell phone service for a short time and attempted to call Arizona State Parks, Tonto National Forest and Arizona Game and Fish offices. She was seeking directions to get back to "civilization." All she got was answering machines. They were definitely in strange country and had no clue how to get back on the right road to Young.

In any event, they took another wrong turn and came to a barricade blocking the road, posted TOTAL CLOSURE of the reservation beyond that point, due to extreme fire danger. They moved the barricade and continued on, hoping that they would find services on up the road, or at least someone's house, where they might get better directions and maybe purchase some gasoline.

Road Closure Barricade. Photo by USFS, Apache-Sitgreaves National Forest.

Finding nothing but more forest and a climbing, twisting mountain road, they soon ran out of gas. After a fitful night in the truck, Mr. Olmsted decided to hike back down the road to find help. Off he went, leaving Valinda at his white 1996 Dodge truck. He would have to walk 30 miles to get help from some local men, who gave him a ride to Cibeque. There he bought gas and Tribal Game and Fish Officers assisted him back to his truck. He then filed a "missing persons" report, when he could not find Valinda Jo Elliott anywhere near the truck.

Ms. Elliott could not get cell phone service at the truck. She could not understand why and thought that if she could only get high enough to reach a cell phone tower, she would be able to call out and get help. She decided to take a little hike and climb the nearest mountain.

She was dressed in shorts and a tank top, with only flip-flops for foot wear, certainly not what most would have considered appropriate attire for a trip to the woods or for hiking. She had little to no preparation for the experience that she was about to undergo. She had no water bottle and took only two cigarettes, her lighter and a towel. Going up the mountain was much harder than she had anticipated and after what seemed an eternity of climbing and slip-sliding, she was able to get cell phone service.

She called 911 six times, but the signal was lost before the call was completed each time. So, higher she must go, she surmised. The scenery on the hike was quite nice, as the Ponderosa Pine forest was so green, cool and serene and the higher she climbed, the more splendid the views were. However, sundown caught her on the mountain with no flashlight and no idea how to get back to the road and to the security of her boss' vehicle.

Even though it was severely "self inflicted," she was now "lost." She spent the second night alone and unprotected somewhere on a mountain. Only God knew where she was, she was sure. She found nothing to eat or drink and had no shelter other than the forest. The forest that initially seemed cool and refreshing, now became more intimidating and foreboding.

She continued on the next day, going higher and trying her cell phone, but to no avail. A third night was spent on the mountain, again without food, water or shelter. Due to the occasional checking for service, the cell phone was now dead. A close encounter with a young black bear unnerved her so that she slept on a large flat rock, up on the side of a steep hill. The timid bear was as surprised as she… and took off in the opposite direction with great haste.

Elliott was becoming desperate and on the verge of panic, not to mention consumed with thirst and hunger. The mountain and Mother Nature had given her some harsh lessons and now she was being challenged with life's biggest test… that of survival.

Her challenges and obstacles were the same that the Ancient Ones faced, only they had been to Mother Nature's school and most had passed. She must soon find water and she must find a way to contact civilization and get help. The alternative to failing the test was losing her life. She also began to understand something of Mother Nature's harshness as a schoolmaster. Not many second chances in this program.

Early in the pre-dawn of June 20, 2002, Valinda Jo Elliott crossed a ridge and saw what looked like farm fields below. She also saw a murky pool of standing water. Valinda had come to Chediski Farms, still on the White Mountain Apache Reservation, still below the Mogollon Rim. Chediski in Apache means "tall white woman," which refers to the limestone promontories above the meadow where the old farm fields are located.

She descended to the meadow, hoping to find a house or someone to give her much needed assistance. Instead, she found only dilapidated corrals and abandoned fields. She never contemplated how wild and remote this land actually was. There was water in a shallow pool and she finally was able to get a drink. It must have been sweet as nectar, as thirsty as she was, even though it would have been stagnant and repugnant to one used to iced fountain drinks and cool bottled water. Still, it met the first need of survival and gave Valinda Jo Elliott a bit of reassurance.

Then she heard the rotor noise from a passing helicopter overhead. She scrambled back up the hill to a spot with an opening and some low brush and dried grass. She stopped about halfway between the meadow and the eastern ridge of Chediski Mountain. There, she lit two clumps of brush and grass with her lighter. It was shortly after 7:00 a.m. [7.a]

At approximately 6:30 a.m., a father and son team, Scott Clifton, son/pilot and Jerry Clifton, dad/videographer were in K.P.H.O.-Channel 5's News Hawk-5 helicopter, departing Scottsdale Airport. They were enroute to cover the Rodeo Fire. Cruising at about 11,000 feet elevation, Jerry saw a thin tendril of grey smoke below. They were concerned that the smoke might be from a plane or helicopter crash. Scott descended to take a closer look.

When they got near, they saw a woman waving something like a cloth or towel, just a bit below the small fires. Jerry recorded the new fire activity, location and size, using the external nose camera on the helicopter, while Scott noted the latitude and longitude on his G.P.S. system and radioed the location into the Engineering Dispatcher at Channel 5's studio, back in Phoenix (North 34 degrees, 8 minutes, 39 seconds and West 110 degrees, 42 minutes, 9 seconds).

He asked Ms. Kim Pappas, an assignment editor at the station to notify authorities that there was another fire. He also informed Pappas that they were approximately 10 miles east of Young and, he thought, 20 miles west of the Rodeo Fire. Scott landed NewsHawk-5 in the meadow below. He observed another helicopter pass by and called the pilot, Rick Crabbs in KPNX Sky-12's news helicopter and asked him to pass the information and location on the new fire to Rodeo Fire Air Attack, so that action could be initiated by firefighters to suppress this new fire, before it got away. The signal fire had served its purpose and the rescue of one lost woman was in progress.

Once on the ground, Scott could no longer communicate with anyone out of "line of sight." Scott shut the engine down and both men exited the helicopter as the young woman slipped and slid down the hill approximately a quarter of a mile to their landing site. When she got there, her first question was if they had any water and could they please help her. She told of being stranded and her boss going for help and that she had been wandering in the forest for two days and nights. She was bone weary and on the verge of hysteria. Jerry captured her story on video.

Ms. Elliott asked to be taken to a hospital. The News Hawk 5 helicopter was an Aerospatiale A-Star, B-2 model. That model would normally hold the pilot and four passengers, but with all the camera equipment, editing computers and additional communications equipment, there was only room for the pilot and the videographer in the news conversion model.

Jerry Clifton removed his portable cameras and some other equipment and made room for the now rescued Valinda Jo Elliot to be transported. The nearest hospital was approximately 40 miles to the west in Payson. Once airborne, Scott radioed Kim Pappas at Engineering in the Phoenix studio and informed the station that they had picked up a lost woman and were transporting her to Payson Hospital for evaluation and any necessary treatment. Jerry also transmitted a video package that was the story of the young lady's trials and rescue by News Hawk 5, which was immediately put on the air.

Ms. Pappas confirmed that she had called the Arizona Department of Public Safety's Phoenix Dispatch, the Tonto National Forest, Gila County Sheriff's Office and the Southwest Coordination Center in Albuquerque, with the coordinates of the new fire. The time of the calls spanned from 6:57 a.m. to about 7:04 a.m. D.P.S. did call the White Mountain Apache Tribal police, but they are not connected by either proximity or radio communications to Ft. Apache Fire Dispatch.

All those were appropriate and worthy calls, except the information had to pass through various bureaucratic filters… and did not get passed to Ft. Apache Fire Dispatch for more than an hour. According to interagency protocol, Ft. Apache Fire had the primary responsibility to respond to this new wildland fire, since it was on the reservation and inside their jurisdiction. Other agencies would support as needed and requested, but initial attack belonged to Ft. Apache. [7.b, 7.c]

In addition, Fire Weather Forecasters with the National Weather Service had forecast Red Flag Warnings for most of the Mogollon Rim Country, which included both the Rodeo Fire and the Chediski Fire. That meant that the relative humidity would be less than 15%, sustained winds would be greater than 25 miles per hour, and 10 hour fuel sticks would be less than 10%. Red Flag Conditions are a warning that indicates fire behavior will be extreme, causing any wildfire to be very difficult to suppress. It is a 'Watch Out" situation that firefighters pay close attention to. Experience has proven that Red Flag Warnings and fire can produce fatality situations in explosive, blowup fire conditions.

Jerry Beddow had been a long-term firefighter on the Apache Sitgreaves National Forest. His day job was as the Fire Management Officer on the Springerville Ranger District. One of his fire qualifications was as an Aerial Observer, until a fire was spotted. Then the position would convert to tactical operations and become "Air Attack." Jerry was "home-grown," and was both knowledgeable and experienced in fire. He knew the White Mountains very well. He was well qualified as an Air Attack (Type I) with over 20 years' experience and was the primary Air Attack on the Apache-Sitgreaves National Forest.

An aerial observer looks for fires and locates them to get fire fighting resources on the way, much as a mobile "lookout" in the sky. Air Attack is a "General in the Sky." Fixed wing air resources over a fire are invaluable to engines and crews on the ground as their "eyes in the sky." The Air Attack can route responding ground fire resources in to the fire, give firefighters on the ground constant updates concerning current burning conditions, intensity and direction of spread. And most importantly, Air Attack monitors changes in the activity of the fire, as changes occur, so that firefighters on the ground can work more safely.

Air Attack advises helicopters and air tankers of this same information and also routes air tankers in to the site, suggesting drop zones and coverage levels of retardant to best help firefighters on the ground battling the blaze. Usually, Air Attack uses a moniker of the fire name, such as "Rodeo Air Attack" on a large fire. In initial attack, it may be the abbreviated tail number of the airplane, in this case "3-9-Quebec" for clear radio communications.

Jerry and his pilot, Mike Wray took off from Springerville Airport at approximately 7:30 a.m., enroute to do a reconnaissance flight of the area west of the Rodeo Fire, as new smoke had been reported to White Mountain Zone Dispatch in Springerville. All air operations over the growing Rodeo Fire were under the control of Larry Humphrey's Type I Incident Management. Jerry checked in with Cliff Claridge, Rodeo Air Attack – 700 Sierra Romeo – as he flew over the Rodeo Fire and proceeded west.

At 8:00 a.m., he radioed that he had spotted a new smoke and was going to fly over it. Then he gave a legal location of Township 10 North, Range 15 East, Section 26 with a geographical location of four miles south of the reservation line at the end of Lost Tank Ridge, near the 101 Road. He told the Forest Service Dispatcher at Springerville that the fire was definitely on the White Mountain Apache Reservation. His legal subdivision location matched up to the GPS location that Scott Clifton in Newshawk 5 had given KPHO earlier. White Mountain Dispatch gave the location of the new fire to Ft. Apache Fire Dispatch. [7.d]

Scott and Jerry Clifton took Ms. Elliott to the Payson Hospital Emergency Room and returned to Chediski Farms to retrieve their equipment that had been off-loaded to make room for Ms. Elliott. They arrived shortly after 8:00 a.m. and noticed that there were no firefighters on the scene, which surprised them.

There was an airplane overhead and they radioed 39-Quebec for permission to land and pick up their equipment. Their GPS coordinates of the fire location were given to 39-Quebec and a brief version of the rescue. Permission was granted and they were informed that firefighters were on the way. They retrieved their equipment and flew on to cover the Rodeo Fire.

Here is a summary of events from Ft. Apache Dispatch Logs, Tonto National Forest Dispatch Logs and White Mountain Zone Dispatch Logs:

- 0837 hrs. – Ft. Apache Fire Dispatch received confirmation on the new fire and named it Chediski, since it was near the Chediski Farms and Chediski Peak. Immediately, Helicopter 355, Patrol Airplane Papa-1 and two S.E.A.T.s (Single Engine Air Tankers) were launched to begin suppression of the fire.

- 0900 hrs. – both S.E.A.T.s dropped retardant on the upper ends of the fire and returned to Cibeque Airstrip to reload with retardant and return. Helicopter 355 arrived in the area and did an aerial recon.

- 0905 hrs. --Initial Attack Incident Commander Reginald Armstrong and two firefighters off loaded from H-355 at 9:05 a.m. They landed in the same meadow where NewsHawk 5 had picked up Valinda Jo Elliot. Armstrong's crew hiked up to the fire.

- 0913 hrs. – Armstrong and his two firefighters began digging line. The Chediski Fire was already three acres with flames of three to four feet at the upper end as the fire grew to the northwest. I. C. Armstrong immediately called Floyd Walker, the Helicopter Manager in H-355 and asked for more helitack firefighters and for the return of both S.E.A.T.s with another load of retardant.

- 0915 hrs. – Papa 1 with Aubrey Aday on board as Ft. Apache's Air Attack arrives over the fire. Jerry Beddow in 39-Quebec is relieved and returns to Springerville. Two heavy air tankers, diverted from the Rodeo Fire are cancelled and return to the Rodeo to deliver retardant near Pinedale. The S.E.A.T.s continued working the fire. Ft. Apache Fire resources once again were convinced that they would be able to "catch" this new Chediski Fire.

- 0936 hrs. – Maurice Williams arrived from Cibeque. He was the Operations Section Chief on Kvale's Type II Incident Management Team and was given verbal authorization over the radio to assume command of the fire. He immediately ordered the Prescott Hotshots, Apache Crews 1, 2, 3 & 8, which were 20-person handcrews, 7 Type 6 engines, and four D-6 bulldozers. He also requested that the three Pleasant Valley Forest Service engines be re-ordered and asked to continue to this new fire to assist with suppression.

- 0945 hrs. – I.C. Williams requested two heavy air tankers. Told none were available. Request was sent to Southwest Coordination Center to be put on priority list.

- 1017 hrs. – Promontory Lookout called White Mountain Zone Dispatch to report status on the Chediski Fire. The lookout reported a change in the smoke from white to dark and that fire activity appeared to be picking up significantly. Even though early, the day was not looking very positive for firefighters. Promontory Lookout would continue to monitor and report the status of the Chediski Fire.

Chediski Fire Column from Black Canyon Lake about noon June 20, 2002.
Photo by USFS, Apache-Sitgreaves National Forest.

- 1035 hrs. – 23 tribal Timber Stand Improvement crewmembers were sent to the top of the mesa to begin flanking the fire.
- 1045 hrs. -- Prescott Hotshots and Apache 1, 2, 3 & 8 crews arrive and began to dig indirect line from a safe anchor point in the canyon bottom to the rock bluff on the south side of the fire. The fireline would require burnout when constructed and support was given from the three Pleasant Valley engines that had also arrived.
- 1054 hrs. – Armstrong took a weather reading. The temperature was 90 degrees and the relative humidity was 17 %. Winds were about 5-7 miles per hour. Fire activity was increasing, but the initial attack "direct" line close to the edge of the fire was becoming too hot to continue.
- 1130 hrs. — Chediski Lookout reported that the winds had increased to 25 miles per hour with gusts to 35 m.p.h. The winds were out of the Southeast, due to the drainage orientation of Lost Tank Canyon and the uphill draft of Chediski Peak. Daytime winds usually flow up canyon, until air reaches the top of the ridges. Then the predominant Southwest winds override local canyon winds, often causing a curl or vortex where winds are most turbulent in chutes, saddles and on the lee side of the ridge.
- 11:40 hrs. – Armstrong took another weather reading. The temperature had risen to 97 degrees, the humidity dropped to 9%, and winds were increasing. In only 46 minutes, the temperature had risen seven degrees and the humidity had dropped by eight percent. That is a HUGE change in the burning conditions, even without the increase in winds. If the winds had doubled to 15 miles per hour, down in the canyon where they were fighting the fire, the added winds would have meant an acceleration of at least four times in the rate of spread at the head of the Chediski Fire. When the head or top of the fire reached a steep, narrow chute, it literally exploded up the mountain. Both Colcord Lookout and Chediski Lookout reported the smoke changed from white to dark and increased dramatically in volume. That meant that the fire was burning with much more energy and growing rapidly. It also meant that the fuels were changing from grass and

light brush to heavy brush and some timber. All the firefighters were forced to switch from Direct Attack, which is digging fireline right at the edge of the flames to an Indirect Attack. When flames exceed four feet in height, firefighters cannot safely continue to battle the fire right at the edge of the flames. The heat is just too intense. They have to fall back to a safe distance to dig fireline. Then they burn out between their dug fireline and the edge of the fire, to secure the line and rob the area between the line and the fire of fuel. The main fire will actually pull the smaller burnout fire into it, as it drafts air from the sides and smoke and heat rise off the top. It is an old firefighter truism that the only "Safe fireline" is a "black fireline!!" However, the wider the black, the better. By noon, winds had increased to more than 35 miles per hour, so that aircraft were no longer safe to operate. The Red Flag Warning had come into effect and all planes and most helicopters were grounded. Ground resources responding to the request for assistance were slow, due to long distances on primitive roads and crews and engines starting from other areas, such as Cibeque, Ft. Apache, Pleasant Valley, Payson and Heber.

Chediski Fire flamefront. Photo by U.S.F.S, Apache-Sitgreaves National Forest.

- 1200 hrs. – the Chediski Fire was estimated at 120 acres.
- 1354 hrs. — Chediski L.O. reported spot fires with "red smoke" way out in front of main fire in Sec 23. Fire had crossed Lost Tank Canyon and was leaping up the canyon wall. This was most likely a combination of fire whirls and unburned gases mixing with oxygen and burning in the air. This was extreme fire behavior.

*   *   *   *   *

Chief Mel Epps of the Heber/Overgaard Fire Department heard of the new fire at Chediski Farms over the radio and was extremely concerned with the now-named Chediski Fire, since his town was directly in the path of potential disaster, if the fire escaped initial attack and burned up over the Mogollon Rim. His concern led him to ask his friend and neighbor, Pat McLeod if he would fly him over and have a look at the fire. At approximately 10:30 a.m., they lifted off from Heber/Overgaard's Air Park and flew the 19 air miles south to the Chediski Fire.

They saw the helicopters and S.E.A.T.s working and saw firefighters on the ground. Radio traffic indicated that additional crews, engines and bulldozers were enroute to assist in the fire fighting effort. Mel and Pat reconned the area for some time, although they had to remain at 12,000 feet above ground level due to an F.A.A. Temporary Flight Restriction, already in place. They returned to the Air Park with some confidence that the fire was being "handled."

When they landed at just before noon, Chief Epps looked back to the south and saw the black mushrooming smoke plume of the Chediski. That short-lived confidence melted and was replaced with a dark sense of dread. Mel viewed the same change in smoke and building column that the two lookouts reported. He was fearful that the firestorm would certainly reach his community.

Chediski Fire. Column growing and becoming much darker, indicating hotter burn and heavier fuels.
Photo by U.S.F.S, Apache-Sitgreaves National Forest.

Another complication arose. Once the Chediski Fire climbed over the 6,589 foot tall Chediski Peak and raced through Lost Tank Canyon, ground access by roads was extremely limited and there were few escape routes and safety zones for any firefighters on the east side of the fire.

The Rodeo Fire was less than 15 miles to the east in very rugged country with only a few primitive roads on that side as well. As the fires burned, even though some distance apart, there was a very good chance that they could burn towards each other and merge with an awesome multiplication of energy and destruction.

A conscious decision was made to not bring resources in from above the Rim, nor from the east side of the Chediski Fire in response to concerns for firefighter safety. Resources of engines and at least six more crews continued to arrive at Chediski Farms and were immediately put to work on the fire suppression efforts. Two bulldozers were dispatched to the fire at 10:18 a.m., but would not arrive for four hours.

Notes from dispatch logs and summaries continue:

- 1500 hrs. – the fire had grown to an estimated 1,200 acres.
- 1530 hrs. — Papa 1 Air Observer reported the Chediski Fire was more than 2,000 acres and a call went out to evacuate the Canyon Creek Fish Hatchery and the OW Ranch.
- 1542 hrs. – Ft. Apache Fire Management Officer, Ken Butler requested Rich Kvale's Type II Incident Management Team be formally assigned to take command of the Chediski Fire at 1800 hrs. This was the local Arizona fire team that had first been assigned when the Rodeo Fire blew up. They were still in the area, assisting the transition to Larry Humphrey's Type I Team on the Rodeo Fire and had set up camp and a base of operations in Cibeque. Maurice Williams, Operations Section Chief on Kvale's Team had actually commanded the extended attack for Ft. Apache Fire Management.
- 1600 hrs. – a one hour standby to evacuate order was suggested to Navajo County Sheriff Gary Butler for all the residents of Heber/Overgaard and all the isolated homes, campgrounds and recreationists in the path of the Chediski Fire. Law enforcement officers began spreading the word and clearing the area of people in front of the fire's path.
- 2055 hrs. – Helicopter H-355 flew a recon and estimated the fire at more than 7,000 acres.

Chediski Fire mid afternoon on June 20, 2002. Photo by Rob Schumacher, Arizona Republic

But for the irresponsible actions with absolutely "zero" common sense and little outdoor knowledge on two people's part, Olmsted and Elliott, the Chediski Fire should never have been ignited. While it was true that Valinda Jo Elliot was lost and desperate, was her life in immediate danger? Who knows, although her appearance on the Channel 5 video was more of fatigue and confusion than it was life threatening.

They had been made aware of the fire danger and had seen the road signs and warnings. They even moved a reservation road barricade posting the closure of the road beyond that point. In a statement to authorities, Ms. Elliott said that she lit the signal fire to get attention. **IT DID!!**

Now, there were two multi-headed monsters on the loose, raging and ravaging the White Mountains. Radio traffic amongst firefighters in the area referred to the smoke columns of the two fires as the "Twin Towers of Fire," reflecting on the disaster of 9/11 and the twin towers in New York City just nine months prior.

Looking west from Highway 60. Rodeo Fire column is nearest and Chediski Fire column is farther west. Mid-afternoon photo by Jerry Beddow in 39-Quebec.

*Looking east with Chediski Fire in the foreground and the Rodeo Fire in the background.
Photo by Rob Schumacher, Arizona Republic.*

The perfect storm predicted by Stephen Pyne and others was just beginning and the "royal flush" of disaster had been drawn and shown, cards face up.

*Looking northwest from Cibeque up Salt Creek at the Chediski Fire, afternoon of June 22nd.
Photo by Paul Bead.*

CH. 8: TWO WEEKS OF "HELL" IN THE WHITE MOUNTAINS

"Earth is a fire planet. For four hundred million years it has had the ingredients to sustain fire; an oxygenated atmosphere, terrestrial fuels... and lightning. Homo Sapiens is a fire creature, with a species monopoly over fire's manipulation.
~ Stephen Pyne, America's Fires

Larry Humphrey's Southwest Type I Incident Management Team was dispatched to a fire north of Cuba, New Mexico on Sunday, June 16, 2002. That was a fire that resulted from a natural gas line rupture and an ignition that burned the forest around it like a blowtorch in a haystack. Cooperation among the gas company, local fire departments and the initial attack resources of the Santa Fe National Forest got the gas shut off and had the fire well in hand by the time we assembled in Cuba to receive our line officer briefing.

It did not appear that the services of our Type I Team were needed and we never did receive command of the B.M.G. Fire, but we stayed for 48 hours just to be sure that the fire did not get away, as burning conditions were extreme all across the Southwest.

On Tuesday, June 19th, we left Cuba and were to meet at a hotel in Albuquerque at noon. At that point, plans were that we would go into a holding pattern, staged, until another fire broke out. It is advantageous to have a Type I Team assembled and collected in one place, as the 40+ members of Humphrey's Team came from all over Arizona and New Mexico. Staging of teams and resources is a common practice in extreme fire conditions. That way, assembly and travel time do not delay team response on major fires. On June 18th, there were no less than thirteen large fires in the western U.S. with incident management teams on them. These included:

- Haymen Fire, started by a Forest Service Fire Prevention Technician who was enraged by a domestic dispute. The fire burned 113,000 acres and 39 homes, and burned almost to the southwestern edge of Denver, Colorado.
- Missionary Ridge Fire near Durango, Colorado, which burned 70,085 acres and 57 homes.
- Coal Seam Fire near Grand Junction, Colorado burned 12,105 acres and 43 homes.

There were more than 85 new fires reported throughout the west, just on this one day. Critical resources of heavy air tankers, helicopters and hotshot crews were in high demand and very short supply. [8.a] The National Multiple Agency Coordination Group (M.A.C.) at the national fire headquarters in Boise handled competition for these resources. As priorities changed, those scarce resources were allocated one at a time or dealt much like cards in a poker game. The stakes were communities and millions of acres of parks, forests and watersheds. Every incident management team working on a fire was in competition for the 38 heavy air tankers, 78 hotshot crews and approximately 300 fire-ready helicopters that were available nationwide.

*   *   *   *   *

June 19th. Wednesday

We did not have long to wait in a holding pattern. At 1115 hours on June 19th, Incident Commander Larry Humphrey received a call from the Southwest Coordination Center in Albuquerque, before we even got to Espanola, enroute to Albuquerque. In fact, by cell phone and radio, each Command Officer and General Staff Chief got the message from Larry Humphrey or his Deputy, Jeff Whitney, that we were not going to meet at the hotel. Instead, we were being dispatched to a fire on the White Mountain Apache Reservation that had the potential to burn onto the Apache-Sitgreaves National Forest and threaten communities.

Through a pre-arranged call system, the message was relayed to every person on the team. Our instructions were to proceed on I-40 west to Holbrook and then down Arizona Highway 77 to Show Low and on Route 73 to Whiteriver, where we would receive a line officer's briefing and delegation of authority to manage the fire. That letter would also give us objectives that we would adhere to, which often determined how we would battle the fire.

By the time we reached Grants, New Mexico, there was a pall of smoke in the air. By the time we reached Gallup, New Mexico, it was as if we were driving in a fog. We were still 150 air miles from the fire. When we reached Holbrook, there was solid, dense smoke and we knew that we were in for battle with an extreme, climax fire. As we drove through Show Low, we could see the glow of flames off to the southwest. Our meeting was at the Bureau of Indian Affairs Office in Whiteriver at 2100 hours (9:00 p.m.).

Top: Smoke from the Rodeo Fire in Holbrook late afternoon of June 19, 2002. Photo by Jeff Clark
Left: Smoke Column on the evening of June 19th. Photo by George Leech
Right: Rodeo Fire Smoke Column on afternoon of June 19th from Deuce of Clubs near K-Mart in Show Low.
Photo by USFS, Apache-Sitgreaves National Forest

As we traveled, we began to gather information and intelligence on the Rodeo Fire for each specialty and discipline, as would any Type I Team. Our team had already been out three times this year and we were a well-oiled, firefighting machine. The more information we had, the better and faster we would be able to begin the battle.

This was what we did, and previous fires had shown that our team was very proficient and effective. Just two weeks prior, we had stopped the Bullock Fire from burning into the town of Summerhaven and across the Santa Catalina Highway on Mt. Lemmon near Tucson.

My Deputy Information Officer was Chadeen Palmer, who was the White Mountain Apache Tribal Public Affairs Officer. Her dad, Harry Brewer, had been the Fire Management Officer for Ft. Apache Fire for 17 years. Chadeen grew up with fire and was highly regarded in the White Mountain communities as a public affairs specialist. We also had a trainee with us, Danny Randall, from the Bureau of Land Management out of Grants, New Mexico. Just in the Information function alone, this would be our third season working together.

Deputy Information Officer Chadeen Palmer. Photo by White Mountain Independent News

Several members of our team worked for the Bureau of Indian Affairs on the reservation, or for the Forest Service in Show Low or Springerville. As we called and each of us gathered "intel" on the Rodeo fire activity, we found a uniformity of disbelief in all who had seen the Rodeo Fire develop. None had ever seen this kind of fire before, not even in the Yellowstone Fires of 1988 that burned 1.2 million acres in five weeks. The rate of spread or growth of this Rodeo Fire was off the fire behavior calculation charts.

Flames of 300 feet to 1,000 feet had been witnessed. Several people told us that the fire had already crossed the Mogollon Rim and into the Sitgreaves National Forest. It was headed for the villages of Pinedale, Timberland Acres, Clay Springs and Linden. WHEW!! That this fire was ominous and was going to be more than a challenge grew with almost every cell phone call and bit of information received… and we had not even gotten there, yet.

Above the Rim, Initial Attack Incident Commander Lloyd Wilmes had already ordered 200 fire engines, 100 20-person crews, all the hotshot crews he could get and 50 bulldozers in anticipation of the difficult time ahead. Lloyd and our operations Section Chiefs, Roy Hall and Buck Wickham, talked by cell phone several times as our team was enroute. They concurred with Lloyd's resource order and left it in process.

Roy had been on large difficult fires for

Sun obscured by Rodeo Fire smoke on Cibeque Ridge on June 19th. Photo by Varnell Gatewood

most of his entire career. He had recently been promoted to the Assistant Director of Fire and Aviation Management with responsibility for Fuels Management for the Forest Service in Albuquerque. He later told me that of all the fires he has been on, the Rodeo-Chediski "was the battle of a lifetime and it left deep marks in [his] character!" [8.b]

The Type II team commanded by Rich Kvale, Forest Service Fire Staff from the Coronado National Forest in Tucson, had been ordered at 2230 hours (10:30 p.m.) on the 18th and was in Whiteriver. Kvale had not actually received a delegation of authority and had not taken command of the Rodeo Fire. When the Type I Team was called, Kvale's Team was put on hold and assisted with ordering resources and gathering intelligence and initiating plans for daily shift actions. They met with us at the B.I.A office and were then assigned to work the south end of the fire. They would be based out of the Cibeque Community Center and would continue building line from the heel of the fire up both east and west flanks.

When we got to Whiteriver, we had about an hour before the meeting started, to gather more information from initial attack resources, Kvale's Team and from Ft. Apache Dispatch. At 2100 hours (9:00 p.m. Mountain Standard Time), we met with Dallas Massey (Tribal Chairman of the White Mountain Apaches), Ben Nuvamsa (Superintendent of Ft. Apache B.I.A.), John Bedell (Forest Supervisor of the Apache Sitgreaves National Forest), Kirk Rowdibaugh from Arizona State Lands, and a host of local officials.

We were briefed by Varnell Gatewood, Initial Attack Incident Commander, George Leech, Operations Section Chief and Lloyd Wilmes, Incident Commander on the Sitgreaves Forest/ Fire Behavior Analyst/Air Attack for the White Mountain Zone. They all painted a picture of the most extreme fire behavior that any of the three had ever seen, even though they each had been on fires all over the U.S. for the last 20 to 30 years, and were each expert and experienced firemen.

Varnell Gatewood told us that Ft. Apache Fire had thrown everything that they had at this fire, which was definitely human caused. They called in extra crews and bulldozers and hoped to flank the head of the fire and pinch it off at Carrizo Creek, which was flowing water, early in the morning of the 19th. The fire actually burned hotter during the night of the 18th than it did during the day of ignition. It had burned hot enough at night that it created its own weather, where winds had not died down, temperatures on the fire had not cooled off and there had been no humidity recovery during the dark hours. Anomalous fire behavior, almost beyond comprehension!!

Rodeo Fire Whirl on Cibeque Ridge. Photo by Varnell Gatewood

Varnell re-emphasized that the fire had burned more aggressively during the midnight hours than it did in the daylight of the 18th and it just beat the firefighters to the creek. Once fire crossed Carrizo Creek, intensity increased with extreme fire behavior, to the point where firefighters were not able to work the flanks safely and were pulled off the firelines to safety zones.

Multiple plumes of Rodeo Fire as flame front climbs the Mogollon Rim. Note the spot fires out in front (to the right of photo). Photo taken early afternoon by George Leech

George Leech had been in a helicopter most of the morning of the 19th and told us that fire crossed Carrizo Creek before 1000 hours, like it was not even there, much less a green riparian area with a 20 foot wide, flowing stream. Normally, that green belt of the riparian area with flowing water in the stream would have been a barrier or at least should have slowed the fire temporarily. Flames exceeded 400 feet in height. Lofted embers or firebrands were starting spot fires as much as ½ mile out in front of the flames.

Shortly after 1000 hours, the winds began to increase from the southwest. By 1300 hours (1:00 p.m.), all of the air support (air tankers and helicopters) was grounded for safety reasons due to the high and erratic winds. Air Attack and Operations continued to fly, as did the Phoenix media helicopters, although they were buffeted violently in the strong winds and updrafts from the fire. Crews were in such steep, broken terrain with no escape routes and no safety zones and smoke was so thick, that Incident Commander Gatewood made a decision to move crews from the firelines to safe zones on *all* sides of the fire at 1529 hours (3:29 p.m.).

Crews and dozers began a safer, indirect attack from the flanks of the fire. Perimeter protection was set up around the community of Cibeque. I.C. Gatewood and Ops. Chief Leech knew that this fire was growing into a monster and that once it reached the steep canyons below the Mogollon Rim, it would accelerate uphill and burn with astounding, increased intensity. The call was made to Sheriff Gary Butler that Linden, Pinedale, Timberland Acres and Clay Springs should be evacuated immediately and Arizona Highway 260 should be closed to traffic. The fire was on its way and nothing could stop it from reaching these small rural communities!

Rodeo Fire at the Mogollon Rim and Forest Road 300 at 5:32 p.m. on June 19th. Photo by Jerry Beddow

Lloyd Wilmes explained to us that the fire crossed the Mogollon Rim and Forest Road 300 at 1732 hours (5:32 p.m.) on a six-mile wide fire front that was moving approximately 20 miles per hour when it topped the Rim. In simple terms, that meant that *it burned 10,000 acres in about 15 minutes*, as shown above . Also note in the photo, that the trees were approximately 60-80 feet tall on the Rim. Flames were three to four times the heights of the trees. Both Leech and Wilmes reported witnessing flames of 800 to 1,000 feet. Temperatures at the flame fronts were estimated to be in excess of 2,000 degrees. This is unbelievable fire behavior!!

Lloyd also related that the Rodeo Fire had burned about 1,100 acres in the first ten hours it burned, which was significant growth. Yet, it gained an additional 54,000 acres by the time of our briefing, which was only an additional 20 hours. *That is more than 2,000 acres burned per hour since ignition... incredible!*

More than half of Humphrey's 40-person team had 20+ years of fire fighting experience. We had been on many complex Type I fires that never exceeded 10,000 acres... and very few that had ever exceeded 50,000 acres. Now this monster had grown by 54,000 acres in only the second day of the fire. Lloyd finished by informing us that fuels (dead logs, brush, pine needles and dead grass) were drier and more explosive than had ever been measured/recorded in all of the 20th Century.

Weather was going to be against us, in that we could expect Red Flag Warnings for at least the next four days or longer. A "Red Flag Warning" is issued by the National Weather Service and indicates that burning conditions will be extreme or worse, with high temperatures, low humidity (less than 15%) and sustained winds in excess of 25 miles per hour. That would limit typical fire fighting tactics and was a "Situation that Shouted 'Watch Out!'" Some were wondering what in the world we had encountered on this assignment!

Tribal Chairman Dallas Massey, Ft. Apache Superintendent Ben Nuvamsa and Mr. Robert Lacapa addressed the team as to the impact of this fire on the tribe and how they wanted to limit the damage to their neighbors to the north. Mr. Lacapa spoke to this fire consuming a major portion of their timber resource.

Apache-Sitgreaves National Forest Supervisor, John Bedell, spoke briefly about keeping firefighters and the public safe. He asked us to take whatever measures we deemed necessary to contain this fire with the least amount of damage to communities, but that safety was Priority-One for both the public and firefighters.

Kirk Rowdibaugh, State Forester from Arizona State Lands stated in his delegation of authority that the state would cooperate and that we needed to include the community and rural fire departments in our plans. The delegation gave Hump's Team authority and responsibility for managing the fire on private lands. A question that was not answered was if we had authority to "command" the local fire departments. [8.c]

Chairman Dallas Massey of the White Mountain Apache Tribe. Photo by White Mountain Independent News

Incident Commander Larry Humphrey addressing morning briefing on June 20, 2002 at the Show Low High School. Photo by USFS, Apache-Sitgreaves National Forest

Incident Commander Larry Humphrey closed our incoming briefing with acknowledgement of the situation. *We inherited a "DISASTER!"* In accepting the challenge before us, he made a statement that "this was not the typical fire and we would not fight it in traditional ways. The forests were going to burn and we could not stop that. There were also communities and lives in harm's way."

Typical firefighting would utilize "anchor and flank" strategies of building line and confining the fire from where it started up each flank, east and west, taking that "safe-black line" with us as the crews moved north. This would eventually pinch off the head of the fire, methods that have not changed in 100 years. Dozers and crews already on the line would now continue that flanking action, with help from Kvale's Type II Team from just north of Cibeque. But that would not help the communities north of the Rim.

Hump's Team and all the resources we could gather would go up ahead of the fire. With the help of our crews, local fire departments, structural fire engines from other departments and what air support we could get, we would prepare areas with homes for a "fire visit." That work would entail emergency cutting of trees and removal of burn-ables and vegetation in close proximity to buildings. Then structures would be foamed with fire retardant from those structural fire engines, just before the fire arrived.

Since safety and protection of life (both firefighters and the public) was our first priority, and since this was already a mega fire, firefighters on the ground would be pulled to safe zones and allow the flaming fire front to pass by. When conditions were deemed safe, they would go back into an area and try to save as many houses as possible.

Such a strategy was totally counter to anything we had ever attempted. History would weigh our success, but that was not our concern. Getting to the battle at hand with a "mega-fire monster" was, and we were ready to spit in his fiery eye.

The next nine hours, prior to our team taking command of the fire, would be a very busy time for the team, getting set up, in place and functioning at the Show Low High School and getting additional resources ordered and enroute. We would try to get our feet on the ground. Since fire had already crossed the Mogollon Rim and put areas of homes at risk, media helicopters had swarmed the area.

ADOT Road Advisory of Closed Road on Highway 60 south of Show Low on June 19th.
- Photo by Varnell Gatewood

Highway 60 south of Show Low to the Junction with Highway 73 to Whiteriver had been closed, as had Highway 260 from Show Low to Heber. Reporters from all over Arizona were coming to Show Low, Whiteriver and Heber-Overgaard. We had inherited a disaster, the scale of which we could not know or anticipate… yet. It was an event to be recorded and reported to America and the world, through the media as something unique in the rate of its destruction, and a phenomenon never before seen in Arizona.

As soon as word spread of our base camp at Show Low High School, the media vehicles and satellite trucks began to pull in and set up. Our Information Center was in the Mormon Seminary, adjacent to the Show Low High School on Old Linden Road. Satellite trucks and news vehicles were parked in the high school auditorium parking lot along Old Linden Road. By day's end, we had seven satellite trucks set up and more to come.

Left: Information Center at Mormon Seminary in Show Low.
Middle: Setting up Information Center.
Right: Information briefing area at Mormon Seminary in Show Low.
All photos by USFS, Apache-Sitgreaves National Forest

*   *   *   *   *

Sid Howard, Pinedale/Clay Springs Fire Chief asked Linden, Heber-Overgaard, Show Low, Lakeside and Pinetop Fire Departments to come to Pinedale and help him prepare homes. Lloyd Wilmes, I.C. above the Rim, and several Forest Service fire engines, dozers and crews also worked in the Pinedale area and down along the Rim Road #300. Paul Watson, Chief of Pinetop Fire went to the south end of Pinedale Estates and directed construction of a one-dozer-width fireline. He was unable to get crews in to accomplish burnout of the line before the fire got there first.

More than a dozen engines and 100 firefighters worked to prepare homes for fire to come against them. Paul served as one of the Structure Protection Specialists on Hump's Team. A Structure Protection Specialist has a depth of experience as a structural fireman and also as a wildland firefighter. He/she directs structural fire engines when protecting homes from a wildfire and coordinates with the Division Supervisor for the team. As a guide to "triage" on houses to protect or not, Paul used the following Go/No Go Reference List. Not all of these apply, as the residents had already evacuated and there was a decision that crews would not remain if fire roared through the area, but rather would prepare, foam and retreat, returning after the fire front passed.

Structure Go-No Go / Protection Reference

Factors that may make a structure too dangerous to protect: If you answer, "yes" to any of the below, don't attempt to protect that structure, move on to the next.

__ Fire is making a sustained run and there is little or no clearance.
__ Water supply will not last as long as the threat.
__ Fire's intensity dictates leaving the area immediately.
__ The roof is more than one-quarter involved.
__ There is fire inside the structure or windows are broken.

If the conditions listed above allow for a structure protection effort to be made then:

__ Check roads before the fire arrives. Know turnouts, and bridge limits.
__ Check each home for an adequate defendable space.
__ Stay mobile; keep vehicle engine running, and red lights on.
__ Back in equipment for a quick escape.
__ Brief resources on strategies, tactics, hazards, and LCES.
__ Coil a short 1½" charged line with a fog nozzle on your engine for safety and quick response.
__ Use short hose-lays.
__ Keep at least 10% capacity of water in your water tank.
__ Determine if residents are home.
__ Advise residents of escape routes, safety zones, evacuation plans and centers.
__ Ask residents to evacuate threatened livestock or pets.
__ Leave home lights on inside and out, day and night.
__ Place owners ladder at a corner of the structure least threatened by the fire.
__ Coil and charge garden hoses.
__ Turn on sprinklers.
__ Identify hazards. (HazMats, gas lines, power lines, etc.)
__ If a home becomes involved, leave it and move to one you can save.

Firefighter safety and survival are the number one priority.

Source: BLM Red Book, January 2002

Smoke from Rodeo Fire as it came over the Mogollon Rim on the evening of June 19ᵗʰ from Pinedale Estates.
Photo by Dewayne Saxton

P-3 Orion Heavy Air Tanker dropping retardant (slurry) near houses in Pinedale.
Photo by Dewayne Saxton

The fire was on the way and time was short. With Paul Watson, Pinetop Fire Chief, as their Structure Protection Specialist, the crews and engines prepared homes during the night. They cut trees and brush around houses and foamed them with retardant.

As the wall of fire approached, some houses were saved with direct retardant drops from heavy air tankers, an anomalous tactic as usually air tankers avoid dropping on houses. Those structures that were not defensible with either too many trees or too much brush and "burn-ables" were identified with fluorescent pink ribbon across the driveway. Those houses that were "red-tagged" were to be passed over by firefighters. This was painful triage to all who worked on it, but there was so little time to prepare that options were few. Firefighters saved those houses they could and grieved those they lost.

Left: J. Jayne's house is defensible while house below burns. Photo by Paul Watson

Right: Linden firefighter attempting to save a house in Timberland Acres. Photo by Dewayne Saxton

June 20th. Thursday

Hump's team assumed command of the fire at 0600 hours (6:00 a.m.). Crews, engines and overhead went out to Pinedale. Because homes were burning in Colorado on both the Hayman Fire near Denver and the Missionary Ridge Fire near Durango, we were lower priority, nationally and were initially only given two heavy air tankers to support our ground forces. One heavy helicopter (Air Crane) was enroute. Governor Jane Dee Hull signed a Disaster Declaration, mobilized state fire fighting resources of the State Lands Department, and asked structural fire departments from around the state to assist the communities about to be assaulted by fire.

Safe Zone in the meadow at Peterson Ranch in Pinedale. Photo by Dewayne Saxton

About 1000 hours (10:00 a.m.), all the engines and crews received radio calls to move to a safe zone at Peterson Ranch in a large meadow. Winds had picked up. The fire topped the Mogollon Rim and moved very quickly through McCleve Canyon and into the southern portion of Pinedale Estates. The preparation work of Wilmes, Chief Watson, Chief Howard and all the structural firefighters on the 19th, served well, as only one house was lost in Pinedale Estates.

Fire whirl on Juniper Ridge in Timberland Acres during the night of June 20th. The small "candles" are 50-60 foot tall trees. The flames and fire whirl that depict the Devil's horned head are approximately 500 feet tall. Photo by Dewayne Saxton

Subsequent waves of fire would take 41 houses in Pinedale and 106 houses in Timberland Acres. (Note: See Navajo County Assessor's tabulation of losses by area, in *Chapter 15: Post Fire*). Summit Fire Chief Don Howard had been assigned as the Linden, Pinedale & Clay Springs Fire Departments Liaison from Hump's Team. Chief Howard began fighting fire as a volunteer on a rural department more than 20 years earlier. He also had extensive experience as a Structure Protection Specialist on wildland fires. He believes that "volunteers are the backbone of America and that small rural fire departments are full of people who give back to their communities" [8.d] Chief Don Howard knew and understood what the Linden, Pinedale and Clay Springs firefighters were going through.

Chief Howard and Division Supervisor Denny Nelson started into the interior of Pinedale when the second wave of fire hit. Explosions of propane tanks were heard and black smoke from burning houses in Pinedale was seen all across the horizon to the south. Div. Sup. Nelson put out a radio call that all resources must move, again… this time, back to Highway 260 for safety reasons, until the flame front had passed. A menacing tower of smoke and heat was building over Pinedale and the plume-dominated thunderhead was building. When it iced out, the plume collapse was imminent. The flame front was even hotter and faster than anticipated and the meadow at Peterson's Ranch where fire resources were assembled was going to receive the fury of climax fire, so safety concerns mandated an immediate pull back.

It was then that Pinedale/Clay Springs firefighters took issue with the idea of not fighting the fire head on. Pulling back was an excruciating concept and many of them felt they were not redeeming their sworn responsibilities. We understood that they had a vested interest in saving all the homes possible. Most of them had never worked with an Incident Management Team and did not understand the concept of delegations of authority. They were not aware that the State Forester had given Hump's Team the responsibility of overseeing the fire departments involved. Also, it was obvious that Hump's Team was only here for two weeks, but they would be here forever after.

None of us had ever seen a fire like this Rodeo "Monster" and many were simply overwhelmed by the speed, devastation and number of homes lost. The actions of Div. Sup. Nelson and Chief Don Howard were warranted and, considering the situation and the withdrawals, most likely saved lives.

Some of the locals either did not believe or did not understand the ferocity of this monster, the Rodeo Fire. When the fire rushed over the hill to the south of their safety zone at Peterson Ranch, Gary Holdcroft, a volunteer fireman with Linden F.D. noted that "Huge, bright orange flames spewed over the top of the hill with an angry black column of smoke on top… a scene out of Hell!" [8.e]

As the rest of the engines and firefighters pulled back to Highway 260, the three Pinedale/Clay Springs Fire engines left the meadow and headed for Clay Springs, where they might be able to work, rather than simply view the fire from Highway 260. Fire was headed in that direction, as well, and they were hoping that perhaps they could take positive action there. For those whose homes hung in the balance, doing anything was better than sitting and waiting for the flames to pass. Tensions were high and tempers were short.

*   *   *   *   *

Left: Clay Springs Engine Task Force with Show Low Engine 302 (yellow truck) on Highway 260 at Clay Springs turnoff. Photo by Darin Whiting.

Right: Show Low Fire Engineer Darin Whiting cutting trees and brush around a home in Clay Springs. Photo by Show Low Fire Dept.

Darin Whiting, Engineer, Show Low Fire Department was a member of a 20-engine task force working in Clay Springs. They were busy prepping houses for the anticipated arrival of fire. Crews cut trees within ten feet of the houses, removed grass and brush, moved woodpiles, cut wooden fences and prepared to foam houses when the flames came close. Darin had his camera out as fire approached Highway 260 and took these five photos as fire moved ever closer. The big Juniper tree in the middle is significant.

In the two photos below, both taken by Darin Whiting from James Ward's house, note the density of the smoke and the formation of a column, as the flames get closer.

Left: Creeping fire putting heat under juniper trees. Note Ward's favorite tree to right of center.

Right: Fire climbing the "ladders" of branches into the crown of the junipers.

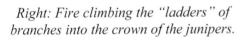

At Left: Trees fully involved with fire.
All photos by Darin Whiting

Darin then moved a little to the south to take the next three photos from a different vantage point. The crew of Show Low Engine #302 was successful in protecting this house and, although fire came right to the edge, it did not burn.

About two months after the fire, Darin met Mr. James Ward who was buying fence posts and wire at a building materials store. His fence and an outbuilding had burned during the fire, but his house was saved. Darin had these same pictures there and offered to show them to Mr. Ward. As he was flipping pictures, Darin looked up and there were tears streaming down Mr. Ward's face. He very quietly said of the big Juniper, "That's MY tree! You guys saved my house. Thank you!"

After the fire, Darin regularly drove Highway 260. He could not pass the turnoff to Clay Springs without thinking of that successful protection action and one house saved. Mr. Ward had not known who was responsible for saving his house, but put this sign up on the side of the highway as a public gesture of his family's gratitude.

Sign from Mr. James Ward after the fire on Highway 260 at the Clay Springs turnoff. Photo by Darin Whiting.

Was it only chance that drew these two men to the same spot and allowed each of them to share their experience of the fire as "neighbors?" One helped the other and the other finally had a chance to express his gratitude. [8.f] Such is life on the mountain.

Above: Rodeo Fire approaching Highway 260 at Juniper Point (milepost 326) at 1:45 p.m. on June 20th.
Photo by Dewayne Saxton
Right: Fire across Highway 260 at Milepost 312.
Photo by USFS, Apache-Sitgreaves National Forest

The second wave of fire ran through Pinedale with unbelievable speed. Our Law Enforcement Liaison Officer, Jim Clawson reported that fire crossed Highway 260 at Juniper Point (Milepost 326) at 1345 hours (1:45 p.m.), and that it was running hard with at least 100-foot flames. Officer Clawson was there trying to get any fire units collected in the area and make sure that everyone was okay. Fire was also very close to the Timberland Acres access off Highway 260.

Flames from Deuce of Clubs in Show Low, afternoon of June 20th.
Photo by Karen Wattenmaker

Fire is so unpredictable. This finger of fire burned like a blowtorch, only one mile wide, but some 5 ½ miles to the north, even out into the pinyon juniper, where fire generally doesn't crown and run hard. Embers were being lofted and landing as much as one mile out in front of the fire, which is unheard of in P-J fuel type. As fire approached the 500 Kilovolt APS power line, it had to be de-energized and shut down. Fire will arc with heavy smoke as a conductor and threaten any personnel in the area with "power-line lightning." The power line was de-energized for two days, until firefighters could get this finger of fire contained and cooled down. Three houses in Victory Heights burned as the fire passed to the north of Highway 60.

Fire was everywhere and few people, firefighters, law enforcement or anyone working in emergency management services had ever seen this much fire up close.

We got a call at the Incident Command Post that local Police and Navajo County Sheriff's Deputies were evacuating Pinetop. The call came from the Forest Service office in Lakeside, which had been asked to help. They were concerned and asked if there was in fact an evacuation order from Hump's team. The answer was an emphatic "No!!" Even though there had been no order for evacuation, the smoke plumes and visible flames in the sky appeared to be on top of the towns, when they were, instead, at least ten miles to the west.

We got that evacuation stopped, as fire had NOT made an advance against the towns. Everyone was on edge and a bit jumpy. The fire was so obvious and filled the sky from horizon to horizon, that it looked much closer than it really was. However, that evacuation exercise was to play out for real, only two days later.

*　　*　　*　　*　　*

104

Salvation Army's mobile kitchen preparing meals for firefighters at Show Low High School until caterer arrives. Photo by David Sherman

Salvation Army volunteers building sack lunches for firefighters at Show Low High School Fire Camp. Photo by David Sherman

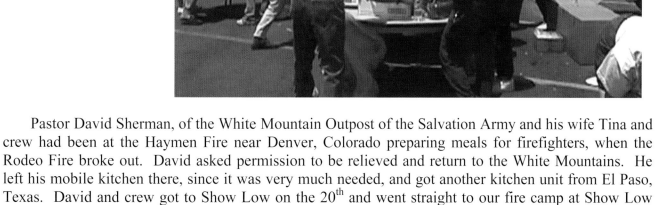

Pastor David Sherman, of the White Mountain Outpost of the Salvation Army and his wife Tina and crew had been at the Haymen Fire near Denver, Colorado preparing meals for firefighters, when the Rodeo Fire broke out. David asked permission to be relieved and return to the White Mountains. He left his mobile kitchen there, since it was very much needed, and got another kitchen unit from El Paso, Texas. David and crew got to Show Low on the 20th and went straight to our fire camp at Show Low High School.

At Fire Camp, he met Incident Commander Larry Humphrey and asked what he could do to help. Larry informed him that our caterer would not arrive and be set up for meal delivery for at least 30 hours. Could he help us feed the fire crews? "Absolutely no problem!" replied Pastor Sherman and he set up the kitchen and started work. His wife Tina got on local radio and the Community TV and asked for volunteers. In short order, 50 volunteers were there to help. Some of the Salvation Army staff got groceries and supplies. All of a sudden, sack lunches for 600 + firefighters began to appear.

The Salvation Army also cooked dinner and breakfast and made sack lunches for the next day. Finally, the caterer arrived and set up. In all, the Salvation Army had mobile kitchens at Heber, Linden

Fire Dept. and the Round Valley Evacuation Center. Before the end of the Rodeo-Chediski Fire emergency, they had four mobile kitchens working in various locations. They prepared several hundred meals per day for more than two weeks and were a great help to fire fighting effort.

*   *   *   *   *

Fire Chief Mel Epps had been one of the first to send engines to help Pinedale/Clay Springs Chief Sid Howard, as soon as it was evident that fire would come against homes in the Pinedale/Clay Springs area. He himself had worked in Pinedale all night on the 19th, doing triage and preparing for the inevitable. About 0845 hours on Thursday, Mel got a call from his administrative assistant, Janie Gonzalez, asking him to return to station, due to a new fire on the reservation south of Heber-Overgaard.

By the time Mel was back in Heber, he could see the smoke plume, just a thin pencil of gray and black well off to the south. Nervously, Chief Epps watched the Chediski Fire smoke column grow, almost by the minute. He closely monitored the radio traffic of resources on the Chediski Fire. After the plane ride with Pat McLeod, to check the fire in person (detailed in Chapter 7), his apprehension grew, once he was back on the ground.

As the fire outpaced efforts to contain it, he began calling all Heber-Overgaard firemen, both fulltime and volunteer into duty. He asked for the three H-O (Heber-Overgaard) engines that were assisting Pinedale to be returned to station, and they were released from the Rodeo Fire. Mel went outside often to view the towering inferno as the column grew in size and darkness.

The rate of change in the sky and the fire's growth was just so shocking as to be beyond comprehension. He had never seen a fire build so fast and look so close, yet be so far away. By 1400 hours (2:00 p.m.), Mel met with Navajo County Sheriff's Deputies. He informed them that he was making Heber-Overgaard Fire Station a command center and asked them to use the facility, to which they agreed. He also asked for the Sheriff to give notice of pending evacuation to all the residents in the area, which deputies began to do.

At 1600 hours (4:00 p.m.), after a call from Ken Butler, Ft. Apache Fire Management Officer, telling Chief Epps that the Chediski Fire was headed up the Mogollon Rim and would be moving toward his communities, Chief Epps asked Sheriff Butler to go ahead and evacuate.

Several TV stations' reporters were in the area. They were asked to interrupt regular programming with the notice of evacuation, which was done. Sheriff's deputies and firemen went door to door and also gave notification. They used their siren-public address systems to announce the evacuation over loudspeakers, as well. Residents were given one hour to begin their exodus. A few went to Holbrook, but most folks went to the middle school in Payson or stayed with family or friends in the valley or elsewhere.

*   *   *   *   *

As residents were leaving Heber-Overgaard to the west, some locals with dozers, backhoes and trucks began to appear at the H-O fire station, wanting to help. Chief Epps was in a real "no win" situation, as he was required to adhere to Arizona State Lands Department policy on equipment and "volunteer firefighters," which mirrored federal policy. Equipment was required to be inspected and put into a formal contract for services. Firefighters were required to have attended the 40-hour basic fire training, passed the physical fitness test and be equipped with Nomex fire clothes and all the basic safety equipment. None of those wanting to help could meet any of these three requirements.

Chief Epps told them that they could not be signed up and put to work. In frustration, faces were red, fists were shaken and names were called. The group eventually left.

About 20 men in the Whiterock area refused to evacuate. They cached food and supplies in Ron Squire's house, which became known locally as the Whiterock Command Center. They worked around the Whiterock and Buckskin areas on private lands to help reduce risk by cutting trees, removing fuels and dozing firelines. Mel asked Kvale's team to get an inspection crew to sign up as many of the dozers, backhoes and other pieces of equipment as possible… and then to put them to work. He knew that Heber-Overgaard would need all the help they could get in short order.

About 2300 hours (11:00 p.m.), Chief Epps met with Forest Service Black Mesa District Ranger Kate Klein and Kvale's Type II Team. They asked for Mel's concurrence in constructing a dozer line across private lands in Section 31, south of the H-O fire station. Their hope was to build the line and burnout as fire approached, in an effort to keep fire out of as many housing areas as possible, but the plan sought concurrence from the Fire Chief to operate across the private lands. Mel readily agreed and endorsed the idea. It was in essence a unified command decision, since both federal and private land jurisdictions were involved.

Chief Epps was demoralized, "feeling as lost as a softball in tall grass," when the phone rang and Cottonwood Fire Chief, Mike Casson asked how he was. Epps replied "overwhelmed and exhausted!" Chief Casson asked if he could come over and provide some relief to Chief Epps. Mel's answer was, "How fast can you get here?"

Chief Casson had seen quite a bit of wildfire and was also bringing engines and additional firefighters with him. He came to shadow, take notes, drive, support and just give some relief to Chief Epps in a tense and exhausting situation. That allowed Mel to focus on the immediate issues at hand and was most appreciated. [8.g]

Chief Epps really had a good handle on all his resources. He had set up a command center at the fire department and co-located the Navajo County Sheriff's Office there as well. The evacuation had been orderly and efficient. His plans for preparation of areas at most risk was very good. All he lacked was about 50 more fire engines and 200+ more firefighters that could have helped implement the plan faster.

*   *   *   *   *

Information Officer Jim Paxon during a press briefing at fire camp in Show Low High School/Mormon Seminary. Photo by Guy Atchley

The first news conference for Hump's Team was at 1800 hours (6:00 p.m.). As the spokesman, I told news media and a few locals that we had inherited a fire-breathing dragon and that the Rodeo fire "kicked our butts today!" I also related that "the fire is burning like pouring gasoline on a bonfire and then setting up a big fan to blow on it… only much bigger and hotter than you can even imagine!" For the first of many times, I told the audience that, "Mother Nature is in control in a big way. We will be a long time getting this fire contained and sadly, many houses are directly in the path of her wrath."

It was not pleasant to relate this much negative information, but I did tell them that, "Larry Humphrey, for whom I work, is one of the gutsiest Incident Commanders in the entire United States. This is not a traditional firefight. We are going to the front of the fire and working with local fire departments to try and save as many homes as possible."

Also, for the first of many times, I emphasized that, "Safety of firefighters and the public is absolutely our first priority. There is not a tree, an acre or a house worth a firefighter's life, so we will be working hard at battling the monster, but with one eye on the sky. If conditions become dangerous, firefighters will withdraw and move to safety zones, where they can watch the fire go by… and then go back in to save homes from burning."

I did tell the media in Show Low that we had another fire on the reservation and to the south of Heber-Overgaard, but I did not have full information on that situation. Getting accurate and timely information on the Chediski Fire was to be a severe headache for the next several days.

*   *   *   *   *

June 21st, Friday

Summer Solstice occurred on this day. It was the longest day of the year with 14¾ hours of sunlight. Fuels would be the most sun heated, most dried and most available for fire, more so than any other day of the year. The National Weather Service forecast another red flag day with temperatures on the fire in the 90's, terribly hot at the elevation of the fire. Relative humidity would be less than 5%. Strong breezes would change to strong winds before noon, with gusts of 35 miles per hour and more in the afternoon, a forecast that bode ill for the firefighting efforts.

The forecast was accurate. By mid-day, smoke in Holbrook (50+ miles to the north) was so thick that driver's had to turn on their vehicle's headlights. Visibility was less than 200 feet… and it was mid-day! Not even a "London fog" is any thicker. Several evacuees in Holbrook with respiratory problems had to be moved to a less smoky environment.

*   *   *   *   *

The Today Show requested that I do an on camera interview with Matt Lauer and Katie Couric. Remember that New York is three hours ahead of Arizona in the summer, which meant that I had to be up at 3:30 a.m. for the 7:00 a.m. Today Show interview. We had already scheduled a daily briefing at 11:00 a.m., after our morning Command & General Staff meeting and our shift planning session, to share summaries and updates from the night shift. We also had the scheduled evening briefing at 10:00 p.m. every night, so we could relate the day's activities and accomplishments just after the 9:00 p.m. shift planning session.

Most Arizona TV stations interrupted their 10:00 p.m. newscasts or extended their format to one hour, to carry us live. Usually, I would do two or more one-on-one interviews after the 10:00 p.m. briefing. These times were firm in order to accommodate newsprint and radio media needs and deadlines. We had the briefing area set up in the fenced, grassy area of the Show Low Mormon Seminary, where our information center was located.

When interviews were finished, I would simply lay my sleeping bag out, right on the ground by the podium. Sleep usually came quickly. Arizona Game and Fish Officers were assigned security for all of the fire camp.

At 3:15 a.m., an officer would gently rouse me with a cup of coffee and get me up for the east coast morning talk shows. I splashed a little water on my face and jammed a team ball cap on my head and we were good to go. Once the Today Show asked for an early interview, all the networks including CNN got in line and wanted the latest information… every morning. Seldom did I get four hours sleep a night for the next ten days.

*   *   *   *   *

Maricopa County Sheriff, Joe Arpaio sent 250 deputies, his Sheriff's Office helicopter and 150 members of his Sheriff's Posse to assist Navajo County Sheriff Gary Butler with evacuations, road closures and patrol of evacuated areas. Sheriff Butler was extremely glad to get the help. A small problem arose with some of the deputies taking news media with them into hot zones and none of them having any personal protective equipment or any wildland fire training. Coordination with Sheriff Butler by Liaison Officer Jim Clawson, a Forest Service Law Enforcement Officer and firefighter curtailed the practice of ride-alongs of news media with Sheriff's Officers and also kept them safe from a danger that they did not understand.

Other law enforcement agencies also jumped in to assist. Hundreds of officers from Arizona Department of Public Safety, Arizona Game and Fish, Apache County Sheriff's Office and the Arizona National Guard helped staff roadblocks, assisted local officers in patrols, delivered plans, maps and supplies to various points on the perimeter of the fire and served as camp security. Their contributions were priceless and most helpful.

*　　*　　*　　*　　*

Dozers and several hand crews worked to build a fireline between Juniper Ridge and Timberland Acres subdivision. Pinedale/Clay Springs and Linden Fire Departments were assisted by several structural departments from the valley as well as Pinetop F.D, Lakeside F.D. and Show Low F.D. in preparing homes for fire to come against them. By noon, the dozer lines were breached and firefighters were again ordered to safe zones.

Once again, engines in Pinedale and Timberland Acres were pulled to large meadows or to Highway 260, while the several flame fronts roared through the countryside, taking houses and consuming forests. Firefighters could hear propane tanks exploding, and as houses caught fire, thick black smoke would fill the sky for only a few minutes as the monster devoured another "fuel depot," which he considered no more than a snack, as he looked for the next house to attack. This was de-ja-vu unimaginable, but it was to happen several times in Pinedale and Timberland Acres before the monster lay down.

The Arizona Republic's June 21st front page carried a historic, full-page photo of a huge, menacing smoke column looming over two houses in Pinedale. Photographer Pat Shannahan took the photo. It was up close and personal evidence of a "plume dominated" fire's smoke column.

At the morning briefing for the day shift crews at Show Low High School, at about 0600 hours, Roy Hall, Operations Section Chief, explained that these towering columns would rise and fall as a phenomenon of the fire's intensity in that area at that specific point of time.

Roy warned that if things got eerily

Smoke column closing in on Pinedale on June 20th. Photo was full front page of June 21st Arizona Republic newspaper. Photo by Pat Shannahan, Arizona Republic

quiet and/or firefighters felt a light sprinkle, it was a warning to get out immediately, or sooner... as the collapse of the plume would send gale force winds down to the ground in a microburst that would spread fire explosively in all directions. Firefighters would not be able to run to safety nor could vehicles negotiate meandering mountain roads fast enough to escape its wake. Once a plume built and began to ice out with the big white cloud on top, standard operations would require a withdrawal from the fireline to safe zones. Roy spoke from personal experience.

Engineer Darin Whiting of Show Low Fire Engine #302 was busy protecting homes in the Clay Springs area, while his own home in Timberland Acres on Juniper Ridge Road was burning to the ground. The next day, Darin was able to get in and have a look at what was left of his home. Smoke was so thick that he had a difficult time even in finding where his house had stood.

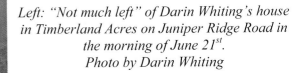

Left: "Not much left" of Darin Whiting's house in Timberland Acres on Juniper Ridge Road in the morning of June 21st. Photo by Darin Whiting

Right: Same location as above approximately June 29th. Photo by Sandy Whiting

Above Left: Nothing left but rubble. Note small figure in lower right hand corner of photo. Photo by Darin Whiting

Above Right: This ceramic "friar" is about all that the Whitings were able to salvage from their former home. Photo by Darin Whiting

Several days later, when the fire cooled and the public was allowed to return, Darin and his wife, Sandy got a good look at what remained from exactly the same viewpoint as the picture above. Note the small figurine on the porch in the lower right of the photo. That porcelain "Friar" is about all that was salvageable from his dream home.

That house had been Darin's refuge from the rigors and stresses of everyday life. It was the place where he found peace and tranquility. His three children spent many hours on the creek in joyous, carefree play. Darin regularly rode his mountain bike up to Juniper Ridge Lookout for exercise and to take in the forest views from there that had been so scenic.

First rain in July across from Whiting's house location. Darin's three children used this tire swing. Note the water flow looks like used motor oil. Photo by Darin Whiting

All that peace and tranquility had vanished as quickly as the passage of the flames. You can see the remains of the house across the creek after the first rain in Juniper Ridge in July. The children would no longer swing out over the creek and play in the forest. Truly heartbroken, Darin and his family have seldom been back.

The change from his little piece of paradise to barren moonscape was just too painful to endure. Darin reflected on the way the burn ravaged the draw where his house and many others were lost. Looking at the moonscape and total devastation, he was glad that no firefighters had been there when fire came through, for it would surely have been their "deathtrap"… and he would not want that on his conscience. He has since sold the lot. He and his family have chosen to remember what their home was before the fire. They now live in the City of Show Low… and life goes on. (8.f)

*   *   *   *   *

The Chediski Fire, (detailed in Chapter 7) came under the command of Rich Kvale's Type II Team from Southeastern Arizona officially at 0600 on June 21st. The Chediski Fire was already more than 15,000 acres. Red Flag warnings foretold of another day where winds and fire conditions hampered firefighter efforts. Helicopters and air tankers were in scarce supply, but the winds limited their use and severely reduced their effectiveness.

Dozers and hand crews continued to anchor the heel of the Rodeo Fire, and now included work to the north on the east and west flanks from the ignition point near Chediski Farms. Large areas of the west end of the White Mountain Apache Reservation were densely forested and had been managed for the production of logs. Timber sales, thinning and post sale prescribed burns had been implemented and fuels were less dense in those areas, which greatly slowed the advance of the raging flame front.

By mid afternoon, fire was "seeded" (established and cooking) in several steep canyons below the Mogollon Rim, where no thinning or burning had been done. Kvale's Operations Section Chief, Maurice Williams, was working with the Black Mesa Ranger District engine crews, two hotshot crews and 10 dozers building a dozer fireline to the south of houses in Heber-Overgaard, that could be burned out as the flame front of the Chediski Fire approached, and hopefully the burned-out line would stop the fire from coming into the communities.

Sun at 3:00 p.m. on June 20th. Photo by Dewayne Saxton

At 1330 hours (1:30 p.m.) Mel Epps did a phone interview with the White Mountain Independent. He told the reporter that, "everything was so dark, that it's like being in a fog at dusk. The sun looks like a little thumbnail, only it's pink… and it's so quiet. Heber-Overgaard is a ghost town." (8.g)

*   *   *   *   *

Cell phone gridlock began on June 19th and continued to get worse every day. Many members of the team had cell phones that did not have service, or sketchy service at best, in the Show Low area. Richard Watkins of Cellular One, the local cell phone company in the White Mountains, brought 30 cell phones to camp, with unlimited use and donated them to the fire effort. He asked that the phones be returned when the fire emergency was over. We used those phones to great advantage. There was so much radio traffic that overhead and command used the phones so as to not tie up the radios, unless a large number of people needed to hear the message. (8.h)

*   *   *   *   *

Air traffic became a severe problem in the area of the Show Low Airport. We had established an F.A.A. temporary flight restriction (TFR) over the fire, so that only fire-associated aircraft would be in the area. Media and other aircraft had to maintain a 12,000-foot elevation or get specific clearance to enter an area from Air Attack. The Show Low Airport was still open and traffic was congested there as well.

The team worked with Dennis Wiss, Manager of the airport, who accommodated us very well. We had six helicopters, two of them the giant Air Cranes, three air attack planes and at least one lead plane for the big air tankers based at the airport. There were both fixed and rotor wing media aircraft working out of the airport, as well as private planes. F.A.A. brought in a temporary control tower, which was on wheels, much like a mobile office. It had an extendable control tower and a self-contained radio/telephone communications system. Several Air Traffic Controllers staffed the tower anytime there was takeoff and landing traffic, for the duration of the fire.

Eventually, there was an F.A.A. "T-1" total closure of the airspace around the fire and the airport for safety reasons. This type closure has only been used twice previously on wildland fires and one of them was the 1.2 million acre fire in Yellowstone in 1988. The other time was the Musecbrod Fire in Montana in August of 2001, to which Hump's team was assigned.

*   *   *   *   *

In the late afternoon and evening of the 21st, fire crossed Highway 260 at milepost 302 between Heber and Forest Lakes. The fire was losing its energy when it crossed, so it did *not* roar across and keep on running to the north. Quick response from structural and wildland fire engines in the area kept the fire from running on past the highway to the north. Fire was to bump up against Highway 260 several more times.

*   *   *   *   *

The news of the huge, house-gobbling Rodeo Fire and the growing Chediski Fire had spread far and wide. Our Information Center had grown to overflowing. There were at least a dozen TV satellite trucks parked in the Show Low High School Auditorium parking lot. New York and L.A. Times reporters as well as an international contingent of reporters had come to Show Low. The local and Arizona newsprint reporters and many radio station broadcasters were in Show Low.

Every Arizona TV station and the national networks, including CNN and national bureaus/reporters from ABC, CBS, Fox, NBC, Telemundo and Univision were on hand. Each of the satellite trucks ran cables to the podium on the east side of Mormon Seminary where we posted a daily summary and progress maps before each briefing. Some of the "sat trucks" (satellite trucks) were as far away as 500 feet. With cables pre-run and camera positions setup, TV news media could be ready for a briefing in about five minutes.

Left: News satellite trucks setting up in Show Low High School Auditorium parking lot. Photo by USFS, Rocky Mountain Research Station-Flagstaff

Center Right: News setup camp at Show Low High School on Old Linden Road. Photo by USFS, Rocky Mountain Research Station-Flagstaff

Bottom Right: Looking west from Information Center at smoke plume. Photo by USFS, Rocky Mountain Research Station-Flagstaff

We set standard briefing times of 11:00 a.m. and 10:00 p.m. Most of the briefings were carried live on TV and radio. We tried to hold the 10:00 p.m. briefing to less than 20 minutes, so that Phoenix and Tucson TV could finish a brief newscast in regular programming time. In addition, my staff and I went around to each news media unit and did personal interviews during the day. Anytime there was special news, we would call for an impromptu briefing and give media the time to coordinate with home units and prepare, before we began.

We had set up a Rodeo Fire Website, through the Southwest Coordination Center and had an onsite computer specialist to update the website at least once a day. We also got eight phone lines wired into a rollover receiver bank in the Mormon Seminary conference room. Whenever a phone rang, it would be answered by the next available information officer. Phone calls were such that we staffed the phones from 0700 hours (7:00 a.m.) until 2200 hours (10:00 p.m.). During the life of the information center, we received more than 40,000 phone calls and twice that many hits on the website.

As we were able, tours were taken to high vantage points, so that the media could get "flame art" or "flamage" and see the development of the fire situation. Even then, the media had to be in nomex clothes and safety gear, including 8" tall lace-up leatherwork boots, hardhats and fire shelters. Safety dictated that we not get the media too close to the lines where firefighters were working. We could not, must not interfere with fire operations. It would be difficult to extract media in their own vehicles and without communication, in the event fire moved rapidly in their direction."

This lack of access to the very edge of the fire really rubbed some of the media types the wrong way. They felt that this historic event demanded that they be able to document the fire and loss of homes first hand. First Amendment issues came up from some of the National network reporters. Law Enforcement Liaison Officer Jim Clawson and I met with them and explained the situation. We sought alternatives, but there were not many. Officer Clawson and I were both very clear that we wanted to work with the media and considered them partners in getting critical information out to the public… but for their safety and that of our firefighters, there was no flexibility in the rules.

Photo from space by USGS Landsat satellite showing Rodeo Fire to right and Chediski Fire left. Note the arm of Chediski "reaching" toward the bigger Rodeo Fire. Photo taken June 21, 2002

The Rodeo Fire had grown to 150,000 acres. The Chediski Fire was almost 30,000 acres. Notice the phenomenon of attraction as shown in this photo taken from space by a Landsat satellite. The image from space shows that the smoke plumes of both fires are drifting almost due north (to the top of the photo), yet a finger of fire on the east side of the Chediski Fire was drawn to the much bigger main body of the Rodeo Fire.

When the Chediski made its first run up and over Lost Tank Ridge, it was approximately 15 miles from the nearest point on the Rodeo Fire. When this picture was taken in the evening of June 21st, the fires were still eight miles apart. The much bigger mass of the Rodeo Fire somehow drew the Chediski Fire like a ball bearing is drawn to a magnet. When the two burned together, Bill Jackson, our Fire Behavior Analyst (FBAN) predicted that the energy release from the two fires united would be more than anyone had ever witnessed. Bill thought that the two fires might merge on the 22nd or 23rd.

The Kinishba Devil. Photo by Paul Bead.

CH. 9: EVACUATION OF SHOW LOW, PINETOP-LAKESIDE, HONDAH, MCNARY & FOREST LAKES

Fire… "In two-needled pine groves, thousands burn at once in one continuous flame, flying like storm-clouds with terrific grandeur—an ocean of billowing flame reddening the sky at night!"
John Muir, <u>John of the Mountains</u>

June 22nd, Saturday

The Chediski Fire was reported at 29,800 acres, but grew through the night as the plume dominated fire created its own weather. Fire ran up and over the Mogollon Rim and made a major advance toward Heber-Overgaard. Crews and engines braced for the onslaught of fire. About noon, Navajo County Sheriff Gary Butler issued Forest Lakes residents an evacuation order. At this time, the fire was growing to the west, along with a major flame front running directly towards Heber-Overgaard. The flame front was within three miles of Heber by early afternoon. Crews prepared to burnout firelines around Heber-Overgaard as the flame front drew near.

At approximately 1600 hours (4:00 p.m.) a finger of fire bumped up against State Highway 260 between Heber and Forest Lakes. Embers on the north side of the highway ignited several spot fires, but engines and crews from the Heber-Overgaard Fire Department and the Forest Service were able to contain the spot fires.

Fire approaching Highway 260 west of Heber-Overgaard on June 22nd. Photo by Dewayne Saxton.

Huge columns of smoke and fire would rise in prominence, making a distinct tower and growing the tell-tale white ice cap of a thundercloud on top, only to collapse as another column rose. It became very difficult to tell the difference between the Chediski Fire and the Rodeo Fire to the east.

Rodeo Fire Column, morning of June 22ⁿᵈ. Photo by Rob Scumacher, Arizona Republic.

Sun attempting to shine through the smoke in Chediski Canyon. Photo by USFS, Apache-Sitgreaves National Forest

Fire entered Overgaard at about 2200 hours (10:00 p.m.). Firefighters worked through the night, burning out around subdivisions as the main fire approached, and then going back into subdivisions to extinguish burning houses. By midnight, the Chediski Fire had grown to 94,000 acres and at least 165 Overgaard residences and six businesses had been lost. Hardest hit were Pinecrest Lakes Mobile Home Village and Bison Ranch. Fire had not run through Heber to the west. The excellent work of structural fire engine crews and wildland hand crews working together saved many homes.

*   *   *   *   *

Bill Beecroft came to Heber when he was nine years old, and has been there ever since. He retired from the school system in 2002, after 40 years with the Heber-Overgaard school system as a teacher, coach, principal and athletic director. He met Bob Worsley in 1996, when Worsley began building a 22,000 square foot log lodge on the old Gibson Ranch, 10 miles south of Heber on the Black Canyon Lake Road. Bob was looking for a caretaker and asked Bill's help in finding a good one. Bill volunteered himself and has been at "Legacy Lodge" ever since.

The ranch is only two miles from Turkey Springs where in 1975, Travis Walton was abducted by aliens for five days. *Fire in the Sky,* written by Walton and made into a movie, documents that experience. Baca Ranch, a historic stage stop on the old General Crook Trail is only two miles west of Legacy Lodge. Building the lodge required 3.5 years. It has been used as a family and corporate retreat and is a magnificent example of log and stone masonry construction.

Legacy Ranch from the air. Photo by USFS, Apache-Sitgreaves National Forest.

Legacy Ranch from the front gate. Photo by Ken Palmrose.

Upon receiving notice of the Rodeo Fire, a concerned Bob Worsley and his son Brad took actions to protect the lodge and other buildings on the property during the afternoon of June 20th. There is a lake between the lodge and a large Dutch-roofed barn. On the north end of the meadow there are the caretaker's cabin (which is a historic log building with a shake roof), an old board-and-batten barn/garage and various outbuildings. Of particular concern was a 20,000-gallon propane tank, which was full and located on the south side of the ranch property.

This is the first area on the ranch most likely to be hit by the Chediski Fire. The Worsleys put a hose and sprinkler aimed at the propane tank and left it sprinkling. They also moved a wheeled generator and several vehicles into the middle of the irrigated meadow and then they returned to Gilbert to their regular lives. [9.a]

Bill Beecroft was on vacation in Canada, on June 20th, when his daughter called with news of fire in Clay Springs and Pinedale and houses burning. Out of concern for long time neighbors, Bill decided to head back to Arizona, but could only get to Seattle by plane. He drove a rental car all night and all day, arriving in Phoenix at 6:00 p.m. on June 21st.

Bill and his wife drove to Heber, but were stopped at the roadblock at Highway 260 and the 300 Road, just east of Forest Lakes. Bill knew the deputy and pled his need, but still could not gain permission to drive on to Heber. No one except fire and law enforcement was allowed access. He and wife, Jo then drove a back route north of Highway 260 on the 99 Road, which brought them to the north side of Heber. Once again they were stopped at a roadblock and turned around. Bill did turn around, but only drove down the road a ways and pulled off to take a nap, since he had been awake continuously, since early on June 20th, two days earlier.

Meanwhile, Bob Worsley had driven to Young from Roosevelt Lake in an attempt to reach the lodge. He, too, was stopped and turned around at a roadblock near the turnoff to Colcord Lookout. It appeared that neither man would be able to get to the Lodge.

Bill Beecroft is a woodsman who had spent half a century tramping woods and trails in the White Mountains. Bill's wife dropped him off about ½ mile from the roadblock at 3:30 a.m. on the 22nd and returned to the valley. Bill walked behind the westernmost Heber Circle K Faststop and down Turkey Hollow into Heber to Monty Williams' house. There, his good friend, Monty and he rode four-wheelers to Legacy Lodge, down Forest Road 86 from Heber. No one else was on the road, all the way to the Lodge. Monty returned to Heber while Bill checked on the buildings, llamas and chickens.

Sometime after 10:30 a.m., Bill received a phone call at the lodge, informing him that the fire was on its way. The caller pleaded with him to leave, immediately! Bill replied that it wasn't there, yet, and he had just a few more things to do before leaving, but when he looked outside… it *was* there. At exactly 11:00 a.m., the fire came over the ridge with a banshee howl and waves of 600-foot surreal red, yellow and orange flames, dancing and weaving, with solid black sky above.

Bill had never heard noise like the fire. It was more intense than standing next to a jet taking off and louder than standing right next to a locomotive barreling by on a set of railroad tracks. He was less than 200 yards from the flame front as it passed just to the east of the lodge. He watched as five different, large pine trees exploded and burst into flame, even before the flame front got to them.

Bill decided that it was time to leave and jumped on his four-wheeler. He returned to Heber on Forest Road 86 and only looked back at the fire when he reached the top of Chipmunk Hill. He didn't pause long as the entire sky was black and orange, and it appeared that the fire was closing in on him.

Bill went to the Mogollon High School in Heber, which was being used as a spike camp and supply depot. There, he met Mikahlo Medina and Judy Alley, reporters from Channel 12-KPNX in Phoenix. A helicopter from another TV station had reported that Legacy Lodge had burned. Bill told them his hair-raising tale and countered the helicopter report, based on his most recent personal experience. They asked if he would guide them to the Lodge and let them do a story on it. He figured that the main flame front had passed, so he agreed and went back down Forest Road 86 in their SUV.

Fire was on the ridge to the east of the road and had crossed Turkey Springs Canyon. When they got to the Lodge, it was still standing. It amazed Bill that the llamas were non-plussed and very laid back, just walking around in the green meadow, nibbling on grass. That green meadow had much to do with the lessening of fire intensity that came against the lodge.

On the return trip to Heber, a finger of fire had come down a canyon and trees were on fire on both sides of the road as they drove through in the Channel 12 SUV. [9.b]

* * * * *

Rick Lupe's crews and bulldozers had been building line in upper Hop Canyon near the eastern edge of the Rodeo fire, 12 miles west of Show Low. Due to the intensity of the fire, an indirect fireline was being constructed as much as a quarter mile from the flames. The combination dozer and hand constructed fireline was completed, but needed to be burned out to remove or rob fuel from the main fire and stop its advance. Remember, "the only safe line is a black line." Hotshot crews were tasked with burning out inside the fireline. Air Attack Frank Hayes had flown over the burnout and launched an Air Crane helicopter to support the burnout operation.

In Command and General Staff strategy meetings, Hump's team and local officials had designated Hop Canyon as the trigger point for evacuation of the communities to the east, Show Low, Pinetop-Lakeside and others. If the lines held, no evacuation would be necessary. If fire crossed Hop Canyon, there was absolutely no place to make a stand against this house gobbling monster fire, as trees and fuels were continuous up to and through Show Low. If fire crossed U.S. Highway 60 at Forestdale Canyon or anywhere below Rim Road 300, it would have burned east through Wagon Wheel and Lakeside and on possibly through Vernon to the grasslands north of Antelope Mountain some 30+ miles to the east. Hump's Team looked at both scenarios closely in a W.F.S.A (Wildland Fire Situation Analysis)..

Had fire crossed Highway 60, the Rodeo Fire surely would have exceeded a million acres and cost thousands of homes lost. These were most sobering considerations that weighed on each and every member of Humphrey's team. We were trying desperately to slow the advance of this ravenous monster, but Mother Nature held all the cards. We felt like she was dealing from the bottom.

Rick Lupe, Division Supervisor and four hotshot crews (Ft. Apache, Heber, Silver City and Mormon Lake) had been burning out through the night to secure the fireline and stop the eastward advance of the fire, working the top of Hop Canyon up to the Mogollon Rim. They continued the burnout action during the day, as the Rodeo fire was growing to the east and north.

Conditions were questionable, with tremendous heat from the fire and the burnout combined, since the action was in the middle of the day, even into the hottest portion of the burning period. Crews on the ground had to apply fire in short sections and then let each section burn back into the main fire, while watching vigilantly for spots over the fireline to the east. Spots were extinguished before they flamed and took off.

Erickson Air Crane preparing to drop water on the fire. Photo by Pat Shannahan, Arizona Republic.

Frank Hayes, Air Attack, was over Lupe's operation and remembered distinctly talking to Heber Hotshot superintendent, Chris Willcox, as his crew moved with the burners. Frank's words:

"They had started picking up small spot fires, but were catching them, when the Heber Super asked me to focus the one helitanker (Erickson S-64 Air Crane #747 with 1,200 gallons of water that was inbound, to an area of the burnout, still inside the fireline, but upslope, that was beginning to show a pretty good bit of heat (black smoke, not grey). 'Cool it off, so we don't get spots,' the Heber Super requested.

"I was monitoring both Air to Ground frequencies (normal channel used for Air Attack, helicopter, and ground troop contact) and also TAC freq (normal channel unique to that specific division only for ground forces communication). The helitanker was inbound to the drop when I overheard radio traffic on the TAC freq to the Heber Super from a crew member that they had a spot fire, up slope across the line, and that it was burning across Hop Canyon. This was not good news. I fortunately had an excellent Air Attack pilot who also overheard this "radio traffic," and banked to the spot, so that I got an eye on it, immediately.

"It was no more than 50 feet across when we spotted it. I got the helitanker dialed in to it immediately. He dropped on it in less than two minutes. It was growing rapidly as he made his approach. He made an excellent drop and knocked down the head of the fire, but was only able to soak about half of the entire spot fire. I did not have another helicopter nor air tanker in the area. The Air Crane went to the pumpkin, reloaded was back in less than 10 minutes, but the fire literally had erupted to more than 100 acres in size in just that short time.

"The hotshot crews had to be withdrawn. In an hour, the newest head of the monster was over 1000 acres and running northeast, parallel to Highway 60. Every individual and resource gave their all… the fire just beat us to the punch and Show Low had to be evacuated." [9.c]

*   *   *   *   *

Hump's Incident Management Team and local officials decided to call a special briefing session at the Show Low High School for 7:00 p.m. (1900 hrs). We asked the radio and TV media to work with their producers and interrupt normal programming to carry this briefing live, as the public needed this information.

Evacuation Day from Fire Camp. Fire is more than 10 miles away. Note the sun. Photo by USFS, Apache-Sitgreaves National Forest.

Press briefing to announce the evacuation of Show Low, Pinetop-Lakeside, Hondah and McNary at 7:00 p.m. Photo by USFS, Apache-Sitgreaves National Forest.

We did not mention, but everyone knew that it was for the evacuation of several communities east of the fire. I opened the session and thanked everyone for coming. Then I asked Incident Commander Larry Humphrey to come to the podium. Larry told folks that we had set up a trigger point whereby if fire crossed it, we would need to evacuate the communities to the east of the fire, as there was no place to stop the fire. That trigger point was Hop Canyon and the fire had simply beat us there.

Then, I introduced Show Low Mayor Gene Kelley (not the dancer), who in an emotion-charged voice, told residents of Show Low, Pinetop-Lakeside, Hondah and McNary that they had only a very few hours to load up precious items, take care of pets and livestock and head out of town. He asked them to be safe and maintain calm. Mayor Kelly asked all who viewed/listened to, "Pray for the firefighters, pray for us and pray for rain!" Mayor Kelley asked residents to "post" their house as being vacated with a white towel or rag tied to their front door so that it could be seen from the street. [9.d]

200 West Cooley
Show Low, AZ 85901-4724
(520) 537-5724

FAX: (520) 537-2338
E-MAIL: info@ci.show-low.az.us
URL: www.ci.show-low.az.us

City of Show Low

ORDER OF EVACUATION

The Rodeo Fire is at a point where it is presenting a considerable danger to our citizens and visitors. For this reason, we are initiating an evacuation order for all persons in the City of Show Low. People should evacuate these areas immediately and not re-enter until this order is rescinded. The evacuation center for Show Low is at the Round Valley High School in Eagar.

When you leave your house or residence, please leave a white towel or rag tied on your door that is visible from the front of the residence. If you are in this affected area, please leave at once in an orderly manner. We appreciate your cooperation and understanding.

John A. Corder
Chief of Police

Gene Kelley
Mayor

Date: 6-22-02

 Spisske Podhradie, Slovakia ♣ Sister City

The primary evacuation center for Show Low and the communities to the south would be located at the Round Valley High School Dome in Eagar. Additionally, the towns of Springerville, St. Johns, Greer, Globe, Snowflake-Taylor and Whiteriver volunteered to receive evacuees with open arms. Pinetop-Lakeside Mayor, Ginny Handorf's short speech was the lead in to Dan Rather's June 23rd. Evening News on CBS. She said simply. "We are the White Mountains. We are Arizona. We will get through this!" [9.e] She also asked residents to leave in a calm and reasonable manner.

Sheriff Gary Butler told the cameras and the audience that a state of "martial law" was being declared and law enforcement and National Guard troops would be patrolling evacuated areas. Anyone, other than firefighters and emergency personnel would be arrested if found wandering around in the towns that had been evacuated. Those who refused to evacuate would be required to remain on their own property.

During the briefing, I realized that we had a unique situation with the media that was present at that time, especially those with satellite trucks set up and in place. It would serve us better, in the dissemination of information to the public, if they were able to stay in Show Low. Incident Commander, Larry Humphrey and I put our heads together and came up with a quick decision that was extremely rare… media would be given the option of staying or evacuating, but if they left, they would not be allowed back in until the evacuation order was lifted. Media had become our partners and good information was getting to all facets of the public from our twice-daily briefings.

Of 120 media personnel in camp, only about four individuals left. All the rest signed waivers and came under the control of the team for their welfare and subsistance. Never before had media been sequestered in the midst of a fire camp and made/allowed to experience the same conditions that firefighters do on every assignment… *living in the dirt*! That meant that we would provide their sleeping bags and tents, fire clothes, food, showers and sanitary facilities.

We gave them only two rules: First, no skullduggery and sneaking around to "get the scoop," outside of camp, without an Information Officer escort. And second, the chow line and showers were off limits to interviews. Sleeping areas were not to be invaded for interviews, either, as that was for necessary down time for crews. Information Officers would coordinate interviews. Art Morrison, a Type I Information Officer and former Smokejumper from Albuquerque was the media coordinator and handled all I.O assignments and media trips, tours and interviews with crews. Show Low Police Sergeant Jeff Hansen would also be working with us as a liaison from the local law enforcement side. We promised media that we would get them out as close to the fire as was safe, as often as we could.

Not all the media was overjoyed at being sequestered in fire camp. They wanted free access to the firelines, action shots of firefighters working and of course, close-up views of the fires burning. Some of them took the fire team to task for alleged violations of the First Amendment. The Arizona First Amendment Coalition, numerous elected officials and agency officials statewide continue a dialogue to this day on news media access to fires.

Media field tour to fireline. Photo by USFS, Apache-Sitgreaves National Forest.

*   *   *   *   *

Ben Nuvamsa, Superintendent of Ft. Apache B.I.A and his assistant, Robert Lacapa, John Bedell, Apache Sitgreaves National Forest Supervisor, Bob Wagenfehr of State Lands, I.C. Humphrey and some of the command folks got together and all reached the same conclusion… that the two fires were bigger than Hump's team was and the Rodeo Fire alone had exceeded our capability to manage. We never did assume command of the Chediski Fire.

Dave Dash's Alaska Type I Team was on the way to the Chediski Fire, to assume command from Kvale's Southeast Arizona Type II Team, who was in place and working out of Cibeque. We needed more help and we needed it fast. A call was made to the Southwest Coordination Center in Albuquerque and Van Bateman's Type I Team (our sister organization) was committed to the Rodeo Fire on the south end.

Kim Martin's Intermountain Type I Team from the Boise area was dispatched to take command of the Chediski Fire in the Heber-Overgaard and Forest Lakes area, but it would take him at least 24 hours to arrive in Heber. Joe Ribar's Area Command Team would set up at the Hondah Resort and would handle coordination between the four teams.

One of Area Command's primary functions would be to allocate scarce resources amongst the four teams, based on risk analysis as well as predictions of the next day's fire behavior. Those scarce resources were air tankers, helicopters, Hotshot crews and fire engines. The fire was renamed the Rodeo-Chediski Fire Complex and had now become the Number One Priority in the United States for resources. With so many fires and so few critical resources nationwide, we would still not be "fat," but more of our needs would be met more quickly than before, as resources became available.

*   *   *   *   *

Richard Watkins of Cellular One put a notice on the local radio stations and Cable One TV that if anyone needed a cell phone for emergency purposes, Cellular One would provide a phone with a national call plan and unlimited minutes. They gave almost 500 phones out to recipients based on the honor system. Cellular One's only request was that the phones be returned when the emergency was over. Very few phones were lost. [9.f]

*   *   *   *   *

Tom Brown, Show Low Fire Dept. Chaplain, was working with us in information, coordinating field tours for media. He attended the morning and evening briefings at shift change to get the latest updates and the plans for action against the dragon on that shift. He told me that this was his first experience with a team on a large fire.

Tom said, "The briefings were painful to endure, even though the information was excellent. I felt like the whole community was a cancer patient learning that the surgery did not work and now our body (i.e. community) was going to have to undergo radical treatment of radiation and chemotherapy…and oh, by the way, if that doesn't work, then we will need to do an emergency amputation."

Shift briefing for crews going out on shift. Photo by USFS, Apache-Sitgreaves National Forest.

124

His head reeled and he felt nauseous with the outlook, but he did not have any alternatives or options to offer. He really felt that at times he and others were in shock. Tense times, to say the least.
9.g

*　　*　　*　　*　　*

Exodus from Show Low on Highway 60 East. Flames on Juniper Ridge showing in the background are eight miles from Show Low. Photo by Arizona D.P.S. Highway Patrol.

Smoke from Rodeo Fire on Evac. Day, June 22nd from airport. Photo by Arizona D.P.S. Highway Patrol.

The line of cars leaving Show Low was something out of a science fiction movie. Many of those who left have told me since that it was similar to a funeral procession and that all the traffic was in the east bound lane moving only about 30-40 miles an hour in a 55 mile per hour speed zone. Rearview mirrors and rear windows were filled with an entire horizon of flames eight miles to the west of Show Low. Many thought that fire would knock on Show Low's door that night.

Distance and flames at night are deceptive, but the emotion and heartache were real. Many of these people were born in the White Mountains. Others moved here because of the beauty, mountain serenity and the charm of the local populace. Leaving their homes had people in shock. Most of these "refugees" had no idea what they would return to, or when. Would it be to their homes and towns, or only to the ghosts of rubble and ashes? This photo shows Juniper Ridge the day after the flames in evacuees' rear view mirrors as they left Show Low. Note that it is now a "moonscape."

Juniper Ridge Lookout Tower on June 24th after fire passage. Photo by USFS, Apache-Sitgreaves National Forest.

By now, approximately 30,000+ people from a dozen communities had been displaced and uprooted. One distraught woman told me, "Things like this are not supposed to happen HERE!!" I asked Ed Muder, the acting Show Low City Manager what he remembered most about the fire and the evacuation, and he replied, "After being raised here, I knew most of the people in the area. I was genuinely lonesome when they and my family were evacuated and town was so empty, so alone. I, too, could not believe that this was happening here, now… to us." [9.h]

*   *   *   *   *

Show Low empty streets after evacuation on June 23rd. Photos by George Leech.

126

(c) 2002 - Brian Buswell

(c) 2002 - Brian Buswell

(c) 2002 - Brian Buswell

(c) 2002 - Brian Buswell

(c) 2002 - Brian Buswell

Sequential photos of a tanker drop, all by Brian Buswell

Rick Lupe's crews on the ground and the air resources under Air Attack's direction never gave up… they just kept chasing spot fires and slopovers on the east flank of the fire. As the edge of the fire moved, so did they. By mid-afternoon, the smoke was so dense and dark that neither lead planes nor air tankers could get through to smoke columns inside the fire, so retardant drops were limited to the southeastern flank, outside of the dense smoke.

Frank Hayes related another interesting story that illustrates just how huge a battle and what kind of monster we were in the grips of. Four air tankers had run all day out of the Winslow Tanker Base, one trip after another, returning time and again for fuel and retardant. That is a standard procedure known as "Load and Return," communicated to the tanker driver by Air Attack. It means basically, get back here with another load of retardant as quick as possible. Other air tankers on the fire were working out of airports with retardant mixing bases at Williams Gateway in Mesa and Silver City, New Mexico. An example of the magnitude of this fire is shown when Frank recalled:

"Late that evening (June 22nd), my lead plane had gone home, due to timing out (used all available hours under FAA regulations), and I thought that all the air tankers were also finished. When I checked with White Mountain Dispatch, they advised that one lone tanker had reloaded at Winslow and was inbound. It was Tanker 25, an Aero Union, P-3 Orion driven by the notorious Bill Waldman. Bill has decades jockeying air tankers and is legend, even amongst tanker drivers, for being able to deliver in tight spots, when needed.

"I was able to reach Bill on normal air-air AM frequency, and asked his ETA (estimated time of arrival). It was getting pretty shadowy, that late in the afternoon, to drop in the canyons. Bill replied that he was out of Winslow about five minutes, was going to have to skirt the Chediski Fire first and he would be there in a few. He called back to let me know he was approaching a very large column, 'Can you see me?' he asked. 'Nope, keep coming,' I replied.

This conversation repeated itself several times, each time same answer: "Just keep peddling, Bill. We are way around the corner on the southeast flank, parallel but well to the west of Highway 60. He eventually did show up. 'Ah, that column,' he exclaimed as he got sight of us banking into the late afternoon sun.

"He had traversed seven major fire columns or plumes, all from the Chediski fire, except the last two, which were on the Rodeo Fire, as he was en route to the eastern most point of fire activity. Bill did his customary excellent size up and drop, which was the last of the evening." [9.i]

*   *   *   *   *

Orion P-3 Heavy Air Tanker dropping retardant on a ridge. Photo by Ken Palmrose.

Gary Martinson, owner of Bison Ranch, had developed a western resort, complete with a boardwalk-lined, false-front structured town, even to include a small bison herd in corrals adjacent to Highway 260. Gary and several of his staff had loaded valuables from their homes and offices during the day of the 22nd. They really felt that they were going through the motions, to satisfy the authorities, fire really wouldn't reach Bison Ranch... would it?? As a precaution, Gary had his staff load up the dude horses and the four-horse team of Percheron draft horses. They truly believed that in a couple of days, they would return and life would go on as normal.

A law enforcement officer came by as they were leaving and asked about the bison. He suggested that the gates be opened so that the bison could fend for themselves if the fire got too close. Gary assured him that the bison were fine in their pens with no grass or weeds around the corrals and that the worst thing for firefighters and emergency traffic would be to meet an angry 1000-pound bison standing in the road or on a fireline. The officer reconsidered and passed the word on to others. The bison stayed put and weathered the smoke from the fire just fine. They were in a large open safe-zone that was shared later with firefighters when fire made its big run through the ranch.

About a dozen vehicles, including two semis of horses, left Overgaard about 6:00 p.m. and headed to Payson. In Payson, their rooms, along with those of many other refugees, were comped by the Mazatzal Casino and Hotel. Each evacuee was issued a meal ticket for use at the Casino restaurant. Horses were boarded at the Payson Rodeo Grounds. Such was the generosity of a community who greeted fire refugees with open arms.

Bobby Crandall was Martinson's caretaker/handyman at Bison Ranch. He stayed behind and began watering houses with sprinklers. He filled the ranch water truck and moved vehicles parked in driveways to the big meadow. When fire came through Bison Ranch at approximately 10:00 p.m., Bobby watched from his cabin. It got too hot to stay in his cabin, so he got in his truck, drove to the meadow and remained there, with the engine and the air conditioner running.

As soon as the flame front passed, Bobby got in the ranch water truck and drove the main roads, putting out fires that approached cabins. He is solely responsible for saving a number of homes in Bison Ranch, before fire crews and engines arrived later in the night to assist. He bypassed those cabins that were already burning, and used his water on those he thought there was a chance of saving. Bison Ranch lost 35 cabins that night.

Bison Ranch looking northeast after fire's passage. 35 homes/cabins burned along the fringes of the development. Photo by USFS, Apache-Sitgreaves National Forest.

Cabins burned in Bison Ranch. Photo by USFS, Apache-Sitgreaves National Forest.

One cabin survived the fire. Photo by USFS, Apache-Sitgreaves National Forest.

Looking northeast through the damage to Pinecrest Lakes R-V Village. Note the almost total devastation. Photo by USFS, Apache-Sitgreaves National Forest.

Nothing left but ashes and rubble in Pinecrest Lakes Mobile Home Village. Photo by USFS, Apache-Sitgreaves National Forest.

But, the flag flew during the fire and survived. Promise and Hope. Photo by USFS, Apache-Sitgreaves National Forest.

Bobby had no fire training, but with an ample dose of common sense, he applied triage techniques quite successfully and safely. Without Bobby's good efforts, Bison Ranch might have lost double the 35 cabins burned, or even more. One crew boss from California told Bobby that he had not even imagined that there were cabins back in that far from the highway, as he only knew of those that they could see from the road. [9.j]

Pinecrest Lakes Mobile Home Village was not so lucky. When the flame front roared through, it took 166 of the 200 motor homes, R.V.'s and mobile homes in one pass. Most of those went up in smoke in a matter of seconds as the fire moved through the area. An aerial view in this photo shows the fire's destruction. A close-up at the entrance shows a flag that withstood the onslaught of fire that destroyed the community center and all the mobile homes around it. Look closely and you will see that the flag's edges are singed. Another 16 homes in Pinecrest Lakes would burn in the next wave of fire. Heber also lost their community and senior citizens centers.

The Chediski Fire gained an additional 64,200 acres, while the Rodeo Fire burned 49,200 acres. Think about it, that is a "one day only" total of 113,400 acres burned. There was no way that fire crews and command could even keep up with the progress of the two fires. The Chediski Fire was now estimated at 93,990 acres total, while the Rodeo Fire had grown to 199,300 acres. Even those of us who had been in wildland firefighting for 30 years and more had never seen or imagined anything like this many-headed monster. This photo from a Modis Satellite in space shows the two fires and their smoke plumes.

Communities across Arizona responded with assistance. Forty-one communities sent 104 fire engines from structural fire departments across the state. Every fire department in the valley had apparatus and firefighters on one or both of these house-gobbling monsters. Phoenix sent seven engines and 28 personnel to help out. It was the first time that Phoenix Fire engines had ever responded out of the valley. There were also more than 150 wildland fire engines from all the agencies that were assigned duties on the firelines. [9.k]

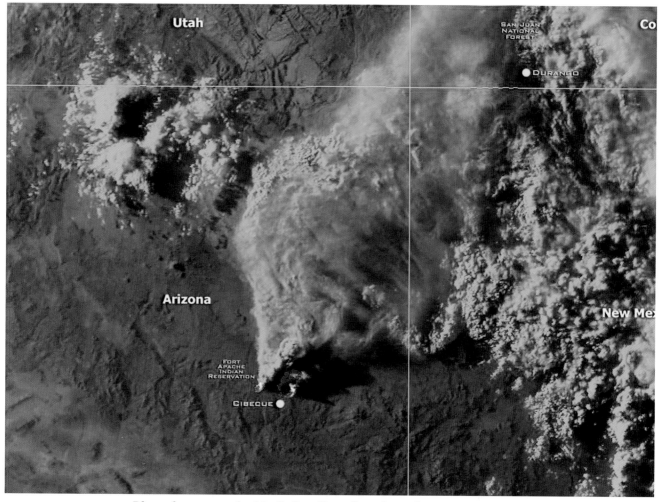

Photo from space by Modis Satellite. State boundaries superimposed.
Note the Missionary Ridge Fire north of Durango, Colorado.

*   *   *   *   *

June 23rd, Sunday

Rodeo Fire and Chediski Fires combine about 2:30 p.m. on June 23rd.
Photo by USFS, Apache-Sitgreaves National Forest.

This Sunday will be remembered as the day that the Rodeo and Chediski Fires burned together at approximately 1433 hours (2:33 p.m.). An additional 40,000 acres burned, bringing the total of the now named Rodeo-Chediski Fire to more than 331,000 acres. The fire grew on its entire perimeter and in every direction. Fire behavior was so extreme that it was unpredictable. For example, *Probability of Ignition* (P.I.) is one of the indices used by Fire Behavior Analysts in predicting how severe a fire may burn. The "P.I." was "10," meaning that, out of ten embers or firebrands that might land on a receptive fuel bed, all 10 would ignite and start a new fire. Embers lofted in the smoke columns of the many flame fronts were in the millions per hour.

*   *   *   *   *

Governor Jane Dee Hull flew the fire and witnessed the destruction. Ater landing, she was interviewed and blasted environmentalists for stopping logging and thinning. She also directed part of the blame to policy makers in Washington D.C., when she said "Westerners cannot have these fires burning, because Easterners don't know how to manage forests. Basically, when we start to cut trees or clear brush, someone sues. We must have the authority to manage these lands. We live here!" [9.1]

Rodeo Fire News:

After to big pulse burn days the Rodeo fire has pulled the Chediski fire in to it on Sunday at 2:33 p.m. to form one huge inferno of over 330,000 acres, as predicted by the FBAN. The blaze is now known as the Rodeo-Chediski. The fires continue to burn very intensely with extreme fire behavior and erratic crowning runs with profuse spotting causing burnout and holding problems.

-Rodeo Situation Unit

Sign posted by the Situation Unit from Hump's Team on the Rodeo and Chediski Fires combining. Photo by USFS, Rocky Mountain Research Station-Flagstaff.

Since almost all the residents evacuated, he could not in good conscience stay in his house, so Show Low Mayor Gene Kelley had taken up residence in the Show Low Police Station's interview room on a cot. His wife and parents had evacuated to the Round Valley Dome in Eagar. The Mayor was often seen checking the wind by watching Show Low Fire Department's 40-foot tall flagpole and large flag. Then he was often seen praying for Heavenly intervention to keep fire out of Show Low. The seemingly never changing wind out of the west had the flag held stiff and popping. Once it even blew the ball cap off Gene's head and he chased it across the street before catching it. He also had a prayer chain of thousands of people all over the nation joining him.

As Mayor, he attended every single team strategy session during the entire time Hump's Team was on the fire and gave input regarding the City, which was extremely helpful. He also made daily trips to Round Valley Dome to visit with and give the latest news to the evacuees. The Mayor considered his job to be that of enabler for the city departments, the voice of direct reassurance and bearer of daily information updates to the evacuees at the Dome. There were constant rumors of looting and fire in Show Low. One radio station had reported that the mayor's house near Show Low High School had burned. He spoke from just having been there that those rumors were not true. He also recommended to the evacuees that they not watch T.V., except during our 11:00 a.m. and 10:00 p.m. briefings, so that they would get accurate information.

*   *   *   *   *

On the fire scene, this was the fourth straight day of Red Flag conditions. Once again, as individual columns rose and collapsed, firefighters were pulled off the firelines to safety zones. They watched as fires burned by and then would go back in to subdivisions to salvage what they could. More houses were lost all across the Highway 260 corridor of the fire.

Roy Hall, Operations Section Chief referred to this event as another "bleacher day" for firefighters. Conditions were so extreme that any efforts by firefighters were wiped out and temporary gains became losses by the end of the day. Risk to life was just too great and the conditions too unpredictable to put people close to the fire.

This precaution once again caused great discontent amongst the locals and rural fire departments. Many firefighters from the local departments just could not understand why Hump's team was not more aggressive in going "head to head" with the dragon. We tried to convey to them the danger and risk to firefighters of these plume collapses and how neither I.C. Humphrey nor the Operations Section Chiefs Roy Hall and Buck Wickham were willing to take that risk.

It is ironic that many of the locals blamed the Forest Service for this caution, when it was totally our Incident Management Team. Their issues are understandable, I just do not believe they understood the power and severity of these plume dominated columns of fire. I am sure if my house were threatened, I would want to do more as well.

Dave Dash's Alaska Type I Team arrived to take command of the Chediski Fire. They were based in Cibeque, as was Kvale's Type II Team, which was being replaced. Another Type I Team commanded by Kim Martin from the Boise, Idaho was ordered for the Heber-Overgaard area. Van Bateman's Southwest Type I Team (our sister team) was ordered, confirmed and enroute to manage the southeast side of the Rodeo Fire. They were coming off a fire near Santa Fe in New Mexico.

Joe Ribar's Area Command Team would oversee all of the incident management teams, prioritizing resource orders and allocation of scarce resources (air tankers, helicopters, hotshot crews and engines) and providing logistical support to all four teams' operations. Each Incident Management Team would have a quadrant that amounts to an equal portion of area + complexity + communities at risk.

Hump's team now managed only the area from Mogollon Rim Road 300 on Highway 60, below Show Low around the Northeast side of the Rodeo Fire to Airipine on Highway 260. It would take a full day or more for these other teams to arrive and another day for transition (getting settled and set up for action) before becoming functional. We were now the number one priority in the nation for resources. All of the fire crews and contract resources nationwide were stretched thin and becoming fatigued after a very active fire season all over the U.S.

*   *   *   *   *

Crews began building a dozer line down Joe Tank Road (Forest Road #136), adjacent to Bison Ridge sub-division, at the very northwest edge of Show Low. It was considered a secondary line, in that it would only be used if the fire made a significant run toward Show Low. Crews continued building hand and dozer fireline to the east of the fire, just below Linden Ridge subdivision and Cheney Ranch in a southerly line down Forest Roads 135 and 136, east on Rim Road 300 and then south along Highway 60. Where they could use Joe Tank Road and some two-track Forest roads, they widened the line and readied for a burnout operation to begin on June 24th.

*   *   *   *   *

Once again, fingers of fire made mid-day runs through Overgaard. A burnout operation in Sections 30 and 31 kept the fire from making a frontal assault against homes in that area of Heber. The tactic worked to a degree, although there were many spots and some slopovers that burned beyond the firelines.

A second wave of flame ran through Overgaard. It crossed Highway 260 and ran through Mogollon Air Park and past the Baptist Church on Highway 260. The church is a brick building with a composition shingle roof. All the hedges and the front door were burned, but the building stands today.

Top Left: Overgaard Southern Baptist Church sign. Fire crossed Highway 260 and burned north through the Airpark. Photo by USFS, Apache-Sitgreaves National Forest

Top Right: Church showing shrubs burned as fire passed. Photo by USFS, Apache-Sitgreaves National Forest

Left: Close up of the church showing damage to screens and all shrubs burned, but the church survived. Photo by USFS, Apache-Sitgreaves National Forest

Eight homes in the Airpark burned. Approximately 20 homes in the Buckskin Artist Draw, Section 30 and Black Canyon area below Heber also burned. These fire runs occurred in narrow, wind driven, topography-influenced "strips" that burned parallel to the path that the first onslaught of the Chediski Fire took on the 22nd. Now, unbelievably, more than 331,000 acres had burned in only six days.

*　　　*　　　*　　　*　　　*

Incident Commander Dave Dash and his Alaska Type I Team had become heroes to the White Mountain Apaches in Cibeque. Dash's fire camp was there and he worked out of the Cibeque Community Center. The Apaches were watching a large part of their economic viability in future timber harvests go up in smoke on the two fires. Their community of Cibeque was also threatened, if fire turned and came their way. More than 800 firefighters worked out of this camp and a few of the news media made it into their area.

The world was not very aware of the damage caused to the White Mountain Apaches, and the information flow to our information center was limited and somewhat disconnected. We had most of the media sequestered in Show Low. Show Low was what they could see and what I knew most about… so that was what was reported the most.

With the advent of Area Command overseeing the information function and gathering twice-daily reports from each of the four zones, the flow of information to us improved dramatically for the duration of the fire. Mrs. Carrie Templin of the B.L.M. in Phoenix became the Area Command Information Coordinator. As of June 26th, each zone had a representative who spoke directly about the activity on their zone at both the 11:00 a.m. and 10:00 p.m. news briefings. [9.m]

*　　*　　*　　*　　*

Heber-Overgaard Chief Mel Epps was getting meals from Cibeque in "hot-tainers" (cans with insulation and food by entrée in each can. His problem was that the food was about three to four hours late and very cold. He had almost 1,000 people to feed, including the "Heber Rebels." You can't fight the battle, if you can't keep the troops fed, so Mel requested the Salvation Army set up a portable kitchen at the H-O Fire Station and food began to be made available to firefighters and those still in town on a regular basis.

He also had vehicles that were having tire, air filter and maintenance problems and no garage to work on them. Parts were even harder to get, since Heber-Overgaard had been evacuated. Mel actually resorted to using the power of eminent domain and breaking into auto parts houses and restaurants and grocery stores. He had his people run an inventory of everything taken from each store. All of the bills were submitted for payment and every broken lock was fixed or replaced.

*　　*　　*　　*　　*

Bill Beecroft returned to Legacy Lodge in the afternoon. As he rode his four-wheeler down Forest Road 86 to the south, he noticed what looked like a blue tarp up in the top of a tree close to the road and he thought that to be curious. He went on to the ranch to check on buildings and animals. First thing he saw was the woodpile at the caretaker's house was on fire and fire was creeping towards the house. He went after creeping flames with a garden hose and was able to quench the fire.

On the other side of the caretaker's house, the well house had burned and the copper roof was a "puddle" on the slab where it had melted. Thank goodness for the water storage tanks, as he still had water available to put out fires. The metal gate at the boundary fence was too hot to touch, even though fire had already burned through that area and was by this time, no more than smoldering. The chicken coop had burned, but Bill found most of the chickens and the llamas in the big pasture, just grazing and walking around.

When Bill got down to the Lodge, it was standing, unscathed, as was the barn. He walked past the lake and noticed that a 12' diameter water trampoline was gone. It was mounted on an aluminum rim with a blue jumping surface and styrofoam flotation pads. The trampoline had been secured to the bottom of the lake with log chains and concrete anchor piers. Now Bill knew what the "blue tarp" was 50' up in that pine tree on the road… it was the water trampoline.

So much for his idea of taking refuge in the pond, if the fire had burned the lodge and barn, and he had been at the ranch. When the main fire roared through, winds must have been close to 100 miles per hour. This would explain the uprooting of an anchored, very heavy trampoline, which ended up several hundred yards away, in the top of that pine tree.

Bill spent the night in the Lodge and told me that it was as smoky inside as outside. He marveled at the kaleidoscope display of burning tree "candles" in the night sky. Entire hillsides both to the east and west of the Lodge were lit up with stumps and trees burning. As one blaze would die down and go out, another would blaze up and wink in the night. It was an awesome display of God's fireworks. [9.0]

*　　*　　*　　*　　*

At the 10:00 p.m. news briefing, I gave results of the day's activity and told the audience that an estimated 331,430 acres had burned, now that the two fires had combined. This was an area bigger than the corporate city limits of Mesa, Arizona. Then I took a deep breath and asked the good Lord for the right words.

Fire moving closer to Show Low's Deuce of Clubs Ave. on June 24th. Photo by Karen Wattenmaker.

I told the audience that I was going to draw our Fire Behavior Analyst, Bill Jackson's predictions for the next two days fire advance in the Show Low area. The line for the 25th arced from Torreon through Fool's Hollow Reservoir. The line for the 26th was from the junction of Highways 60 and 260 up toward the Show Low Airport. Our team and FBAN Jackson were convinced that if fire behavior continued and conditions remained as volatile as they were, there was no way to keep fire out of Show Low. There were audible gasps followed by ghastly silence, even among the hardest of news reporters.

When I returned to the podium with its 20+ microphones, I told the crowd and the viewers that we needed a miracle and we really needed conditions to cool down and a change in the weather, so that firefighters could press the attack closer, against the edge of the fire. I announced that we would attempt a burnout operation to the west of Show Low in a last ditch effort to rob the fire of fuels and stop its advance. Otherwise, the team and all our cooperators were preparing for fire to invade Show Low and possibly Pinetop-Lakeside.

*　　*　　*　　*　　*

Friends Martin and Eunice Kent were on a Mediterranean cruise with an airline flight that landed in Milan, Italy. As they were deplaning and walking the concourse, Eunice cocked her ear and then looked up. She heard a familiar voice and when she saw me on a widescreen T.V., she gasped and pulled Marty up and said, "Oh my God, look, Marty, it's Jim. There's a forest fire near Show Low." They were shocked that CNN Europe was carrying reports of the fire. They were able to keep up with the fire's progress during most of their cruise. Small world, isn't it? [9.p]

* * * * *

June 24th, Monday

Proof that life carries on and a boost to the morale of evacuees in the Round Valley Dome occurred when at 1:01 a.m. on June 24th, Alexia Blaze Crowther was born at the White Mountain Medical Center in Springerville. Her mother had been one of the evacuees at the Dome and her birth lifted everyone's spirits in the Dome and Springerville/Eagar. What an appropriate middle name. In all, there would be eight babies born to evacuees during the fire. [9.q]

* * * * *

Once again, the day began with active fire behavior on all flanks. Measuring the fire perimeter by infrared flight documented 43,000+ additional acres burned. Fire even burned to the south, downhill and against the wind toward the town of Cibeque. Crews and dozers were able to stop the fire before it reached the town. The fire now stood at 374,950 acres and still no containment. The dragon was flexing his muscles and still bragging about his ability and desire to consume forests and towns. On large fires, infrared photos are taken about midnight by a contract jet that flies the fire. They accurately detect heat on the ground. The fire was flown in strips or lines from north to south about one mile apart. An infrared photo frame is taken every mile as the plane flies a line.

A fire as big as the Rodeo-Chediski takes considerable time to fly and photograph. When the mission is accomplished, the plane must land and the infrared film must be developed. The images are then taken to an infrared interpreter, who transfers new boundary lines and areas of greatest heat to a paper map. Usually we want the infrared interpretation with new boundaries on the map for the 0600 morning shift briefing for crews going to the fireline that day. Infrared also gives Operations an idea of where the fire might burn hottest the next day, due to the amount of bright red and the size of the area of greatest heat that shows on the photos. Due to the size of the fire and the number of photo frames that had to be taken, we were not getting the latest infrared information until about 1000 hours, which we incorporated into our morning planning session for the evening shift.

A curious thing had been noted for the last two nights. There was a green area of "unburned" country of several thousand acres near Chuckbox Lake to the northeast of Chediski Peak. It should have burned in the initial run of the Chediski Fire. Finally, Ben Nuvamsa, Ft. Apache Fire & Forestry Superintendent related that the green area might be the Chuckbox Timber Sale area, and if so, timber had been harvested last in 1996/97, the remaining stands of pine thinned in 1997 and slash piles prescribe-burned in 1999.

When members of Ft. Apache Fire/Forestry were later able to get out to that area, they found that fire had burned through the Chuckbox area, but on the ground only. They had hardly lost a single tree to torching and crown fire on 2,000 + acres. It appeared that fire "went to ground," slowed to a crawl and burned with much less intensity, until it reached the northwest side where no treatments had been done and forests were still extremely dense. Then fire climbed the "ladders" of small trees and branches and crept into the crowns, running through the forest and burning nearly everything in its path again. That was absolute proof that thinning and pruning, followed with "cool" prescribed fire to reduce fuels and clean the forest floor really does work. This is an inarguable lesson from Mother Nature for us all to remember and apply to our lands.

The Chediski Fire burned through the Chuckbox Timber Sale and did very little damage. Photo by B.I.A., Ft. Apache Forestry.

Chuckbox Timber Sale, thinned, piled and debris burned years before the Chediski Fire. Photo by B.I.A., Ft. Apache Forestry

Area adjacent to Chuckbox, but untreated. Tree mortality is approaching 100%. Photo by B.I.A., Ft. Apache Forestry

Crown fire devastated this un-managed stand and burned everything down to the ground, also adjacent to the Chuckbox Timber Sale. Photo by B.I.A., Ft. Apache Forestry.

*　　*　　*　　*　　*

Show Low Police apprehended a CNN camera crew and reporter driving, unescorted in Torreon subdivision, trying to get close to the fire. They were brought to fire camp. Liaison Officer Jim Clawson, Show Low Police Sergeant Jeff Hanson and I met with the CNN folks. They wanted to argue First Amendment rights and would not agree to play by the rules that we earlier laid out when we allowed all the media to stay in camp rather than be evacuated and denied *any* access to the fire. Officer Clawson expelled them from the fire. I contacted CNN and explained the situation to their management. CNN sent another crew in to replace the "reprobates." Their satellite truck and a second crew remained in camp with us.

The very next day, we had an altercation between a three person national ABC crew and Information Officer Art Morrison, my media coordinator. Brian Rooney of ABC and his producer and cameraman had become abusive and threatening with Mr. Morrison, claiming denial of First Amendment Rights. Once again, Officer Clawson and I conferred and they were also expelled, allowing the network to keep their satellite truck in camp and replace the crew.

Vice President Dick Cheney's office called to find out what was going on with our expulsion of the two national network crews. George Lennon, Director of Public Affairs for the Forest Service in Washington, D.C. was in our Information Center. He was observing our operation and actually working as an Information Officer. George took the call, and once Vice President Cheney had the facts from our side, he had no problem with our actions.

138

*   *   *   *   *

The days shortened by one minute and 30 seconds per day, since Summer Solstice on June 21st. As conditions for monsoons began to build off to the east, the Fire Dragon changed his character slightly. Winds diminished after four days of Red Flag warnings. The dominant winds changed just a few degrees, now blowing from the south, which pushed the fire away from Show Low. Relative humidity increased by at least 5-6% from a low of 2% only a few days earlier. The many headed Monster was still very much in control and flexing his might, but now the columns and towering smoke plumes actually shaded and cooled the east side of the fire.

*   *   *   *   *

Bateman's Team arrived and set up camp at Blue Ridge High School in Pinetop-Lakeside. Dugger Hughes, Operations Section Chief and his crews planned to continue the burnout through Cottonwood, Corduroy and Carrizo Canyons on June 25th. The only way to secure the fireline and stop growth of the fire toward Pinetop-Lakeside was to rob the fire of fuel, by burning it before the fire got there. Recent fires in Cottonwood (1990) and Carrizo (1993) Canyons helped the burnout operation. [9.r] There was enough grass and brush to carry fire, but not enough timber and dead fuels to generate a tremendous amount of energy. Both dozer and hand crews built some line. Due to severe winds on the 25th, the earliest the burnout on that stretch could be done was the 26th.

*   *   *   *   *

Charles Peterson, a fireman with Heber-Overgaard Fire Department was on his way back up to the fire from Scottsdale. Gary Martinson, owner of Bison Ranch had been in constant phone contact with H-O Chief Mel Epps and also Charlie Peterson. He convinced Charlie to take Gary, his son Scott and Pat Bain back up with him in order to get through the roadblocks using Peterson's badge and credentials. All three men owned homes in Bison Ranch and desired to get back up to help Bobby Crandall, who had stayed at the ranch.

Once the three arrived at Bison Ranch, they photographed and videoed each of the 35 burned cabins and 20 other damaged buildings (garages and outbuildings). Then they began contacting each homeowner by phone or email and giving them status of their property. They even opened Twinnie's Coffee & Ice Cream Parlor and the Bison Town Restaurant to help feed firefighters and supply their incidental needs.

Ice cream was a "hot item" with the firefighters. Gary reflected on loading up all the horses and leaving on the 22nd. He, like so many others, was torn between the need to evacuate the families and animals out of harms way and his need/desire to stay and protect his property and that of his neighbors. He described the loss of 35 cabins as "beyond comprehension," and something that took several days to soak in. [9.j]

(June 24th continued in Chapter 10. Firefighter Rick Lupe--Hero).

CH 10: FIREFIGHTER RICK LUPE, HERO

"Can't never did nothing!" Poppa Garrett

June 24th, Monday (Continued)

June 24th was another day for the history books and the source of some relief to the evacuees at the Round Valley Dome and other locales. At the 11:00 a.m. news briefing on June 25th, I used an example of a grease fire in a skillet, and the best way to retard that fire is to put a lid on the skillet.

I.O. Paxon at the podium for a press briefing.
Photo by White Mountain Independent News.

I explained further that yesterday's smoke column did much the same thing to the fire on the eastern flank. That tall column had stood up from Snake Ridge on the southeast corner of the Rodeo Fire (along with the larger column of the Chediski Fire to the northwest), proud and defiant, for most of the day, but the smoke actually shaded and cooled the east flank of the fire by at least ten degrees.

Crews on Highway 60 preparing to support burnout operation. Photo by Varnell Gatewood.

Because the sun was unable to penetrate the smoke, the preheating of fuels on the ground and desiccation of standing trees was somewhat limited. Winds on top of the Rim and on the east side of the fire were less intense and less squirrelly, as well. Since the fire did not heat up and run as it had in the previous six days, the flame front moving toward Show Low slowed from the tireless sprint it had shown in previous days. Although it slowed some, the fire was still extremely active on the east flank. As crews were able to get closer and begin to burnout, creating more fire to stop fire is a tenuous situation that is done with a mix of science and art tempered with experience

Trees torching from burnout operation.
Photo by Varnell Gatewood.

Viewers and listeners at the morning briefing were informed that Operations Section Chief Roy Hall and Division Group Supervisor Rick Lupe. Rick had requested the Ft. Apache Hotshots, led by Superintendent Marco Minjarez and two Type II crews (Navajo and Laguna Pueblo) anchoring to a narrow forest road on the Mogollon Rim and some hand-dug fireline, early in the morning of June 24th.

This was the same team of hotshots and fireline supervisors who had worked so hard, burning out the fireline in the failed attempt at stopping the fire at the top of Hop Canyon two days earlier. Mother Nature and the dragon won that contest and the towns from Show Low south had to be evacuated, another 20,000 people displaced. With the recent "score" of Mother Nature "1" and Hump's Team "0", Rick was most reluctant to undertake another burnout with even tighter conditions and a very good chance of another victory for ol' Ma Nature.

Most burnouts are done in the "coolest" burning conditions, which usually occur at night or very early in the morning. On June 24th, there was an additional complication. The proposed action mandated an extended burnout operation that would have to continue far into the peak burning period of the afternoon and late evening in order to reach the goal of Cottonwood Canyon.

Typically, with sun shining on the trees and ground, mid-afternoon is when temperatures are their highest and fuels the driest, an explosive combination. That was exactly the scenario in the top of Hop Canyon two days prior... except there was no cooling cover of smoke plume then, as there was today.

Timely burnouts from a constructed fireline are the proven method of "fighting fire with fire" and are still one of the very best tools in a firefighter's bag. Burnouts are often responsible for stopping a mega fire's growth, when nothing else has worked. Risks must be weighed with chances of success and what might happen if a burnout is not undertaken and the fire grows legs and makes a run. This is the highest stakes "poker" to be played, as it involved lives and livelihoods. We all were very much aware that Mother Nature was still dealing the cards.

Rick Lupe had taken very personally the beating that the dragon gave firefighters when the fire jumped across the top of Hop Canyon. Now, with a second chance, he wanted a hand in keeping fire out of his neighbors' homes in the towns to the north of the White Mountain Apache Reservation.

Rick was a White Mountain Apache who had worked as a member of the Ft. Apache Hotshots for 19 years, 10 years as its Superintendent. He had been promoted to the job of Fuels Management Specialist with Ft. Apache Fire only a year earlier. This was also Rick's second year on Hump's Team as a Division Group Supervisor, a commander on the fireline, overseeing all the crews and resources on a designated portion of the fire.

A Division Group Supervisor is responsible for implementing the Incident Action Plan for that shift, on his assigned piece of the fire. The "Div. Sup." is also responsible for the safety of his people on the fireline. Finally, he takes part in reporting accomplishments, fire progress for that shift and for helping to plan the next day's work on his division. It is a complex and demanding job that requires extensive fire experience, good people skills and clear decision-making ability.

In addition to being well experienced, Rick was also very determined and goal oriented. He took the Rodeo Fire personally as a White Mountain Apache, since the ignition was on the reservation and the fire had burned onto the Apache-Sitgreaves National Forest and across private lands.

Roy Hall is the Deputy Director of Fire and Aviation Management, with responsibility for fuels management for the Forest Service Southwest Region in Albuquerque. He was one of two Operations Sections Chiefs on Hump's Team. Roy has a 33-year history in fire and came from the ground up. He was the Superintendent of the Flagstaff Hotshots when they were building line on the Butte Fire in Idaho in August of 1985.

Changes in the weather and indicators of an impending plume collapse prompted Roy's Flagstaff Hotshots, the Payson Hotshots, a Nevada engine strike team and several overhead to move quickly to a large clear-cut above the Salmon River Breaks, which served as a Safety Zone, meaning that it was large enough that they did not have to deploy fire shelters as the fire burned by.

They were communicating the danger to other firefighters, when the Butte Fire column collapsed and a tidal wave of fire raged across the fireline, entrapping 118 firefighters and forcing 73 of them, who had not been able to move to safety zones, to use their last resort – deploying fire shelters in place.

To date, this event remains the largest shelter deployment in the history of modern firefighting. All 73 survived and there were only a few minor injuries. The memories of that event temper Roy's actions in putting firefighters at risk without safety measures in place and well-communicated instructions to all on the fireline.

Roy has lived chasing the dragon and has many times looked him in the eye. He is a good person to be with in tense times. Roy, as the architect of the Cottonwood Canyon burnout operation, was firmly convinced that conditions would be ideal for a successful burnout operation for the entire shift. All involved knew that a failed attempt would mean the loss of many more homes in precious communities just a stone's throw to the east.

Roy was also sure that burnouts could extend well into the early morning hours, if need be, so they could reach the goal of the bottom Cottonwood Canyon and cut off the route of the fire into Show Low. Van Bateman's Team had arrived and was getting set up, but they had not yet received their delegation of authority, to manage the Rodeo side of the fire below U.S. Highway 60 and the Cottonwood Creek Road at the lower end of Cottonwood Canyon (Zone 4).

Dugger Hughes, Operations Section Chief for Bateman, was on scene to get oriented and provide assistance to Hump's Team. Roy, Rick Lupe and Dugger Hughes all came to the same conclusion: that this burnout was the only option in keeping fire out of Show Low, Wagon Wheel and Lakeside and that they MUST proceed *immediately*. The two Operations Chiefs, Roy Hall and Dugger Hughes, supervised and directed the initial burnout operation, which proved to be "textbook" in execution and results, as the ignited fire moved quickly away from the highway and toward the main fire. As success bred confidence, the crews became more enthusiastic about the burn and envisioned success this time around.

Roy specifically asked Division Supervisor Rick Lupe to take charge of the march of fire down U.S. 60 with the burnout operation… as long as conditions remained favorable. They would stay in close contact and proximity until the wee hours of the morning of the 25th when Roy left to pay attention to the other divisions on the rest of the fire. There also was the need to finalize plans for the defense and holding action of this huge burnout "investment" before the day shift began at 0600. [10.a]

Rick had grown up in these mountains and knew every inch of them intimately. Rick had been on the prescribed burns south of the Rim Road 300 some years earlier. Rick's old crew, the Ft. Apache Hotshots worked well with him. The Laguna Pueblo and Navajo crews were good, seasoned firefighters, whose job would be to hold the line and prevent spots from crossing the road/fireline and continue burning towards Show Low and Lakeside.

Heber, Mormon Lake and Silver City Hotshots, under the direction of Operations Section Chief Buck Wickham and Division Group Supervisor Denny Nelson also began a critical burnout to the northwest along Joe Tank Road 135 that tied back into a hand-and-dozer-cut fireline across the bottom of Linden Ridge and Cheney Ranch subdivisions and tied directly into Highway 260. This burnout would secure the northeast corner of the fire and prevent a running flame front from coming around to the north and entering Show Low from above in the Fool's Hollow Lake State Park area.

Crews begin a burnout in a meadow where fuels are light. Holding on the blackline is much more probable. Photo by U.S.F.S. Apache Sitgreaves National Forest.

To understand just how close the fire came to entering Show Low, one needs to study this photo. Torreon is a gated golf community. At the junction of Falling Leaf Road and Shaggy Bark Road, the "scratch" fireline and edge of the burnout was only 300 yards to the west. You can also see just how continuous the trees and fuels were into Torreon and on to the east.

Aerial view of Rodeo Fire's edge. The burnout of Joe Tank Road held. Fire's edge is only 300 yards from houses in the Torreon golf community. Photo by U.S.F.S. Apache Sitgreaves National Forest.

This line is the closest point the Rodeo Fire would burn to Show Low. There is a tall knob in Torreon on Wild Rose Lane that is a good promontory and was used during the fire as an observation point/lookout post. Information Officers also used it as a photo point for media opportunities.

The Hall/Lupe burnout began at the junction of Rim Road 300 and Forest Road 135 to Highway 60, and then on down to lower Cottonwood Canyon, below the Rim to where a large, open Juniper flat made a logical stopping point and the fire's edge turned back to the southwest, away from the highway. It would take Rick Lupe, the Ft. Apache Hotshots and the two Type II crews (Navajo and Laguna Pueblo) more than 18 hours to complete the burnout.

Clockwise from top left: Burnout showing curl of smoke rising over the road. The main fire will draw the burnout back into it, robbing the main fire of fuel and stopping fires advance. Photo by Varnell Gatewood. // Burnouts are typically done in strips using drip torches and fuses. Photo by Phoenix Fire Dept. // Firefighter shooting a flare gun to ignite fuels up to 120 yards inside the fireline and burnout edge. Photo by Karen Wattenmaker. // Igniter using a driptorch. Photo by Phoenix Fire Dept.

Top to Bottom: Burnouts are planned to be less intense than the fire being fought. Photo by U.S.F.S, Rocky Mountain Research Station-Flagstaff. // Crewmember "holding" and watching for spots across the line. Photo by Dave Cruz, Arizona Republic. // Igniter burning with driptorch and crew spreading out to watch for embers. Photo by Phoenix Fire Dept. //

146

Top to Bottom: "Watching and waiting..." Burnouts require patience on the part of the crew. Photo by Phoenix Fire Dept. // Sawyer ready to jump into action if spots land in larger fuels requiring cutting. Photo by Phoenix Fire Dept. // Moving to the next section. Guards will be left to patrol. Photo by Phoenix Fire Dept.

On the 25th, Dugger Hughes and four Hotshot crews (Ft. Apache, Heber, Mormon Lake and Silver City) would continue to burn the remaining line to be burned out to the southwest of Cottonwood down Corduroy and Carrizo Canyons and tie "black" in to the original fireline that Ft. Apache firefighters had built on the 18th and 19th. That first day of the fire, only six days prior, seemed like months ago to us all.

This burnout was truly a last ditch effort… *that worked!* Consider for a moment the effort involved in this burnout. There are about 2,000 steps per mile on level ground. This certainly was not level ground. Eighteen hours is a very long shift, working hard on the fireline the entire time. Not only is it taxing to the body, it is mentally and emotionally stressful. The need for success and the pressure of "what if?" weighs heavily on one's mind.

While igniting the burnout, these firefighters were constantly in close proximity to the very flames that they created, an extremely hot, smoky environment, to say the least. They drank at least a quart of water per hour, just to stay hydrated. There was little time for meals or rest breaks, as the entire ten miles had to be burned out in the one continuous operation in order to rob the advancing wildfire of fuel and stop it in its tracks.

Halting the burnout at any point would have meant that wildfire, which was close by and advancing, would have had an "open gate" to go around the fuel-robbing burnout fire. If the wildfire had been able to get past the burnout operation, like it did earlier at Hop Canyon, there would have been no stopping its movement straight into Show Low and homes to the south.

Only a few firefighters at a time are actually applying fire to the ground. The rest of the crew is in a vigilant watch, monitoring fire behavior and also searching for spots across the line. Sometimes, when the fire became more active than desired, burners would hold up and let the fire move away from the fireline, before continuing. Other times, they would actually have to put more fire on the ground to get it to burn with enough intensity to draw towards the main fire.

Divine intervention also played a part in the success of the burnout. Spot fires and slopovers are always a consideration and a contingency to be prepared for and dealt with. That is why so few igniters actually burn while all the rest of the crew watches the line, ready to take action.

Many spots crossed the line as the burnout progressed, but firefighters were waiting like "ducks ready to jump on a Junebug" and embers were extinguished before flames could get established and grow. There was only one spot fire of approximately one acre that required a great effort to line and contain. It was at the very north end of Cottonwood Canyon and the lighting stopped while all firefighters attacked it and contained it. Only one spot… another miracle and something that just doesn't normally happen in a burnout. The whole reason that 3/4 of the crew is in "watching and holding" mode is to catch the spots that come across and keep them from getting away.

Air support for the burnout operation involved several heavy air tankers, until smoke got too thick for them to operate safely and be effective. Air tankers "painted" a line to the east of the constructed firelines and on the west side of Highway 60, ahead of the burnout, to minimize the risk of escaped fire on the wrong side of the line. Two Sky Cranes – heavy helicopters – were used as needed. When a specific area of the burnout got a little too hot, the helicopters dropped on the hotter areas, just to cool them down so the burnout could progress.[10.b]

Left: Helo 747, an Air Crane leaving Fool's Hollow Reservoir with 1,200 gallons of water. Rodeo Fire in the background, but still 5+ miles away. Photo by Terry Corrigan, White Mountain Independent News.

A record of 86,000 gallons of retardant in one day on a single fire was dropped on the firelines all around the perimeter of the fire. From the vantage point in Torreon, Fire Observers and many others were able to watch this burnout operation as it progressed from this high vantage point. It was amazing as the curl of smoke rose from the burnout and then turned back to the west as the main fire drafted air in from the side much like a huge, pulsing bellows. Observers and firefighters on the burnout could actually feel the dragon breathe as air was drawn into the main fire. Eventually, the two fires would burn together, halting the Rodeo's relentless advance to the east.

Success of this burnout meant that a running flame front would *not* invade Show Low above the Rim Road. It did not eliminate the possibility of fire crossing Highway 60 below Cottonwood Canyon, or the chance of spot fires in town from lofted embers landing on burnable surfaces and starting new fires. This was a most tense time and a calculated risk that was undertaken as the *only* option… the only card we had to play in our challenge of Mother Nature's hand.

And it worked! Had it failed, we were sure there would have been Hell to pay. It is a tribute to all who formulated the plan and executed so well on the ground. This kind of action is what makes hotshot crews and a Type I Incident Management Team the elite firefighters that they are. Hump's team was absolutely one of the best. It is what they train for. It is what they live for… peak performance under the greatest adversity. Success itself is reward enough.

In a television interview days later, Rick Lupe told reporters, "This is my land and I really did not want the fire to jump Highway 60. I have many relatives and friends that live here (in the White Mountain communities)." He was so humble and an excellent firefighter.

B.I.A. Fuels Management Officer, Rick Lupe discussing prescribed-burn plans.
Photo by White Mountain Independent News.

* * * * *

June 25th, Tuesday

The burns progressed well into Tuesday, June 25th as crews continued on down Highway 60 through the "three C's" – Cottonwood, Corduroy and Carrizo Canyons – so the east side of the Rodeo Fire was stopped cold and could be buttoned up. There was still the chance lofted embers could be sent east over the fireline. Patrols would watch for spot fires as well as beginning mop-up operations for many days.

As the monster began to run out of fuel/food, flames began to die down on the east side of the fire. Just because the burnout had been completed, still there was no containment claimed for that piece of fireline, until fires had died down, cooled and the risk of escape or slopovers was truly minimal. Yet progress had been achieved and once more, genuine smiles appeared on sooty faces. These men and women, led by Roy Hall and Rick Lupe, had spit in the eye of the dragon… and made him stumble and take a step backwards. Advantage: Hump's Team.

* * * * *

Less than a year later, on May 14, 2003 at approximately 2:45 p.m., Rick Lupe was working on a prescribed fire near the ancient Kinishba ruins of the Mogollon, which is about six miles west of Whiteriver, Arizona. The Sawtooth Prescribed Burn was in its second day and the actual firing had been completed. Crews were mopping up and using helicopter bucket drops to extinguish fires close to the line.

Rick walked down to the southeastern flank of the burn to check a reported smoke. After seeing how serious the situation was, he radioed nearby crews to get into the black for safety. The intense flare-up that occurred was later estimated at 30 acres.

Rick was caught in the middle of a whirlwind of fire. He attempted to escape the intense heat by deploying his shelter and running with it around him, but to no avail. Lookouts observed the increase in fire behavior with the thick black column of smoke that rose in the area where Rick had gone. In a few minutes, B.I.A. radios crackled with a startling message: "Help, its Rick. I've been burned. Need help! Feet burned in hot ash!!" [10.c]

Firefighters raced to his aid and found him with his fire clothes partially burned off of his body. He had sustained 3rd degree burns over 40% of his body and he had inhaled super-heated air, which damaged his lungs and throat. They called for a rescue helicopter, but it could land no closer than ½ mile from the burn scene.

Not being able to withstand a ride on a gurney, Rick walked to the helicopter and was flown to Whiteriver Hospital, where he was stabilized and put into a drug-induced coma. He was then airlifted to the Maricopa Medical Center's Burn Unit, where he received intense medical attention, including an initial six-hour operation and four skin graft operations in five weeks.

Rick's family celebrated his 43rd birthday in his hospital room in surgical masks and scrubs, as they sang native songs and lifted up prayers for his recovery. Although he was in a coma, they were with him *every day*.

Just a few days later, warrior and firefighter, Rick Lupe died on June 19, 2003, the same day that the Aspen Fire blew up and burned over Mt. Lemmon and through the town of Summerhaven. It was also the same day that a year prior, the Rodeo fire had blown up and breached the Mogollon Rim.

The damage to Rick's lung tissues, throat and trachea were just more than could be overcome. [10.d] Rick is survived by his wife, Evelyn, and sons Sean, Daniel and Brent. Both Sean and Daniel have become firefighters and Brent intends to, when he is old enough. Rick was the kind of man that husbands, fathers and fire bosses aspire to be.

Chadeen Palmer, Tribal Public Affairs Officer and Deputy Information Officer on Humphrey's Team summed up the feelings of the 2,000 attendees at the memorial, "Once you join the ranks of the firefighter organization, they become your second family. It is a very close brotherhood and we lost a brother, when Rick died."

Rick's memorial service lasted four hours with firefighters from all across the state and beyond in attendance. The Ft. Apache Hotshots, Rick's crew, were honorary pallbearers. Dressed in fire clothes, they led the funeral procession, along with the B.L.M. Honor Guard, that reverently carried Rick to his final resting place at Canyon Day Cemetery.

Larry Humphrey, the Incident Commander on the Rodeo-Chediski Fire had worked with Rick when he was the Ft. Apache Hotshot Superintendent. Larry recalled, "Years ago, I was in some tough spots with Rick. He and I stood there shoulder-to-shoulder in support of each other." Rick Lupe epitomized firefighter professionalism and had the highest regard for safety. [10.e]

Congress posthumously awarded Rick the "Firefighter of Year Award" in a unanimous resolution passed on October 29, 2003. [10.f] In 2004, a young Eagle Scout candidate, Richard Genck came up with the idea of a bronze statute of Rick that would be dedicated to all wildland firefighters.

Richard Genck, Eagle Scout who coordinated the Firefighter Memorial, standing beside the statue of Rick Lupe at the dedication of the Firefighter Memorial in front of the Pinetop Library. Photo by White Mountain Independent.

After more than a year's hard work and his refusal to accept "no," Richard convinced and got commitments from city governments, local communities involved in the fire and local businesses to get the statute cast and located in front of the Pinetop-Lakeside Library. The White Mountain Apache Tribe appreciated and supported Genck's efforts. Local artist and teacher, Randy White created the sculpture. It is very much the image of Rick Lupe in fire gear.

The unveiling dedication was held on September 17, 2006. [10.g] In the dedication, Rick's wife Evelyn recalled that Rick had called her on his cell phone before the burnout west of Show Low and told her that, "we are going to stop the fire and keep it out of Show Low."

Now all who gaze on the statute and read the inscription will know and understand the connection of "hero" with firefighter Richard Gene Lupe... our friend, Rick. As in so many things, the mountain knew and would remember.

White Mountain Apache Tribal Chairman Ronnie Lupe speaking at the dedication of the Firefighter Memorial on September 17, 2005. Photo by White Mountain Independent.

Some of Rick Lupe's family at the statue. Photo by White Mountain Independent.

CH. 11: PRESIDENTIAL SUPPORT

"When "you" and "I" become "we," everyone wins." Poppa Garrett

On June 25, 2002, shortly after 8:30 a.m. two small business jets landed at the Springerville Airport. One was a decoy, the other delivered President George W. Bush to the White Mountains. The two were identical, white business jets with only an American Flag adorning the tail to indicate the status of the cargo they might carry. Air Force One landed in Phoenix and one of the smaller jets carried the President and his staff to Springerville.

President Bush made a detour to the fire while enroute to a "G-8 Summit" in Toronto, Canada. He stepped off the plane and strode smartly into a large hanger where he greeted a select audience of firefighters and officials of less than 100 persons, total. Almost half that number was media and press corps with video and still photo cameras thrust at every angle, and reporters' notebooks and pencils in abundance.

Accompanying the President were Governor Jane D. Hull, Congressman J.D. Hayworth and F.E.M.A. Director Joe Allbaugh. The President was casually dressed in a gray shirt with sleeves rolled up, slacks, cowboy boots and his trademark western belt, as if he were on his way to visit a friend. After all, how many times does a president come to an area so remote and seemingly politically insignificant? Can it be that the purpose of his visit was to touch a spot where America really lives? His rolled up sleeves seemed to say that he came to work.

President Bush preparing to take off from Springerville Airport. Photo by USFS, Apache-Sitgreaves National Forest.

As he approached the crowd, "W" announced that he brought with him the best wishes of the American people. He and they wished that God bless all those involved or affected by the Rodeo-Chediski Fire.

This visit had only been spawned two days earlier and the Secret Service and presidential staff had worked with Governor Hull, Arizona DPS and Apache County/Springerville officials around the clock to make necessary arrangements, security precautions and all that goes with such a prestigious event. Hump's Fire Team got confirmation and scheduling at 7:00 p.m. the night before and personal identification and background information was submitted for security clearance of all fire personnel that would attend. Only those with clearance and on the "final list" would be allowed into the Springerville airport.

My function was to get the latest updated maps and statistics of the fire from the incident command post's G.I.S staff and take them to the airport. The gates would close at 7:30 a.m. sharp. If anyone was late, they would simply be turned away. I got the maps from Dave Wilson, G.I.S. Specialist at 6:55 a.m. It is 46 miles from Show Low High School to the Springerville Airport. With the use of red lights and the advantage of very little traffic, I checked into the secure area at 7:25 a.m. Just five minutes to spare. Sure enough at 7:30, the gates were closed and guards posted. No one else was admitted until the President had departed.

All vehicles were screened at the entrance and everyone had to empty their pockets and pass through Secret Service staffed metal detectors. Explosive sniffing dogs and their handlers also screened vehicles and us as we passed by. There were two men dressed in black fatigues and carrying what looked like the "boys in the band"... guitars and amplifiers in nylon cases. However their cases contained sniper rifles and spotting equipment. They climbed to the top of the hanger and took positions on the north and south sides of the roof to cover the immediate area of the airport.

Out to the west, an Apache gunship helicopter was seen patrolling the perimeter of the airport and two F-16 fighter jets passed by high overhead. At precisely 7:30 a.m., all access to the airport, ground and air was closed. Even the Forest Service twin engine King Air plane, carrying fire officials from the Regional Office in Albuquerque was waved off and held out, due to not arriving before the 7:30 cutoff time. "Smokey Air" had to go to Show Low, since they were not allowed to land until after the President had departed.

"W" came to help! He came to see what was happening with the monster that threatened some of his own and their homes and livelihoods. He came to offer help with Presidential declarations and throw the assistance of the F.E.M.A machine into the fray. He came to meet those in the thick of the battle and those displaced by the monster's fury.

President Bush reviewing the fire status and actions with Arizona Governor Jane D. Hull and Incident Commander Larry Humphrey. Photo by Tom Schafer, White Mountain Independent News.

Incident Commander Larry Humphrey and Governor Jane D. Hull briefed the President on the current situation, evacuations, fire team strategies and tactics and a projection of possible damages, if the Rodeo and Chediski Fires continued unchecked. President Bush got a closeup of fire fighting tools and explanation of tactics used in battling the monster. At one point, he hefted a Stihl 044 Chainsaw and remarked, "I have one of these at the ranch, only it's just not quite this big."

After the briefing and remarks, the Commander in Chief made his way about the room and greeted each person, one by one. If he was talking to you, it was as if there was no one else in the room. Tom Morgan, a Lakeside Ranger District firefighter had just come off the line that morning, having worked the night in heavy smoke and ash, his fire clothes stained with sweat and soot. He asked for a personal picture with the "Pres." and "W" responded with a smile and a hug. His genuine interest and concern for everyone was very evident.

When he got around to me, he extended his hand and we shook firmly. I said "Hello, Mr. President." He leaned forward and asked, "Where are you from?" I answered "Lubbock, Texas," to which he responded with a big thumbs-up and a hearty, "ALL RIGHT!!" President Bush was raised in Midland, Texas only 120 miles south of Lubbock. He recognized the accent, even though a Southern dialect is still very distinctly West Texan. Still clasping my hand, he said, "We've been watching you… and you're doing a good job. Keep it up and we WILL beat this thing!"

President Bush greeting firefighters. Photo by Tom Schafer, White Mountain Independent News.

President Bush greeting Jim Paxon. Photo by Apache County Sheriff's Office.

Wow, talk about uplifting and encouraging. His confidence and personal words made the endless twenty-hour days seem much less fatiguing. I believe his presence and personal interest motivated everyone who met him and perhaps helped turn the tide of battle, that very moment. It was almost as if he proclaimed to the many headed dragon that his day had come and he would lose his many heads, one by one, until all were dead and out.

After our visit, a motorcade of the dignitaries took a short trip to the Round Valley Dome where President Bush greeted 300 evacuees and Red Cross workers. There the President signed the formal declaration of the Rodeo-Chediski Fire as a Federal Disaster. That meant that F.E.M.A was now involved and that victims of the fire would be eligible for federal assistance. The President also dedicated his administration to pursuing legislation and initiating programs for better forest management

155

and the prevention of future disasters from "Mega Fires" like the Rodeo-Chediski. The Healthy Forest Restoration Legislation came about with total support from Arizona Congressmen and Senators, but it all started in the White Mountains.

President Bush greeting evacuees at the Round Valley Dome. His visit really raised morale.
Photo by USFS, Apache-Sitgreaves National Forest

Before leaving, "W" asked folks at the Dome to "have faith in their firefighters, who would not quit until the monster was whipped." His appearance and personal interest lifted those evacuees in the Dome as much as his visit with us did. It was a good day and better days were ahead. [11.a]

*   *   *   *   *   *

Wall of flames coming out of Canyon Creek on the Chediski Fire.
Photo by USFS, Apache-Sitgreaves National Forest.

On the west side of the Chediski Fire, flame fronts roared out of Canyon Creek and across the 109 Road. Arizona Public Service operates a 500-kilovolt electric transmission line to the west of Forest Lakes that had to be de-energized as fire got close. It was the second major power line to be de-energized due to the proximity of smoke. Heavy smoke is a conductor of electricity. When it passes under or through a major power line, "arcing" occurs and literal bolts of "power line lightning" will strike the ground, possibly starting fires or endangering firefighters.

This stretch of power line would be de-energized for 36 hours, until the fire intensity lessened and firefighters could build fireline on both sides for approximately one half mile to either side of the power line. This power line went to Flagstaff and then transmitted electricity to the Valley of the Sun. The reduction in power and required change of available electricity on the APS grid caused some problems to APS managers, as many air conditioners run continuously in Phoenix in June and power demands are the highest of the year.

A nighttime burnout from the indirect fireline

Fire crosses the 109 Road on the Chediski.
Photo by USFS, Apache-Sitgreaves National Forest.

under the 500 KV APS power line was completed while the power line was de-energized. The burnout was a success, but 31 elk were caught between the burnout and the main fire and literally died in mid-step from the tremendous heat closing in from two sides as the fires burned together.

Elk and other large wildlife are usually very aware of fire, before it gets close to them. Animals will often go perpendicular to the fire and seek refuge in the next drainage over. The hysterical stampede scene from the motion picture "Bambi" is pure fiction.

Fire continued to burn with Forest Lakes in its path. Crews also continued work in Heber-Overgaard to prevent loss of additional homes, although there was some relief from the daily waves of running crown fire threatening the community.

Kim Martin and his Intermountain Type I Team arrived and set up camp at the Salvation Army's Camp Ponderosa northwest of Heber. They immediately made a plan for a burnout along Highway 260 and to the south of Forest Lakes, to tie into the Young Highway, Road 512. If that tactic was successful, it would stop the fire from advancing to the north. If fire crossed Highway 260 near Forest Lakes, not only would it burn many homes, but it could also burn all the way to Chevelon Lake some 30+ miles to the north.

Cow elk burned in burnout of the Devil's Claw.
Photo by USFS, Apache-Sitgreaves National Forest.

Herd of Elk moving as the fire approaches. Photo by USFS, Apache-Sitgreaves National Forest.

Again, solid canopies of pine trees and continuous ground fuels were in the direction the fire would burn, with no good place to make a stand and stop a climax wildfire. The Chediski part of the fire could then grow to be near one million acres. Now the emphasis changed from a protection strategy to building a fireline for an offensive action, a burnout operation.

To the west of Heber, hotshot crews had begun a burnout along Highway 260 from the old Heber Job Corp Work Center towards Rim Road 300, east of Forest Lakes. Crews dug a fireline around the south side of Forest Lakes. Tonto National Forest engines and hand crews were preparing the Young Road (Forest Road 512) for a burnout operation that would tie into Highway 260. Burnouts would be staged along both roads and below Forest Lakes that would tie continuous "black" along Highway 260 into the Young Road and back into the main fire. Of greatest concern was the top end of Canyon Creek, which terminates into five very steep canyons that became known as the "Devil's Claw!" These burnouts were done with precision and would take four days to complete.

*Map of "Devil's Claw of five finger draws at top of Canyon Creek.
Map by U.S.F.S, Apache-Sitgreaves National Forest.*

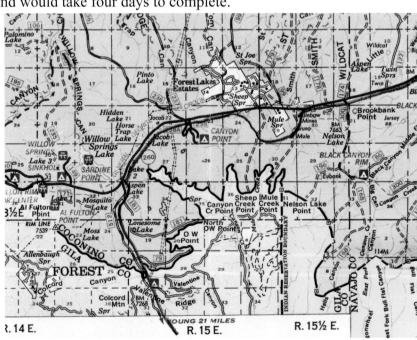

The firing operation would have to creep downhill in each of the canyons, one at a time, and firefighters sought to avoid major uphill runs that could jump the fireline and invade Forest Lakes. The operation was a calculated risk, but it, too, was the only option left to Kim Martin's team of firefighters. If the burnout were successful, then the fire's advance of the Chediski on the whole northwest corner would be stalled.

This would be the classic "fighting fire with fire" operation, using the same tools as the monster, but in a controlled, orchestrated and almost choreographed operation. Although fire suppression is a science, burnouts are a combination of science and experience that approaches art. When a well-executed burnout stops a fire, it is a celebratory experience. To lose a burnout and have the fire go "over the hill" is a defeat that often causes fire commanders to face severe scrutiny and sometimes agency and political retribution. It was a calculated risk that had to be taken as the only way to stop the advance of the Chediski.

This reduced map shows where the most intense heat was on the night of June 25th. Note the burnout operations show intense red areas to the south of Show Low and southwest of Heber-Overgaard. These were fires set to stop the wildfire.

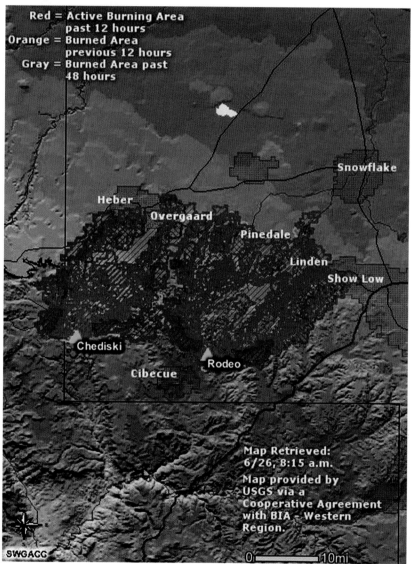

Infrared Map of the Rodeo-Chediski Fire by U.S. Geological Survey/Bureau of Indian Affairs.

*   *   *   *   *

Every day, since June 18th, the Rodeo Fire had "grown legs" and run from the Mogollon Rim to the north. Daily, it burned a narrow strip, as fuels, canyons and winds encouraged, next to and just to the east of yesterday's burn. From this point of fire closest to Show Low, the fire's edge angles back to the northwest to Cheney Ranch. Firefighters continued to build line and burnout, when conditions permitted, in an attempt to keep fire from coming into Show Low.

At approximately 1420 hours (2:20 p.m.), a plume collapsed over the Mogollon Rim as firefighters on Bateman's team worked reinforcing a fireline on the Rim Road and down Highway 60. Extreme fire behavior with 40-mile-plus per hour winds and fire burning horizontally in every direction caused the withdrawal of firefighters to safe zones, once again. It was an extremely close call, but fire did not cross Highway 60. Another one of the many miracles revealed on this fire.

Sunrise in the Salt River Canyon, 6-25-02. Nighttime smoke drift obscures like a heavy fog.
Photo by Varnell Gatewood.

CH. 12: ON THE SCOREBOARD

"If any man's work is burned up, he shall suffer loss, but he himself shall be saved,
even though he has been through the fire." 1 Cor.3:15

June 26th, Wednesday

In a bit of twisted humor, at one of our strategy/planning sessions, Bill Jackson, Fire Behavior Analyst for Hump's Team, showed a "Distorted Fire Intensity" graphic that depicted how extreme the fire behavior had been on the Rodeo-Chediski Fire. Look closely at the graphic, as it tells much. At the far right end, the rate of spread is almost six miles per hour in heavy timber, an unheard-of speed for fire burning in tall timber. Also the fire intensity in B.T.U.'s at one million is like the energy release of a small atomic bomb. "Rompin' & stompin', raging and ripping" are really what we saw and experienced.

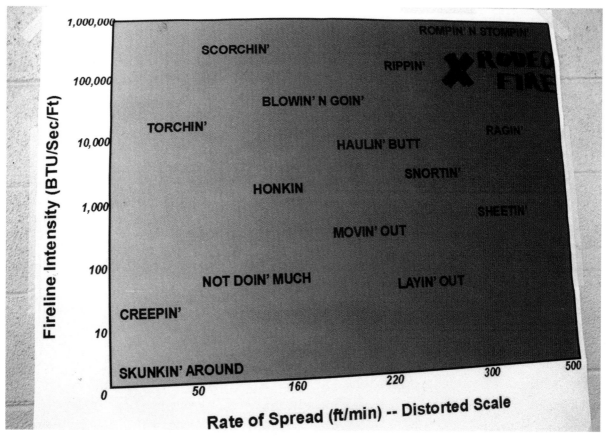

Fire Intensity Chart prepared by Bill Jackson, FBAN

The Rodeo Fire made its initial run through the communities of Pinedale, Timberland Acres and Clay Springs on June 20th. Much of Highway 260 west of Show Low marks a transition of fuel types from Ponderosa Pine on the south to Pinyon-Juniper on the north. For several days after, the fire would burn a new swath from south to north and bump against Highway 260.

The Pinyon-Juniper woodland fuel type does not carry fire as well, or as intensely as Ponderosa Pine forests since the fuels are lighter and more sparse. Even though Highway 260 was accessible to fire apparatus and command personnel, and it served as something of a fire barrier, fire crossed in several locations, usually by spotting across the highway right-of-way and starting new fires on the northern side. In many cases, fireline construction was completed using the highway as a barrier. Dozers and handcrews worked at removing fuels close to the blacktop.

Engines and crews holding fireline on a road adjacent to Highway 260. Photo by USFS, Apache-Sitgreaves National Forest.

Bulldozer building line in the Pinedale area. Photo by Steve Campbell.

Crews took some burnout actions to clean up the fuels on the south side of the paved road before the fire got there. Remember that, "the only safe fireline is a black line." In this case, the "black" had to be one mile wide or more to prevent lofted embers from crossing the road and starting new fires. This is just one more indicator of how intense the fire was each day.

After eight grueling days of the monster running fire crews off firelines to safety zones and losing houses to uncontrollable, unstoppable flames, we finally got a bit of "containment." When a section of line or part of the perimeter of a fire is declared "contained," it means that there is no additional growth in that particular stretch of fireline, due to the fire having been stopped by firefighter actions… and that the risk of fire breaking out, burning across the line and continuing to grow is minimal.

At the evening briefing, I was authorized to announce that we had confirmed 5% Containment and we were finally "on the scoreboard." I did say that, "Either the monster was napping and never raised his ugly head… or the Good Lord blessed us today!"

162

The tide had turned and now firefighters would gain on the monster's run of destruction, day by day. It was the first time in eight days that anyone had smiled… and the smiles were genuine. The first of many heads was removed from the dragon. By this time, a total of 417,640 acres had been consumed. The monster was not done, but he was laboring hard and beginning to run out of fiery breath. His many heads would fall one by one, day by day, until firefighters were the victors.

Rumors were reported by some of the media that fire had burned through Heber and destroyed several more homes.

I.O. Paxon interviewed by Guy Atchley of KGUN-9 Tucson. Photo by USFS, Apache-Sitgreaves National Forest.

This was countered at the evening briefing as no homes in Heber burned on this day.

Firefighters and Animal Planet rescue teams were rescuing many animals. As they were checked out and proved healthy, pets were taken to several area humane societies. Injured pets received care from numerous volunteer organizations and individuals. Information was recorded to reunite animals with their owners when the evacuation was lifted. Two burned elk calves were brought in to the animal rescue center at the Show Low camp and cared for. They were docile and seemed to know that they were being helped.

Winds aloft were still very active, as were the plumes in the interior of the fire. Sometime around 1000 hours (10:00 a.m.), a spot fire was discovered near Show Low's Walmart on White Mountain Boulevard. Immediately, six engines and 50 firefighters responded. The fire was drowned and controlled at less than a half acre.

Structural firefighters had been patrolling, completing "Firewise" type fuels reduction around houses, caring for pets left behind and watering plants and gardens. They were more than ready for some fire "action!" During the last week of June, about a dozen small fires were suppressed by structural and wildland firefighters east of Highway 60. At least two of those fires were of questionable origin, but the rest were confirmed to be from embers landing on dry grass, other vegetation or woodpiles.

President Bush's visit had indeed changed outlooks and made for positive results.

Tribal Chairman, Dallas Massey announced a $6,000 reward from the White Mountain Apache Tribe for information leading to the arrest and prosecution of the arsonist(s) of the Rodeo Fire. The Mescalero Apache Nation in New Mexico added $30,000 to the reward fund. Chairman Massey did estimate that some 700 million board feet of timber had burned as well as three million cords of firewood. That was an economic loss to the White Mountain Apache Tribe of approximately $240 million and would take more than 100 years to replace. [12a]

*　　*　　*　　*　　*

Molten aluminum from a vehicle wheel that burned in Pinecrest Lakes Mobile Home Village. Photo by Steve Campbell.

Ten percent containment was announced in the evening briefing. More than 439,000 acres or 686 square miles had burned, which made the fire bigger than the entire area of the City of Los Angeles.

Some residents of Heber-Overgaard expressed feelings that their homes were sacrificed while efforts to save Show Low took precedence. Many evacuees expressed anger and frustration at not knowing the status of their homes. Their angst was understandable and having to sit in an evacuation center with little else to do only added to their agitation.

The Navajo County Assessor's Office was busy completing damage assessments, but with limited manpower, they were slow to get through all of the areas damaged by fire. Some areas were still too hot to allow non-fire personnel access. For those areas that had been surveyed, Navajo County implemented a call line for property owners only, to get information based on their home's physical address. I started making an announcement in every briefing to let folks know the latest areas added and a recap of the areas that had completed damage assessments available. We asked that only residents call due to the limited number of phone lines and phone gridlock. Still, more than 800 calls per day were answered for several days. Homeowners and relatives were desperate for information.

Burned area still too hot to get in and assess damages. Photo by Phoenix Fire Dept.

*　　*　　*　　*　　*

Dolan Ellis has been Arizona's Official State Balladeer, since 1966, through the terms of nine governors. Fire came very close to his Ramsey Canyon home near Sierra Vista, on the Ryan Fire, earlier in the spring. Dolan was very aware of fire issues and had the greatest admiration for firefighters. He decided to make a trip to the White Mountains, as something terrible was happening and he felt a tremendous need to be a part of it and to feel it firsthand. He had been part of a concert in Show Low in the end of March. Dolan loaded up his jeep with guitars, sleeping bags, and food, and he headed off to Payson.

When he drove east on Highway 260, heading up to the fire, he came to the roadblock just east of Star Valley. Officers there acknowledged his status as Arizona's Balladeer, but refused to let him pass. Dolan went back to Payson, found the first dark bar he could and went inside. There, he and the bar's patrons watched news stories of the fire on T.V. Dolan wrote "Wildfire" on a napkin focusing on the "Mogollon Monster," the towns' evacuees, the terrible loss of homes burned, and of course the brave firefighters working at taming the monster.

He returned to Phoenix the next day and recorded the song. It was released as a single on CD with estimates of final totals that were eerily close: ½ million acres, 5,000 firefighters, 500 homes burned. The CD is still available and all the proceeds from sales go to "CD's for New Trees at www.dolanellis.com. [12.b]

Photo of Dolan Ellis, Arizona's Official Balladeer with Jim Paxon. Photo by Kathy Collins.

*   *   *   *   *

June 28th, Friday

Containment increased to 27 % and the total acreage of the fire grew to 452,230 acres. Sen. Jon Kyl visited most of the evacuation centers in a "whirlwind tour." He blasted radical environmentalists for forest woes due to the stoppage of timber sales through appeals and lawsuits.

Fire jumped the fireline south of Forest Lakes, but the slopover was caught less than two miles from Forest Lakes. The shift of resources from Zone 3 in Show Low to Martin's Team in Zone 2 was to bolster forces needed at the northwest corner of the fire. Four hotshot crews moved from our camp at Show Low High School to the Heber firecamp. Several engines and dozer crews also moved to help in the effort of "de-clawing" the five drainages southwest of Forest Lakes that had become known as the Devil's Claw.

The highest priority on the Rodeo-Chediski Fire was now an effort to keep fire out of Forest Lakes, and prevent the possibility of fire crossing Highway 260 and burning to Chevlon Lake some 30+ miles to the north. That could have added an estimated half-million acres to the fire.

Firelines continued to be built along the Young Road and along Highway 260 in preparation for a major burnout action. Each finger of the five canyons that made up the Devil's Claw had to be burned individually. There could be no tolerance for allowing a running, torching crown fire to build and throw embers across the narrow constructed firelines and thwart our firefighters most determined efforts.

Firefighters also worked to save houses in the Heber and Forest Lakes areas, as the fire approached. In one case, an elderly gentlemen had refused to evacuate, but was too frail to do any firefighting. Crews worked to remove fuels from the immediate area of the house, build fireline around the structures and then burnout as the fire approached. The following series of photos shows that action as documented by Eric Williams of the Phoenix Fire Department and Apache-Sitgreaves National Forest.

*   *   *   *   *

Fire backing off a hill towards a group of cabins. Photo by USFS, Apache-Sitgreaves National Forest.

Fireline building and burnout in progress around cabins threatened by fire. Photo by USFS, Apache-Sitgreaves National Forest.

Removing fine fuels around a house. Photo by Phoenix Fire Dept.

166

Pruning a Juniper tree and removing fuels from around a cabin. Photo by Phoenix Fire Dept.

Hand crew removing fine fuels from around a historic barn. Photo by Phoenix Fire Dept.

Burning out around the elderly man's home. Photo by Phoenix Fire Dept.

Those residents of Cheney Ranch, Timberland Acres, Linden and Pinedale who wished were driven on National Guard and local school buses, through their neighborhoods to view houses standing and those lost. There was so much going on with assessments for and cleanup of hazardous materials, mopup operations to extinguish fires near habitation and concentration of firefighters and equipment in the areas impacted by fire that residents were not allowed to exit the buses. It was, however, an opportunity for a first hand, personal experience that answered questions and settled the angst of not knowing the status of their homes. The support of those who grieved their home-gone was universal, empathetic and reverent. Then was when I saw neighbors' concern for each other surpass any compassion that I have ever witnessed. Old disagreements, differences and grudges were forgotten. Survival guilt of those who still had homes was assuaged by reaching out a hand of help to those who had lost all.

*   *   *   *   *

In Zone 4, below Show Low on U.S. Highway 60, Van Bateman's Team used all their available resources to continue the burnout and hold the line down to the origin of the Rodeo Fire above Cibeque. In many cases, the burnouts had moved a mile or more before meeting the main part of the wildfire. Bateman's Operations Section Chief, Dugger Hughes was quoted, "I have been on complex fires that were not as big as our burnout operation alone!" Approximately 40,000 acres were committed to the burnout from Show Low to Carrizo Canyon on the east side of the Rodeo Fire. The only way to stop the advance of the monster fire was with fire.

Final briefing before beginning a burnout adjacent to U.S. 60 below Show Low. Photo by USFS, Apache-Sitgreaves National Forest.

Burnout at Forestdale, west of U.S. 60 at 1500 hrs. June 28th. Photo by Varnell Gatewood.

Burnout west of U.S. 60 in the Carrizo Hill area at 1700 hrs. June 28th. Photo by Varnell Gatewood.

Zone 1 (west of Cibeque) and Zone 3 (Hump's Team in the Show Low area) began final attack (mop-up) on most of the firelines in their respective areas. Firefighters and officials, as well as some of the media, got into the burned areas and looked closely at the damage done. Much of the burned area appeared moonscaped or nuked, and surreal at best. Firefighters' valiant efforts saved many homes. Vinyl siding as shown in this photo does not a "Firewise" home make, but the home was saved.

Nothing left of a burned timber stand. Photo by USFS, Rocky Mountain Research Station-Flagstaff.

Right: "Moonscape" closeup of burned timber. Photo by USFS, Rocky Mountain Research Station-Flagstaff.

Left: House saved by the good work of firefighters, even with flammable vinyl siding. Photo by Dewayne Saxton.

Governor Jane D. Hull visited evacuees at the Payson Middle School after she had toured the west end of the fire by helicopter. She expressed her sympathy to all who had lost homes and been displaced for so long. She also referenced the Dude Fire of 1990, just 10 miles north of Payson where six firefighters lost their lives. She remarked that we were blessed and so fortunate that no lives had been lost on the Rodeo-Chediski Fire. Evacuees expressed their dismay and frustration at the lack of information specific to their homes and the limited information overall on the fire in the Heber-Overgaard and Forest Lakes area. (Photo 12.V.Gov.).

Governor Jane D. Hull meeting with evacuees at the Payson Middle School.
Photo by Mark Henle, Arizona Republic

Kamax helicopter making a drop on a hot spot on the Chediski Fire.
Photo by Tom Beddow, USFS, Apache-Sitgreaves National Forest.

CH 13: REPATRIATION & CELEBRATION

"Mankind has not woven the web of life. We are but one thread within it.
Whatever we do to the web… we do to ourselves.
All things are bound together… all things connect." Chief Seattle

June 29th, Saturday

Containment increased to 38%. There were 4,447 firefighters, including 20 hotshot crews and 88 Type II crews. All four zones were using a total of 13 heavy airtankers and 24 helicopters. Ground resources included 245 structural fire engines, 100 wildland fire engines, 78 water tenders and 81 bulldozers. Final Attack (mopup) had begun west and south of Show Low and in the Linden, Pinedale and Clay Springs areas. Two rehab teams had arrived to plan and begin efforts to recover/rehabilitate firelines and the smoldering forests and watersheds. Crop duster planes, helicopters and hand crews were already spreading grass seed to stabilize soil as much as possible when summer rains came.

Linden firefighters were at last able to catch their breath. Firefighter Ryan Turner, who has the nickname of "Nozzle" as he loves to be on the end of the hose putting fires out, lost his home. He was attempting to save the homes of his "mountain neighbors" in Linden, Pinedale and Timberland Acres during his personal battle against the monster. At Ryan's home, an American Flag flew through the fire and survived, like so many others, along with a newly planted tree in the front yard. Many firefighters attended an impromptu ceremony whereby the flag was lowered to half-staff, mourning the loss of the home that he had only recently built and loved.

Foundation of Linden Firefighter Ryan Turner's house—all that's left. Photo by Dewayne Saxton

Linden Firefighter, Ryan Turner watering the newly planted tree at his lot in Linden where his house burned.
Photo by Dewayne Saxton.

Severe heat of the flame front actually exploded the bark from this live pine tree at Ryan Turner's home in Linden. Photo by Dewayne Saxton.

Flag at Ryan Turner's house lowered to half-staff in mourning the loss of his house and many of his neighbors in Linden and Timberland Acres. Photo by Dewayne Saxton.

*   *   *   *   *

Rick Lupe was introduced to the news media in the morning briefing as the Division Supervisor who led the burnout on the east side of the fire that essentially stopped fire from burning into and through Show Low. He was also introduced as the Fuels Management Officer for Ft. Apache Fire and a White Mountain Apache. Lupe was uncomfortable in the glare of public adoration and did not understand what all the fuss was about. Rick told people that he was bound and determined to prevent fire from burning through Hondah, Pinetop-Lakeside and Show Low, whose residents he considered neighbors. He felt so bad that fire had burned through Linden and Pinedale that he asked for the opportunity to lead the burnout west of Highway 60. He had also requested the Ft. Apache Hotshots be assigned to assist him in that effort. As far as he was concerned, they were all just doing their jobs… and that was enough.

*   *   *   *   *

Residents of Show Low, Pinetop, Lakeside, Hondah and McNary were allowed to return to their homes. Roadblocks were pulled down at 0700 hours on June 29th. Pinetop-Lakeside Mayor, Ginny Handorf stood/sat in the back of a truck at the town limits and waved "welcome home" to everyone who entered a town still standing. Mayor Ginny remained there on the side of the road by Reidhead's Real Estate office as long as evacuees were returning home. Tears of joy abounded.

Many residents were surprised to find their homes with gardens and plants watered and virtually no incidence of vandalism or looting. Structural firefighters and law enforcement personnel had gone above and beyond the call of duty in protecting and caring for the vacated communities.

Pinetop-Lakeside Mayor Ginny Handorf welcoming evacuees home on June 29th. Photo by Jerry Handorf.

*   *   *   *   *

Leonard Gregg was arrested by federal agents and transported to Flagstaff to be arraigned before a federal magistrate. Leonard had been working on the Rodeo Fire since shortly after his alleged arson ignition at the Cibeque Rodeo grounds on June 18th. He was being paid $8.00 an hour as a contract firefighter for the B.I.A.

At the evening briefing, I announced news of the arrest and told all of the media that I did *NOT* know any more to share with them, but that U.S. Attorney Paul Charlton would be at the next morning's briefing and would give everyone full details. I stated, "I don't know any more than that, so don't ask!" Brian Ellis of CNN promptly asked if I could tell them any elements of the investigation and/or arrest.

Having worked ten 20-hour days, my patience was a bit short. I glared at Brian in front of 20 video cameras and said sternly, "Did I stutter?" The rest of that homily that I often use on the grandkids is, "or did your ears flop??"

Debbie was watching CNN from Truth or Consequences and cringed, afraid that I would finish, as usual. I didn't, I simply said, "Some of you guys don't listen very well... Next question!" Brian apologized after the evening briefing ended.

*   *   *   *   *

Firefighter Clint Brown and his fiancée, Carry Maxon had planned a formal wedding for this day. Clint had been on the firelines since fire came over the Rim. Carry, as a member of the Show Low Fire Auxillary had been busy preparing meals and assisting the fire effort at Station One of Show Low

Fire. Clint's dad, Pastor Tom Brown, also a firefighter and the chaplain for Show Low Fire, was to perform the wedding ceremony.

Wedding of Clint Brown and Carry Maxon at Show Low Fire Dept. on June 29, 2002. Photo by Show Low Fire Dept.

With little time to plan and fire clothes as the proper attire, Clint and Carry were married at 1:00 p.m., as scheduled. The "wedding arch" was crossed ladders, provided by two ladder fire trucks in front of Station One. The ceremony was the sweet union of two spirits, but even more, it was symbolic as a celebration of life continuing with the promise of a "tomorrow." The honeymoon would have to wait until the fire emergency was over, but married they were…and on schedule. They sure enough spit in the eye of the dragon.

North of Linden, a person caused fire was suppressed at less than two acres, due to overwhelming response by fire resources. Arson was suspected. A common thread ran through the community of "What were 'they' thinking?"

An interagency "Burned Area Emergency Rehab Team" (BAER Team) made up of soil scientists, watershed hydrologists, engineers and plant specialists from the Departments of Agriculture and Interior assembled and began working with local Forest Service, B.I.A. and state officials on a plan to mitigate damage from erosion and soil sterilization.

As a last gasp, there was a good bit of smoke in the Forest Lakes area, but most of it was from the successful burnout operations of Kim Martin's Team in the Devil's Claw.

June 30th, Sunday

Containment of the 464,000-acre complex increased to 45%. Dugger Hughes, Operations Section Chief in Zone 4 (Bateman's Team) supervised burnouts on the southeast quadrant, along U.S. Highway 60. Dugger told news media at a stop on a fireline tour, "These burnouts are bigger than most fires that we fight, but they have to be done to stop the Rodeo part of the fire from spreading uncontrollably to the east."

At another special news briefing, Arizona's U.S. Attorney, Paul Charlton and B.I.A. Deputy Chief Special Agent Walter Lamar gave information on the arrest of Leonard Gregg for arson in starting the Rodeo Fire. They did not divulge much, as the investigation was still active. They did say that Gregg had been arrested on the fire and taken to Flagstaff. Leonard had been arraigned in Flagstaff before Federal Magistrate Steven L. Verkamp. Gregg attempted to apologize, when the judge cut him off and advised him not to enter a plea nor any statement at that time. The investigation by B.I.A. Special Agents, with assistance from Forest Service, F.B.I. and A.T.F. agents had only taken 11 days from the day of the arson to the arrest of Mr. Gregg.

Show Low Mayor Gene Kelly stated "how ironic, that a Native American, Leonard Gregg, a part time firefighter looking for work, had been arrested and charged with starting the fire. Yet, Show Low was saved by Rick Lupe along with his old crew, the Ft. Apache Hotshots and the other hotshot crews, who gave all they had to stop the monster." [13.b]

Timberland Acres residents were allowed to return. 106 homes were lost to the monster and now the grieving process began for many returnees. It is even bittersweet for many whose homes were spared/saved. Viewsheds were radically changed for decades and survivor guilt is a real life experience, especially when your next-door neighbors lost their home.

Flag in the middle of the three Stabenow houses burned in Timberland Acres. Note the charred edges of the flag that flew throughout the fire storm. Photo by Terence Corrigan, White Mountain Independent News.

*   *   *   *   *

At the 2200 hours media briefing (10:00 p.m.), I told the audience that "I went to my first fire 33 years ago and had been on about 200 large fires in my career. I had never seen a faster moving, more violent or more dangerous fire than the Rodeo-Chediski Fire."

*   *   *   *   *

July 1st, Monday

U. S. Highway 60 South was opened to traffic. There was still considerable smoke to the west. At times, drifting smoke covered the highway and vehicles had to slow down and use headlights.

A thunderstorm moved across Cibeque Creek. Erratic winds and some downbursts caused fire to jump firelines north of Cibeque in a slopover that burned 600 acres. However, it was caught by firefighters by 2200 hours (10:00 p.m.). No moisture was received in the area, but humidity did increase, which helped reduce fire intensities of the slopover. Once the thunderstorm winds died down, fire advance was minimal.

All of the residents to the east of Overgaard were allowed back into their homes.

Signs of gratitude and appreciation sprang up in yards, on fences and telephone poles, the sides of buildings, in the windows of cars and just about any place that a "thank you" could be shown. Here is a collage of just a portion of those remembrances.

SIGNS OF APPRECIATION FOR THE FIREFIGHTERS

Left to Right: Photo by USFS, Apache-Sitgreaves National Forest. Photo by Varnell Gatewood. Photo by USFS, Apache-Sitgreaves National Forest.

Left to Right: Photo by USFS, Apache-Sitgreaves National Forest. Photo by USFS, Apache-Sitgreaves National Forest. Photo by USFS, Apache-Sitgreaves National Forest.

Left to Right: Photo by Paul Bead. Photo by Paul Bead. Photo by Jim Paxon.

* * * * *

July 2nd, Tuesday

Containment increased to 70% and acreage of the fire only increased by 1,200 acres. The Devil's Claw burnout, west of Forest Lakes was completed and was absolutely textbook successful. That was the last piece of major firefighting to be accomplished. Final Attack remained on approximately 70 miles of the 220-mile perimeter.

TFR's (temporary flight restrictions) were cancelled for all but the northwest portion only (Zone 1). The Show Low Airport reopened for regular traffic.

Hump's team closed out. An Executive Summary—Final Report was submitted and accepted by the B.I.A, Forest Service and State Lands representatives. Larry Humphrey also returned the letter of delegation of authority back to forest, reservation and state. In essence, Hump's Team was released and our assignment completed, although none of us would ever be the same after facing the monster for two weeks… a monstrous fire that none of us had ever before witnessed.

Incident Commanders Larry Humphrey and Van Bateman comparing strategies.
Photo by USFS, Apache-Sitgreaves National Forest.

For my last news briefing, I issued a call to all who listened/watched that "We must come together and do things differently. Management must emulate Mother Nature or else we would have "bigger and badder" fires than the Rodeo-Chediski. Fire was neither good nor bad…fire was natural and Mother Nature would not stand for its total exclusion. Also, it was time to stop bickering and arguing over who's right, regarding land management issues. All interests must come to the table and seek solutions instead of attacking each other. I fear that unless we turned the fuels situation around that the future will hold fires worse than the Rodeo-Chediski."

I traveled to Payson and in a media ceremony, transferred my "Fire Ballcap" as well as the mantle of Lead Information Officer to Tim Grier at the Payson Information Center. He would, from July 2nd forward, be the national spokesman for the Rodeo-Chediski Fire. Tim had worked for me on the Dude Fire fatalities back in 1990 and had since left the Forest Service, but came back to work the west end information and evacuation center in Payson with Regional Media Officer Jim Payne. Tim also owned a cross-country ski lodge and cabins in Forest Lakes, so he had a vested interest in information.

July 3rd, Wednesday

80% containment was reported. Only 550 additional acres burned.

Heber-Overgaard residents allowed to return. Many openly expressed their grief and dismay at losing a home. Losses were the greatest of any portion of the fire, but so was the immediate help of neighbors reaching out a hand.

Burned vehicles with burned homes in the background in Overgaard. Photo by USFS, Apache-Sitgreaves National Forest.

Rubble is all that is left of a house in Timberland Acres. Photo by USFS, Apache-Sitgreaves National Forest.

Five vehicles burned, but the house survived. Photo by Dewayne Saxton.

Many "looky-Lou's" were busy driving the burned areas and taking photos/videos. Some of them stopped to visit with those who had lost homes and give their condolences.

Racial slurs ignorantly thrown at Native Americans following Leonard Greg's arrest were fairly common. Even though Native American crews worked tirelessly on every part of the fire and the Ft. Apache Hotshots were instrumental in stopping the fire from entering Show Low. Ft. Apache Hotshot Superintendent Marco Minjarez remarked with some disdain, "Stupidity comes in all colors, I guess."
13.a

Lightning lit up the evening sky with scattered light showers that actually dampened the ground east of Show Low. There were also four new starts, all lightning caused to the northwest of Forest Lakes. The fires were contained and controlled by initial attack forces.

*   *   *   *   *

July 4th, Thursday

Residents of Show Low decided to continue with their traditional July 4th parade, even though there was no time to build floats. Entrants were mostly fire trucks and firefighters with a few scattered "people" floats. An estimated 20,000+ viewers lined streets with cheers, American flags and handheld signs. In addition, firefighter appreciation signs sprang up on roadsides and in front yards.

The Diamondbacks baseball organization had invited Hump's Team down to the July 4th ballgame with the San Francisco Giants. I was asked to throw out the first pitch. That was an honor. Even though I threw a "skip-strike," the crowd gave a standing ovation.

This was recognition not just to me, but was also a tribute to all the firefighters. There were 40 of us in that party suite in right field, watching as Barry Bonds hit a homerun that rang the stadium rafters near our suite. The Diamondbacks won 8 to 7 and the 40 firefighters attending felt like winners as well. It was a good day to be celebrating the birth of our country and the many freedoms we enjoy.

Wedding gift to Debbie Paxon from Trent and Heather Penrod, The Burly Bear.

CH 14: FINAL ATTACK (MOP -UP)

"If anything is worth doing right, it is much easier to do it right...the first time."
Poppa Garrett

Once a fire is "contained" and no longer growing, then comes the crucial work of "putting the blaze to bed." Containment in fire terminology means that the fire is no longer spreading or growing larger in that particular area. Usually that figure is given in percent of line that has been constructed around the perimeter of the fire as a part of the daily fire statistics. Thus if the fire is 10% contained and is ten miles in perimeter, then one mile of constructed fireline is fairly secure and "black," with no growth or expansion on that one mile of line. It does not mean that the fire is out in that area...much to the contrary. What it means is that the grueling, somewhat boring and absolutely most critical part of firefighting now begins, that of "mop-up"!

Mop-up is less than glamorous in that the firefighters are not battling raging flames. It is the extremely critical job of finding and then extinguishing small fires that remain after the flame front has passed. Firefighters spend long hours looking for tendrils of smoke that indicate latent heat, knowing that a mere puff of wind could cause to blaze anew. Especially when close to the fireline, no fire can be allowed to flare up, as embers crossing the fireline could "grow legs" and once again, the fire could run over the hill. To avoid firefighters letting their guard down, some such as Type I Safety Officer, Steve Ripley refer to the mop-up process as "Final Attack." This is where the dragon loses his breath and has his remaining heads removed by firefighters, the coup de gras, so to speak. It is so critical for this work to be done correctly and diligently. Otherwise, the dragon might be able to rear his ugly head and run through the forests once again.

Mop-up uses a combination of available water, ranging from fire engines and water tenders to five gallon rubber or bladder backpack pumps (known to firefighters as "piss bags"), plus the backbreaking work of using hand tools such as shovels, McLeods and Pulaskis to dig out the source of heat, mix water and dirt and stir the mixture until all heat is extinguished. "Catch and Release" is a term that may be good management in fishing, but when used with firefighters it is an admission that mop-up was not properly completed and that the fire has "gone over the hill!" Certainly an event to be avoided at all costs.

Firefighting organizations and most land management agencies use distance measurement in terms shorter than miles by Gunter's or Surveyors Chains. A chain is 66 feet with 100 links per chain or about eight inches per link. There are 80 chains in one mile. We measure a firefighting crew's line building accomplishment in chains of fireline cut or constructed per hour.

When it comes time for mop-up, instructions are passed down to the crews as to how many chains inside the fireline that all burning materials must be totally extinguished. Much depends on the Operations Section Chiefs for determining the distance inside the fireline to mop-up. It involves criteria such as the severity of the fire season, anticipated weather for the duration of the fire, fuels remaining inside the fireline and adjacent unburned fuels, especially in the down wind direction, the proximity of communities and rural homesteads, slope, topography, fuels type and density and a host of other parameters. It is a scientific, calculated decision that is passed down to on-the-ground firefighters in terms of how far in they must mop-up, and the objective is to keep embers from blowing across the line and starting fire anew.

Usually mop-up is one to two chains inside the fireline, or 66 to 132 feet and occasionally three chains or about 200 feet. Well, how do you readily measure that distance you might ask? Simply, all firefighters are trained to be able to pace a chain. I take 11 paces on flat ground to cover the 66 feet of one chain. A pace is a left and right foot step, so you only count, say the left steps. On steeper ground, you would compensate by adding an appropriate number of additional paces per chain according to the steepness of the slope. Each firefighter knows his or her paces per chain and can fairly accurately measure the distance in from the fireline that they need to mop-up. If the instructions are to mop-up two chains in from the fireline and it is on gently sloping ground of about 20% slope, I would pace about 28 to 30 total paces in from the fireline as the inner limit of my crew's mop-up responsibility. On steeper ground, simply add more steps per chain according to the steepness of the slope.

Mop-up also means that considerable "cold trailing" must be done. Cold trailing is a standard firefighting tactic. It involves checking for heat by using the back of your hand, sans glove to check a suspected hotspot area for heat. The back of the hand is used rather than the palm or fingers, so that the sensitive and gripping part of the hand is not exposed to heat that might cause injury to the firefighter and possibly require medical care.

Crew seeking out heat and using water and tools to stir and extinguish any burning materials. Photo by USFS, Apache-Sitgreaves National Forest.

Crew mopping-up 2. Photo by USFS, Apache-Sitgreaves National Forest.

Left: Nelson Billie seeking heat with the back of his hand. Photo by Dave Cruz, Arizona Republic.
Below: Lots of heat. Gene and Slim wetting and stirring. Photo by Dave Cruz, Arizona Republic.

After the flame front passes and much of the aboveground vegetation is consumed by fire, there is still much left to burn. Seldom does the initial flaming fire front cause a total moonscaping and denuding of the entire landscape. Pockets of fuel along ridges and in canyons are often left for secondary fires to move through. Large logs on the ground take considerable time to consume to ash. Dead trees leave behind stumps and root channels that burn readily in times when there has been little winter moisture to saturate the ground. Dense thickets of trees often have a "duff" layers composed of pine needles and leaves that may be as much as three feet thick. In each of these receptive fuel beds, embers can "sleep" in or remain undetected until the sun bears down like a magnifying glass or an enabling puff of wind causes a flame to spring up. Mop-up requires that all burning and/or smoldering materials must be extinguished. Stumps and root channels are a major source of underground burning and must be a consideration in mop-up.

Once a source of heat is found, it is dug up and a combination of water, dirt and constant stirring with shovel or Pulaski until all burning, smoldering material is dead out and confirmed so by "cold trailing." This type of firefighting requires the firefighters to be in the very midst of their work. They come off-shift looking ghostly with raccoon eyes where their goggles rested on their faces and lines of dark/light contrasts where their hardhats and shirt collars show less of the gray and black of smoke and ash and usually black on the more exposed skin and their not-so-yellow fire shirts.

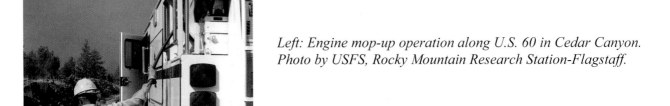

Left: Engine mop-up operation along U.S. 60 in Cedar Canyon. Photo by USFS, Rocky Mountain Research Station-Flagstaff.

Above: Engine mop-up 2. Photo by USFS, Rocky Mountain Research Station-Flagstaff.
Right: Engine mop-up 3. Photo by USFS, Rocky Mountain Research Station-Flagstaff.

While structural firefighters utilize airpacks for breathing assistance, wildland firefighters do not have the same advantage, in that the air packs are too heavy, of short duration, (usually 30-40 minutes to maximum one hour) and are too bulky to carry with a line pack. A wildland firefighter will sometimes use a handkerchief to filter some of the smoke and dust. There have been several patented devices to cover the nose and mouths of firefighters and provide cleaner air, but most inhibit breathing when in arduous aerobic activity and the need to move volumes of air through the lungs prohibits any restriction in breathing. When hiking, carrying a pack and working as you go, firefighters simply live with the smoke, until technology give us breathing devices that filter yet do not inhibit airflow.

Mop-up near Forest Lakes with helicopters, engines and hand crews. Photo by Karen Wattenmaker.

The images we see on television and in our newspapers often show the more dramatic elements of fire fighting, especially raging flames and the air shows. Seldom, if ever has an air tanker or helicopter put a fire out. They do slow the rate of spread and cool the intensity of a fire in many cases, allowing the firefighters on the ground to get close and begin their work. The real work of fire fighting is in mop-up and until that job is accomplished with patience, pride and some "long suffering," there remains the constant threat of a fire growing legs and running off. Line firefighters or "dirt diggers" are the infantry of firefighting and they are still the primary tool in firefighting. Mop-up is the least glamorous, but most essential part of fire fighting. It truly has not changed much in the last 100 years.

Crew near Heber-Overgaard mopping-up. Photo by USFS, Apache-Sitgreaves National Forest.

Below: Left: Crew Photo #2. Photo by USFS, Apache-Sitgreaves National Forest.

Right: Crew Photo #3. Photo by USFS, Apache-Sitgreaves National Forest.

Bottom: Chipper spreading chips for mulch on a roadside near Heber-Overgaard. Photo by Ken Palmrose.

*   *   *   *   *

July 5th, Friday

Fire teams reported that the Rodeo-Chediski Fire was now at 468,638 acres and was 90% contained. Rehab is in full operation with helicopters bombing steeper, more intensely burned areas with hay bales and straw/mulch shredder/blowers treating roads and areas around communities and campgrounds with seed and mulch. Only in the far northwest corner of the fire is there any active fire remaining and crews are patrolling and mopping-up those areas above the Devil's Claw near Forest Lakes.

July 6th, Saturday

Information reported 95% containment had been achieved and no change in acreage. Glen Joki's Type II Team takes over command to oversee mop-up and continue rehabilitation of firelines and burned areas that have cooled down.

An impromptu parade in Heber-Overgaard traveled down Highway 260. Navajo County Sheriff's officers and Arizona DPS-Highway Patrol provided escorts and traffic diversion. Many viewers, residents and tourists remarked that it was one of the best Heber-Overgaard parades ever. The joy of being back in the community after almost two weeks of evacuation is understandable. Those who lost homes or businesses were somewhat better able to cope, being in familiar places instead of not knowing and being far away. Much emotion was openly displayed and many flags and signs of appreciation were evident. Once again, the strength of the White Mountain communities was evident as neighbor reached out to neighbors in need.

The "yard animals" are all that survived this fire visit. Photo by USFS, Apache-Sitgreaves National Forest.

The Payson Media Center closed as media and public interest waned. An interagency recovery information center was maintained in Heber to inform the public on post fire "rehab." activities and also provide an avenue and contact point for volunteers.

The Incident Command Post in Show Low at High School was shutdown. Joki's team operates out of several different locations in the White Mountain area over the next two weeks.

July 7th, Sunday

The Rodeo-Chediski Fire is now 100% contained. More than $43,000,000 has been spent in suppression of this one fire.

Rehab work is in full swing on the 220 miles of fireline/perimeter. It would still be two months until the fire is declared "controlled." There is continuous evidence of remnants of fire in isolated smoke plumes and ash dust devils as interior islands of fuels burn deep within the fire perimeter. Estimates of costs of rehab work are double the costs of suppression or close to $100,000,000. Values lost have not been estimated, but will be staggering.

Many returnees exhibit stress, dispatchers receive many 911 calls due to homeowners apprehensions with all the smoke and occasional flames visible from housing areas. All are checked out by the appropriate fire and/or law enforcement jurisdictions. Those needing suppression action and/or mop-up are handled. Those that do not pose a threat are allowed to consume and go out naturally.

White Mountain Recovery Partnership began to organize in order to effectively "lend a hand" to those in need.

Post fire, a stump burning near a house that survived the fire. Photo by USFS, Apache-Sitgreaves National Forest.

The W.M.R.P. is composed of FEMA representatives, Arizona Department of Mental Health workers and many local civic and church groups and interested individuals. Both Salvation Army and Red Cross are participants. Many volunteers from Show Low and Pinetop-Lakeside want to help and work in W.M.R.P. It is locally led and locally driven to help those in need and those who are hurting. The success of W.M.R.P. is to become one of the major factors in the speedy recovery of communities on the mountain. Some individuals are still reeling from losses and suffering a type of post-traumatic stress disorder (P.T.S.D.).

September 7th

The Rodeo-Chediski Fire was declared controlled by Forest Service and B.I.A. officials. Fire suppression funds could no longer be used after this date. Now rehabilitation funds would be used to accomplish erosion control and watershed stabilization work as well as removal of hazards around campgrounds, trailheads and along roads and trails.

Guardrail burning along Cottonwood Wash on Highway 260. Photo by Steve Campbell

CH 15: POST FIRE

"He who makes no mistakes does nothing. He who does not learn from his mistakes is a fool."
Poppa Garrett.

Final Fire Statistics
- The Rodeo Fire began about 4:00 p.m. on June 18, 2002.
- The Chediski Fire began about 7:00 a.m. on June 20, 2002.
- The two fires merged about 2:30 p.m. on June 23, 2002.
- Rodeo-Chediski Fire Complex was declared "Contained" on July 7, 2002 at 460,182 acres (revised based on better mapping and ground truthing of burn points from the original 468,830 acres reported July 2, 2002).
- Rodeo-Chediski Fire Complex was declared "Controlled" on September 7, 2002 (which meant that the fire was essentially "out").

Jurisdictions involved:
- Ft. Apache Reservation — 276,335 Acres
- Apache-Sitgreaves National Forest — 164,440 Acres
- Tonto National Forest — 10,711 Acres
- Private Lands — 8,673 Acres
- Arizona Game & Fish Lands — 23 Acres

Most acreage burned in one day—June 20th—70,815, although the two fires, while still separate, burned 113,450 acres total on June 22nd. For each of seven days the fire burned in excess of 40,000 acres per day.

Severe + Moderate Acres Burned:
- Ft. Apache — 162,114 Acres
- U.S.F.S. — 94,546 Acres
- Private — 3,069 Acres
- Severe + Moderate Acres Burned — 56.4 % of total

Navajo County Assessor Summary—Improvements Burned

Aripine Area	8	Overgaard Townsite	12
Bear Country	2	Pinecrest Lake	182
Bison Ranch	50	Pinedale	41
Buckskin Artist Draw & Section 30	24	Pinedale Estates	1
Cheney Ranch	3	Pine Meadows	4
Claysprings	6	Section 31, Heber-Overgaard	5
Farnsworth Ranch	3	Timberland Acres	105
Fool Hollow Ranches	2	Victory Heights	3
Miscellaneous Forest Buildings	22		
Mogollon Air Park	8		
North of Pinedale	1	Total structures burned 491, which included 465
Overgaard Store Area	8	homes and 6 businesses.

- Number of homes threatened and saved 2,200+ (does not include structures outside the fire perimeter in Show Low, Pinetop-Lakeside, Hondah & McNary).
- Total estimated people evacuated — 45,000+ (per Navajo County Sheriff)
- Personnel Assigned — 4,447 at one time (total individuals who served over the term of the fire 6,600 +)
- Miles of Fireline (Perimeter) — 220 miles
- Cost of Suppression – $43,000,000
- Anticipated Costs of Rehabilitation – $50,000,000+ (realistically X 2)

Resources on both fires:
- Heavy Air Tankers — 13
- Single Engine Air Tankers — 5
- Helicopters — 26
- Type I Incident Mgmt. Teams — 4
- Type II Incident Mgmt. Teams — 2
- Area Command Team — 1
- Fire Engines — 245
- Bulldozers — 89
- Water Tenders — 95
- Type I Crews (Hotshots) — 20
- Type II Crews – 77

*   *   *   *   *

Special Report

WHITE MOUNTAIN

Independent

A comprehensive look at 'The Monster,' Arizona's largest wildfire

Rodeo-Chediski Complex fire June 18-July 6, 2002

Battle lines
As 400-foot flames advance toward White Mountain communities forces rally to contain 'The Monster.' Page 3

Face of 'The Monster'
Smoke plumes at times achieve a horrible beauty. Scenes of the fire, Page 48

White Mountain Special Report—Rodeo-Chediski Fire, July 2002

The local paper, the White Mountain Independent, published a great special tabloid magazine summarizing the Rodeo-Chediski Fire with some of the most dramatic photos, and inserted 11,000 copies into their regular newspaper in early July, 2002. Those papers sold out in less than 24 hours and demands came into the WMI office asking for additional copies of the special report. W.M.I. printed an additional 3,000 copies, which went almost as fast. The Rodeo-Chediski Fire Special Report is now something of a collector's piece and one that is prized by all those who were impacted by the fire and have one.

*   *   *   *   *

The contributions and response of both the Salvation Army and the Red Cross were immeasurable. Volunteers of each organization came from all across the west to help. Pastor Dave Sherman and his wife Tina of the White Mountain Salvation Army Outpost were anchors to which many clung. The Salvation Army's mobile kitchens were even called upon to feed Hump's Team and all the firefighters at the Show Low High School for two days, until we could get a caterer in and get the camp at Show Low High School fully functional.

The Red Cross liaison, Mai Lindstrom was instrumental in representing Red Cross interests in our strategy sessions. She related the actions that Red Cross had taken and took our needs for Red Cross implementation. They ran the three primary evacuation centers and supported at least five others.

There are many "angel communities" that received refugees from the evacuated areas with open arms and loving hearts. Holbrook, Snowflake-Taylor, St. Johns, Eagar-Springerville, Greer, Whiteriver, Globe and Payson are among the most generous and closest to those affected. Other areas in the Valley of the Sun, Tucson and Flagstaff also helped in many ways with donations, prayers and action. The people of Arizona responded as neighbors and are to be commended. It truly does go back to a time shown in some of the paintings of Norman Rockwell, when neighbors acted as neighbors out of a basic love for their fellow man.

Recovery from a disaster is not an "event," but rather a journey in which each individual and even whole communities recover at differing paces and in varying ways. The fire's damage represented a negative change in so many people's ways of life, including the heartbreaking loss of hopes and dreams. Many people were in shock and suffered extreme stress after returning to the areas burned. Those who suffered loss grieved. Some experienced anger that would not subside. FEMA, Arizona Department of

Behavioral Health Services, the Community Counseling Centers and the Northern Arizona Behavioral Health Authority reached out to residents through the White Mountain Recovery Partnership. WMRP counselors and volunteers went door to door and held countless meetings that helped folks recover.

A major focus of the WMRP efforts was facilitating disaster recovery and getting through miles of red tape in government and insurance adjustment programs. Counseling sessions for individuals and groups made resources available and gave folks outlets for expression. Two documents, "The Rodeo-Chediski Fire Story" and "Writing to Heal" were strength-based initiatives used to help people deal with the changes and loss. Meetings and counseling sessions were held in every community affected by the fire. Memorial tiles were made from artwork by adults and children and placed in public locations for community memory. Quilts made from artwork provided by children all over the White Mountains were given to libraries, local governments, firefighters and officials who helped in the "Kid's Korner" recovery.

Special quilt made from transfers of children's artwork and quilted by Marque Jacobs of Payson. Photo by Jim Paxon

*   *   *   *   *

Canadian warning sign on a highway. Unknown photographer.

2002 was a major fire-year all across the west and even into Canada. Persistent drought and an abnormally warm spring had fire prevention efforts in high gear. This sign shows a sense of humor that our neighbors to the north have. We were home from the Rodeo-Chediski Fire for almost two weeks when Humphrey's Team was dispatched to the McNally Fire on the Kern River above Bakersfield, California. It burned 150,700 acres and 17 homes in July '02 and was another climax type fire in what seemed to be a never-ending fire season.

A camper's overturned barbeque grill in high winds started the fire above the little town of Kernville. Parched forests and up-canyon breezes caused the fire to race seven miles up the Kern River in just three hours, in very heavy timber. Forty head of cattle were caught against a barbed-wire range fence, as they attempted to escape the fire's fury. The heat was so intense that they literally exploded as the fire incinerated their bodies. Fire burned to within one-quarter mile of a stand of Sequoia trees, giants of the forest including the fourth largest tree in the world. Fire burned on three sides of Johnson City, an old sawmill town turned tourist attraction and artists' refuge. It took a full two weeks to get containment on this fire before we returned to our jobs and families at home.

The Los Angeles Times is a rather liberal publication. The public debate on forest management, thinning and prescribed burning had raged on endlessly for decades as showcased in the L.A. Times. The McNally Fire focused on the need to manage with the McNally Fire coming so close to four groves of Giant Sequoia trees along the Sierra

MICHAEL RAMIREZ

LOS ANGELES TIMES

STOP FOREST THINNING

NO PRESCRIBED BURNS

DANGER FLAMMABLE

"Do us a favor . . . stop doing us favors."

Cartoon by Michael Ramirez, Los Angeles Times Aug. 4, 2002

Crest. Cartoonist Michael Ramirez sketched a satirical response to the issues with a pragmatic rather than simply conservative approach, as shown here. There are only two choices, emulate Mother Nature and manage by cutting competing trees, removing excess biomass and allowing cool fire in the Sequoia groves… or lose them! Which will we choose??

*   *   *   *   *

Firefighter Friday, August 25th at Silver Creek Golf Resort.

Show Low City Councilman, Rick Fernau flew to Truth or Consequences, New Mexico and picked Debbie and I up in his Cessna 172. We flew back to Show Low to attend a celebration for firefighters and local officials at the Silver Creek Golf Club. Firefighters were hosted to an impromptu tournament and barbeque. Many officials gave short speeches including Show Low Mayor Gene Kelly, Pinteop-Lakeside Mayor Ginny Handorf, Sheriff Gary Butler, Navajo County Board Supervisor Pete Shumway, Arizona Legislator Jake Flake and others. I complimented all the White Mountain folks who were there for their indomitable spirit and their true sense of neighborliness in extending a helping hand to those who had lost and needed help. It was a grand time for all and a very warm reception for us.

The Rodeo T-Shirts

A White Mountain Recovery Celebration with Steve Basmajian of International Sunprints was held in Phoenix August 27th. T-shirt sales of the rodeo fire with signatures from Gov Jane Dee Hull, Sheriff Gary Butler and the eight area fire chiefs raised over $300,000 for fire recovery. The caption of the t-shirt was "This Ain't My Last Rodeo." Posters were also made up in the same motiff and sold to help raise funds.

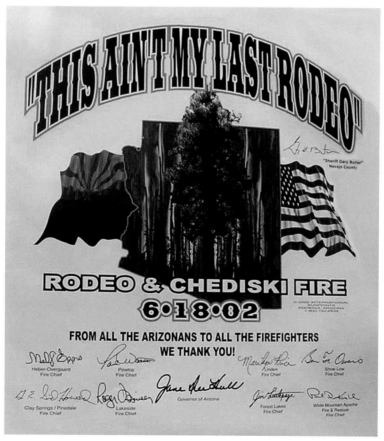

International Sunprints tee shirt. Photo by Jim Paxon

At the celebration in Phoenix at the International Sunprints of Arizona headquarters, Governor Hull, Sheriff Butler and I accepted a check for $157,000. Dolan Ellis performed "Wildfire," the tribute song to the firefighters that he wrote in a Payson bar on June 27th, when he was unable to get up to the fire. Approximately 200 people attended and partook in the celebration and a barbeque that followed. The funds were distributed to the White Mountain Apaches at Cibeque, community Chambers of Commerce and local fire departments.

On Sept 1st. the White Mountain Apache Tribe held a tribute to firefighters at the Sunrise Resort. Firefighters from every Apache fire crew were there, except for the Ft. Apache Hotshots, who were out on a fire assignment. There was a great barbeque and speeches by members of the tribal council. The White Mountain Apache Crown Dancers performed and a good time was had by all, even with an afternoon rain shower.

*   *   *   *   *

The last fire of the 2002 season for Humphrey's Type I Team was the Pack Rat Fire on the Mogollon Rim above the towns of Pine and Strawberry in late August and into September. The monsoon rains had been sporadic with much less than normal precipitation. Our team was called due to the close proximity of the two villages and the numerous youth and organizational camps close to the fire. One of our primary objectives was to keep the fire from climbing the Mogollon Rim and moving through Long Valley and Blue Ridge, where there were several hundred homes. Smoke plumes were visible from Payson on up Arizona Highway 260 past Pine and Strawberry. The Pack Rat Fire never grew legs and ran hard, due in part to the time of year with shorter days, cooler temperatures and some humidity recovery at night. It burned a total of 9,000 acres.

*   *   *   *   *

Sept. 28 Fall Festival Parade in Pinetop-Lakeside. Debbie and I rode atop a Lakeside Fire Department engine as grand marshals. It was both a healing time and a celebration. The crowd was estimated at close to 30,000 people.

*   *   *   *   *

The National Academy of Television Arts and Sciences, southwest Chapter held the 2003 Rocky Mountain Emmy Awards at the Scottsdale Center for the Arts on June 28, 2003. I was awarded a Governor's Award Emmy for service to communities through broadcast journalism. The quote during the award presentation was "Mr. Paxon was our source of information during the Rodeo-Chediski Fires in Northern Arizona last summer, often providing the only hope and humor in a tense and tragic situation. Paxon was reliable and trustworthy during the three weeks of Arizona's most devastating fire. We will remember Jim Paxon. Congratulations on your selection for the 2003 Governor's Award Emmy." I was shocked, pleased and humbled. I accepted the award on behalf of all our firefighters who are "out there" doing the work and will go again whenever called.

*   *   *   *   *

On October 20, 2003, Leonard Gregg pled guilty in federal court to two counts of arson-intentionally starting a fire and destruction of federal forests. (End Note 15.c). His lawyer did not arrange for any plea agreements, rather maintained his innocence. Then on March 8, 2004 Gregg was sentenced the maximum, ten years in prison and $27,000,000 in restitution for starting the Rodeo part of the Rodeo-Chediski Fire. (End Note 15.d). The sentence seems harsh in that Leonard's lawyer purported that he was the victim of Fetal Alcohol Syndrome (F.A.S.) and had limited reasoning and cognitive abilities. It seems even more strange and perhaps unfair in that Valinda Jo Elliot, who admitted starting the Chediski Fire to signal a passing helicopter that she needed rescue. After all, she was in trespass on the White Mountain Apache Reservation and there is a question as to how much in danger she really was. Paul Charlton, Arizona's U.S. Attorney (recently fired) refused to indict Ms. Elliot, claiming lack of evidence that she acted with intent in starting the fire.

*　　*　　*　　*　　*

I chose to retire from the Forest Service after 33 ½ years in January, 2003. I had a blessed career and can honestly say that the days where I did not want to go to work numbered less than the fingers on one hand. It was time for a change. After retirement, I was invited to the Hyatt Regency Hotel in Phoenix to speak to a group of business people on January 13, 2003. While there, I met with News Directors from three Phoenix television stations. All three made offers to work with them as a fire analyst and commentator.

I negotiated a services contract with NBC's affiliate, KPNX Channel 12. KPNX-12 has business relationships with the Arizona Republic newspaper, FM radio station KMML and the news website, azcentral.com. I am asked to assist with the annual TV fire season special and a mid-summer Monsoon special. I go to the scene of wildfires to report on fire team strategies and the progress of fighting the fire. Lastly, I am given the opportunity to write guest editorials for the Arizona Republic and blogs for azcentral.com on fire and land management issues. News Director Mark Casey's desire was that when Channel 12 is covering news of wildfires, he wanted viewers to "feel the heat from the flames and smell the smoke while sitting in their living room!"

KPNX Interview. Nick Calderon with Jim Paxon. Photo by Debbie Paxon

I was honored to accept this unique opportunity. I would still be going to fires and seeing "the old gang" and watching the "kids" that I had trained, mentored and sponsored grow to do great things. A collateral opportunity was to help viewers and the public understand fire and Mother Nature's rules. I am pleased that my contract and relationship with Channel 12 continues today.

*   *   *   *   *

Arizona's Speaker of the House, Jake Flake invited me to address the legislature in Phoenix prior to Governor Janet Napolitano's first State of the State Address on January 13, 2003. I spoke to both houses of Arizona's legislature for about 20 minutes, relating two concerns: First, we would see worse and possibly bigger, more destructive fires than the Rodeo-Chediski Fire. Most certainly people would be at risk in consequent fires and second, Arizona's problems in land management and fire protection needed to be solved and resolved at the negotiation table, or even better yet, out in the woods and **not in the courts.** Land managers, fire experts and researchers must be given an ear. Those who opposed cutting and prescribed burning needed to come to the table as well, where issues would be attacked and not individuals.

Governor Janet Napolitano and Jim Paxon. Photo by Debbie Paxon

*   *   *   *   *

June 17, 2003, two young men were hiking in Sabino Canyon, above Tucson on Mt. Lemmon. Even though there were total closures on smoking and campfires, one of them just had to have a smoke and smoke he did, resulting in the Aspen Fire in the upper canyon. The fire was in severely steep country with heavy fuels. Due to the eight years of drought in the Catalina Mountains, the fire was "climax" and grew as quickly as had the Rodeo-Chediski. Firefighters were not able to work close to the fire in the heavy fuels and steep canyons.

Our warnings to the community during the 2002 Bullock Fire came true. On June 19th, the fire blew up and ran over the top. That was the same day that Rick Lupe died in the Maricopa Burn Center in Phoenix, after suffering burns on the Sawtooth Prescribed Burn near Whiteriver on the White Mountain Apache Reservation.

Humphrey's Type I Team was called to manage the Aspen Fire. The fire ravaged the town of Summerhaven, burning more than 300 summer homes and residences on the Santa Catalina Crest. By the time this monster laid down, the Aspen Fire had burned more than 85,000 acres.

Kinishba Fire Devil. Photo by Paul Bead

*   *   *   *

On July 13, 2003, lightning started the Kinishba Fire, which burned just to the south of the point where Rick Lupe was burned in May. Hump's Team was once again called to attack this fire. For several days it was touch and go. Residents of Pinetop-Lakeside received a lot of daily doses of heavy smoke. Unrest and angst reigned as the communities were put on alert to be ready to evacuate. Governor Napolitano declared another state disaster and freed up $2 million to help in the fire suppression effort. Summer monsoons provided some moisture on the north end, assisting firefighter's efforts. By July 22nd the fire was 70% contained and the risk abated for Pinetop-Lakeside. More than 25,000 acres burned, but no homes were lost and no firefighters were injured.

*   *   *   *   *

In the California Fire Siege of 2003, there were 14 major fires that burned 750,000+ acres, 3,710 homes and 24 lives were lost. Costs of all 14 fires exceeded $123 million. [15.a] In the Cedar Fire alone, in October and November, 273,246 acres and 2,887 homes burned in San Diego County. Fourteen civilians and one firefighter died in the Cedar fire. The accompanying photo shows the Cedar Fire from the Pacific Ocean with Scripps Ranch on the left hand side and the town of Julian in the upper center where firefighter Steven Rucker died. Harbison Canyon is on the lower right hand side of the photo. As evidenced in the photo, the Cedar Fire burned with a vengeance.

Cedar Firestorm October 2003. Photo taken from Pacific Ocean looking east past San Diego.
Unknown photographer.

In Harbison Canyon, only one home survived the fiery blast on the south canyon ridge for almost three miles. This same area burned in the Laguna Fire of 1970, but there were far fewer homes, then. President Bush would tour this area in November and renew his commitment to legislation to address the problem of forest fuel buildup and risk to communities. 28,000 acres burned within the city limits of San Diego.

I was with Channel 12's news team, covering the Cedar Fire for nine days. It wasn't much different than being in fire camp in the old days, only from a perspective of the "other side of the camera lens."

One thing unique to California, by law, the news media cannot be restricted from access to emergency scenes, as long as they do not impede emergency operations. *I think that is a huge step in the right direction.* It will be a long time before it is accepted in Arizona and with the Incident Command community. I.C.'s and the federal government are concerned with liability and control of the situation and what kind of news comes from a mega fire emergency.

I feel strongly, that when full access for media does happen in Arizona and other western states, it will put the onus on the media groups to prepare, train and equip their reporters to be "on the scene." It will also hopefully provide much better information to the public, in a more timely manner. There will still be a huge workload for the team information organizations in providing information from the firefighting side.

*   *   *   *   *

One of Dr. Wally Covington's primary assistants at the Ecological Restoration Institute is H.B. "Doc" Smith, a retired Forest Service District Ranger, Fire Manager and Type I Incident Commander. Doc has worked with Dr. Covington for the last twelve years and assists the Ecological Restoration

Institute with his experience in fire and a ground knowledge that is unsurpassed. He is an interpreter extraordinaire, who condenses much of the science that Covington and his researchers generate into simple terms and comparisons that almost everyone can understand.

I first met Doc on the 1987 Anderson Creek Fire north of Garden Valley, Idaho. Doc was the Incident Commander and his Southwest Incident Management Team was fighting a climax fire in Ponderosa Pine. Four young Jemez Pueblo firefighters died when the National Guard deuce-and-a-half (all-wheel-drive military truck) in which they were riding back to camp, went off a narrow and dusty mountain road and overturned. Fatalities are difficult for every firefighter, but especially hard on the leaders and managers of the young men lost.

The Anderson Creek Fire was the first time I had witnessed mature, large Ponderosas preheated to a kindling temperature suddenly explode into flames, while the flame front was still a quarter of a mile away. It was an awesome sight and one that caused me to pause and wonder at the power of fire… and of God.

Doc Smith now works at getting all the research data and conclusions into "everyday English," which in itself is a daunting task. Doc leads university short courses in restoration ecology and has done countless field trips with every segment of society, government administration and land management interest conceivable.

Doc is a champion of going to Mother Nature's laboratory, the ground, and letting her show us how she would manage, if only we would cooperate… and watch/listen. Doc has been instrumental in shaping many of my philosophies and understandings of Ma Nature's ways. He, too, is a harbinger that has been sounding the clarion for decades that we must change and take action NOW! ... or suffer terrible consequences.

Elk avoid the fire by standing in a shallow river. Photo by John McColgan, BLM Alaska Fire Service.

CH 16.   REFLECTIONS

"Hot heads and cold hearts never solved anything!" – Billy Graham

Over the last four years, I have had many discussions with friends in the fire community, colleagues in all fire and land management agencies at every level. I have completed a mountain of personal research. All of this has given rise to the following, my personal reflections on the events surrounding the Rodeo-Chediski Fire. These might seem obvious, but for those who routinely read the last chapter first, I will restate my conclusions in summary format, for the record:

- 2002 was the worst fire season in the United States in more than 100 years, and certainly the worst since smokechasers began eating smoke and chasing the dragon. Fires burned 6.4 million acres and we spent one billion dollars fighting them. Twenty-two firefighters lost their lives fighting fire. I feel strongly that worse fire seasons are ahead of us until we get our fuels situation reduced and some periodic, managed fire back into all the southwestern ecosystems. (In Fire Season '06, for example, 9.5 million acres burned, 1.25 billion dollars spent and 24 lives lost). One might ask "How much worse can it get?" I would say that we have only just begun to see really *bad* fire seasons!

- Ft. Apache Fire and Forestry resources attacked the Rodeo Fire with an all out effort. Leonard Gregg's arson ignition provided Dr. Stephen Pynes' final card in dealing us the Royal Flush of conditions (detailed in Chapter 2) that provided for the perfect fire-storm. Simply put, it was time and once the dragon awoke, he would not be caught or tamed until his appetite was satisfied for houses burned and forests consumed.

- When homes are lost and property damaged, there is always cause for some to seek "conspiracy" or malfeasance that could be easily blamed for the fire's spread and property losses in Pinedale, Timberland Acres, Linden, Airipine, Clay Springs and Overgaard. There were many who were absolutely certain that resources were diverted to "save" Show Low, Pinetop and Lakeside. To the contrary!! Fire was already forcing its way into Pinedale and ravaging homes when Hump's team took over command of the incident at 6:00 a.m. on June 20th. Incident Commander Larry Humphrey made a decision to not fight this fire in a conservative, traditional way, as many more homes would have been lost. Instead, Hump took a calculated risk and went to the front of the fire to save as many homes as we could. It takes time to assemble resources, transport them to the scene and get them into action on the lines. As resources arrived, they were committed to the areas at greatest risk. For eight days, the fire was far ahead of our actions and Mother Nature was in total control as to where and when the fire took a particular path and how much damage was inflicted. We lost 465 homes, 6 businesses and 23 garages and outbuildings, each one a defeat for all 4,477 firefighters who served. On the other hand, more than 2,200 homes were saved, each one a victory for the same firefighters, and that does not count the homes considered threatened in Show Low, Pinetop-Lakeside, Hondah or McNary.

- I often hear blame placed on the Forest Service for the way the fire was or was not fought. My personal opinion of that type of hindsight is that it is *weak*, even for armchair quarterbacks. Those who were the real players and quarterbacks in the contest of fighting a dangerous wildfire have no problem discussing and defending their plan of attack… as compared with those on the sidelines who merely attack the plans. This fire was never a "Forest Service" fire. Although the Forest Service, the Bureau of Indian Affairs and Arizona State Lands were all three jurisdictionally responsible for portions of the fire, the four incident management teams that managed the fire were all interagency and from different home bases. For example, I.C. Larry Humphrey was a BLM employee out of Safford, Arizona. His deputy I.C. was Jeff Whitney, a U.S. Fish & Wildlife Service fire manager from Albuquerque…and so on. The bottom line was that Hump's Team operated and managed the Rodeo Fire with full authority and autonomy from the B.I.A., State of

Arizona Lands Department and Forest Service with the set of objectives given in the Delegation of Authority. This changed as the situation became more critical with the Rodeo and Chediski fires about to merge, resulting in assignment of an Area Command Team and three additional Type I Teams, assuming their commands on June 25th, each with a portion of the fire to manage.

- The Rodeo Fire was a *disaster* before we got there. We recognized that the forests were going to burn in a big way. Our priorities were to first, get people out of harm's way, second, not lose firefighters or civilians in the fray and third, to save as many homes as humanly possible. Hindsight confirms that we accomplished all three objectives to the best of our abilities.

- Had the Chediski Fire crossed Highway 260 between Heber and Forest Lakes, it most likely would have burned north to Chevelon Lake and added thousands of acres and many more homes lost to the final result. Likewise, if fire had crossed U.S. Highway 60 at Forestdale Canyon, it would have burned through Show Low and Wagon Wheel and may not have stopped until it burned to the east of Vernon. That, too, would have added hundreds of thousand of acres and the possibility of thousands more homes lost. Either way, the Rodeo-Chediski Fire was stopped at 460,000+ acres. It could have been much, much worse… a million acres or more, and who knows how many homes would have been lost?

- The Incident Command System provides for span of control to accomplish objectives in fighting fires. When Valinda Jo Elliott lit her signal fire below Chediski Peak, the span of control from Humphrey's Type I Team was already exceeded. Hump's Team was never in charge of the Chediski Fire battle. Again, Ft. Apache and the rest of the fire organization was way behind the power curve. Remember that there were more than 13 large fires in the western U.S. with teams on them. At least five of those fires, elsewhere, were also losing houses to fire. We ended up with four Type I Teams on the Rodeo-Chediski complex, each with a quadrant of the Rodeo-Chediski Fire, working under the umbrella of Joe Ribar's Area Command Team. Ribar's team actually allocated scarce resources of air tankers, helicopters, fire engines and hotshot crews, based on daily changes in burning conditions and twice daily scientific analysis of predictions for the next day's fire behavior.

- Very few people, even long term firefighters have seen "plume dominated fire" like the Rodeo-Chediski Fire, where at times, there were seven or more distinct plumes or smoke columns with abrupt changes in fire behavior in each that consumed thousands of acres of forests, almost by the minute. To attempt to put people in front of such erratic, volatile and fast moving fire would have been negligent and would have certainly cost many lives. That was a risk that our team (or any other) was not willing to endure. Where there is personal ownership and a vested interest, such as in Heber-Overgaard, Linden, Pinedale and Clay Springs, there are times that "perhaps one is too close to the forest to really see the trees (or the fire, as it may be)" That vested interest sometimes clouds judgment. Waiting out an advancing flame front of fire in a "safe zone" is unbearable torture and wears on one's conscience, when the security of ones own homes and those of their neighbors hang in the balance. Going to firefighter memorials and putting one or more of your peers/friends

Plume dominated Missionary Ridge Fire near Durango, Colorado in June 2002.
Photo by USFS, San Juan National Forest.

in the ground is so much worse! Having been there six times in my fire career, I know!! Imagine a situation like the Esperanza Fire near Riverside, California in October, 2006, where five firefighters died at a single house, trying to keep it from burning, when preliminary investigation is already pointing to a structure that was not defensible to begin with. We certainly could have had the same situation or worse on the Rodeo-Chediski, but for the tough decisions of caring but grizzled, veteran I.C.'s, and heads-up Operations Section Chiefs. I have said many times and believe strongly that *"there is no tree, no acre, no forest, or any house worth a single firefighter's life!!!"* **I pray that never changes in the Incident Command System**.

- Regarding evacuation, when it is your house or that of your neighbor's that is threatened, there is an incredible pull of responsibility to stay, to protect, to do something… anything to make the situation better. Even more so if the place is a dream that has been shaped by your own two hands and the sweat of your brow. I agree, certainly not an easy situation to walk away from. If the choice comes down to either stay… and possibly perish… or leave and perhaps have to rebuild, then the choice might be a little clearer and hopefully easier. Let's remember that eight of the 15 people who died on the Cedar Fire in San Diego in October, 2003 chose to stay, did not evacuate… until the flames came over the hill. When they did decide to evacuate, it was too late and they died in hasty, fatal retreat. *That is a tragedy for which there is no remedy.*

- If I could change one thing in the whole two weeks we were located at the Show Low High School, it would be to have more timely and area-specific information on the communities impacted by fire, especially in those areas where houses burned. I realize that people were agonizing in evacuation shelters, growing restless and needing information. I just did not have specifics to give them. My heart went out to them, but that alone certainly did not fill their need nor ease their suffering.

- Other than one individual who suffered a broken leg and another who received burns to his leg when he stepped into hot coals in a stump hole, there were no life-threatening injuries. On a lighter note, one young man suffered 1st and 2nd degree sunburn when after working the night shift, he fell asleep shirtless on his cot and woke up with a maximum sunburn on his back and shoulders. Of course there were also the endless blisters, colds, bronchitis, bee stings, heat exhaustion, fatigue, work exhaustion, etc. One of the most positive results of this campaign against a formidable monster was that *NO ONE DIED FIGHTING THIS FIRE*, even as huge, unpredictable and dangerous as he was and as aggressively as he was fought. The risk was ever present until the fire was totally contained. The experience and understanding of fire commanders in charge of firefighters, and the commitment of all 4,447 firefighters and support personnel involved, to safety are the reasons for meeting the Delegation of Authority's first objective.

- It seems that today, we battle an enemy who should never have been an enemy at all… fire. Fire, the way it was 130 years ago, was a rejuvenating force. Low intensity, slow moving fire was simply Mother Nature's way of sweeping clean the floors of the forest, every few years. To Ma Nature, the tragedy of black sticks and deep ash are temporary, waiting only on the first rains to send up new shoots of oaks, flowers and grass. The flames of those periodic fires of old were 6" to 12" and no faster than a "turtle in low gear." That kind of fire is so much different than the mega fires we are witnessing today, like the Rodeo-Chediski. The tragedy of lost homes lasts for a lifetime. Lost soil may never be recovered. We can turn this tragedy around, but it entails cutting, pruning, and cleaning and yes, even some prescribed burning. Don't believe the pseudo-science propaganda being fomented that says, "All we have to do is protect a buffer around communities. Let the fires burn in the back country!" The "moat concept" did NOT work in medieval times to keep invaders and monsters out of the castle and it won't work any better now. Haven't we seen that enough times in the recent past to understand?

- There is personal responsibility for each of us who choose to live in the woods. Again, a quote that I used several times: *"Fire is neither good nor bad, fire is natural. If you live in the forest or woodlands, you must expect a fire visit, for it is not "if," but "when!"* It is up to us to emulate

Mother Nature by thinning trees and removing debris and preparing our home for that inevitable fire-visit. The work to be done is no more than modified yard work and building our home in the woods out of less flammable exterior materials. Remember that more than half of the homes burned were lost to creep fire and ember involvement... not to the raging flame front as it passed. Those losses could have been prevented. Again, if you are going to live in the woods, pay attention to the lessons of Mother Nature's school. To do so is to live in peace and security. To do otherwise is really risky business, not only to you, but also to the firefighters who will try to protect your home.

- FIREWISE really works. The elements are at www.firewise.org, but it means thinning, raking, cutting brush and reducing the intensity of fire that might come against the home by zones. Also, fire resistant or less flammable building materials are key to the survival of a cabin or home in the woods. Like Smokey Bear says, "Only YOU can prevent forest fires," but in this case refers to protecting your home or cabin from future forest fires. Why not take advantage of fire department prevention specialists, extension foresters and grants and volunteers to make your house defensible, so that when there is a fire, firefighters have the best chance of ensuring your house will be able to withstand the fire-visit, and it will be there when you come back to it. Here is a sample checklist that any homeowner can use to assess their current situation. Remember the "red tags" across driveways, where there is little chance of saving a home. That fluorescent pink and/or red ribbon across your driveway is a signal to firefighters to go to the next house, a house they might be able to save.

FIRE RISK REDUCTION CHECKLIST

Minimum of 10' cleared from house of trees, brush & leaf litter. _____

Any plants left close to house are fire resistant and irrigated. _____

Trees from 10' to 30' from the house are thinned so that crowns are separated and also pruned up 10' from ground. _____

Any large trees left close to house are pruned 10' above the roof eave. _____

"Ladder Fuels" are removed and broken up in continuity. _____

Grass and ground vegetation maintained, irrigated and mowed. _____

Pine needles, leaves and debris removed from roof and gutters. _____

Pine needles and forest litter no more than 1" thick on the ground. _____

Woodpiles and building materials are stored at least 30' from house. _____

Shake roofs recommended to be replaced. _____

All attic and soffit vents are screened with 1/8" mesh. _____

No open cracks or crevices that allow embers access to interior. _____

Trees from 30' to 100' from house are thinned so that crowns are separated. _____

Big logs and heavy debris on forest floor from 30' to 100' are removed. _____

Street signs and your address are reflective and visible from road. _____

_____   _____   _____

Homeowner   Risk Assessor   Date

Fire Risk Reduction Checklist for assessing properties by Jim Paxon.

*   *   *   *   *

Ed Collins, District Ranger of the Lakeside Ranger District, where more than half of the Rodeo-Chediski Fire burned, has worked hard at emulating Mother Nature. He has received a Forest Service Chief's national award for the largest and very first national "stewardship project" utilizing the Healthy Forest Restoration Act initiative. The White Mountain Stewardship Project is a ten-year plan that will treat a minimum of 8,000 acres per year and a maximum of 15,000 acres per year. It would also implement non-commercial thinning and prescribed burn projects. Mother Nature would manage the forests by burning on about a five-year schedule. Translated to "plain speech" that would mean she would treat about 30,000 acres per year with fire.

Even at the maximum of 15,000 acres per year, the White Mountain Stewardship Project is only accomplishing 50% of what Mother Nature wants us to do… and it is the most aggressive program in the U.S. It seems to me that we should consider getting much busier, much faster, to accomplish more reduction in fire risk. If you take the Lakeside Ranger District's excellent results and apply them across the landscape, we are still falling behind by 50% or more, each and every year. Other areas are not cutting and burning as much as the Lakeside Ranger District. Remember the alternative. If we don't do it, eventually Mother Nature will say, "Stand back, kids, and watch me clean this mess up… with fire!" If only we could understand that there are only two options… and the second one is not in the least desirable.

*   *   *   *   *

Academia, the fire community and land managers have all three recognized that we cannot keep fire out of any of the North American ecosystems. The adage "If it is above the oceans, it burns… periodically" is so true.

Extreme fire behavior in a brush fire in central Arizona in 2004. Photo by USFS, Tonto National Forest.

Mother Nature will not allow her primary tool, that of periodic fire-visits, to be removed from her tool bag for very long. The longer that fire is kept out, the more severe the eventual fire that burns. The dragon will only slumber so long.   When he awakes in a foul mood, he will consume forests with a ravenous appetite. If houses are in the way, he will not stop, for to him, houses are just another easy snack. Now that most have recognized that as a truism, we must begin to emulate Mother Nature. With 130-140 years of fuels buildup, west-wide, it will take more than a few years of work to reverse the trend.

The sun at 3 p.m. on June 21, 2002, in Pinedale, AZ. Photo by Tom Beddow.

Restoration ecology requires that our tools of thinning, pruning, chopping, timber/fuel-wood harvesting and, of course, prescribed burning be used as each situation dictates. The notion of allowing free burning fire without major modification to existing fuel situations is sheer folly, and will lead to greater disasters than we have suffered thus far… and most certainly fatalities of both firefighters and civilians (remember Los Alamos, May 2000, and the prescribed fire that got away). Yet, prescribed fire must be in the mix of tools used by land managers. We must periodically put fire on the ground in a controlled way… or Mother Nature will reduce fuels the same way she did on the Rodeo-Chediski Fire. The biggest problem we have is the backlog/buildup of fuels, live and dead, that are choking our wildlands and forest communities. If your property looks like this, it is unhealthy and dangerous. This represents a biological desert on the verge of ecological collapse, but it is what most of us know as our forests.

Please forgive the use of a repeat photographs; it is important for us to have a mental image of what a healthy forest looks like. Note the space between crowns and the clear boles. Also, take in the abundance of grass and forbs on the forest floor. This is a healthy forest and a biological bonanza with a wealth of insects, butterflies, songbirds and even good habitat for endangered species such as Mexican Spotted Owls and Peregrine Falcons. It is a prime example of a functioning forest.

Doghair pine in the town of Show Low. Photo by Jim Paxon

Healthy ponderosa pine forest, thinned appropriately. Photo by Ron Moody.

We simply must help Mother Nature by cutting, crunching and munching the fuels that are out there. Removal of part of the biomass (or fuels) will help reduce the severity of natural or prescribed fire when it is allowed/encouraged to burn through a treated area. At an estimated average of $1,000 or more per acre for thinning, economics dictate that in order to speed the accomplishment of fuels modification, anything that can be exchanged (products or raw materials for $$) will assist in getting the job done quicker and at less expense. We are not there, yet, with all the various interests that need to come to the table and negotiate, but we are moving in the right direction.

In the meantime, the stage is set and many more monsters are about to rear their many ugly heads. When I am old (whenever that might occur, but at least 30 years from now, ha-ha), all the really old fire dawgs will scratch their heads and say, "Yep! The Rodeo-Chediski Fire was quite a monster… but look what has happened since!" My prediction is that many future fires will destroy large tracts of forests, changing landscapes long term, and may well consume towns, taking a toll of lives.   Truly, our forests and the communities within them are not in good shape. Some towns such as Prescott, Forest Lakes, Pinetop-Lakeside, Ruidoso, New Mexico, and a few others are making great strides in managing portions of their wildland urban interface. Sadly, none of them have total support from all the community residents and property owners.

Forest in Pinetop, Arizona.
Photo by Steve Campbell

Same location thinned by Arizona Corrections Forestry Crews.
Photo by Steve Campbell.

This photo of Wild Iris is at the second switchback above Los Alamos, New Mexico. It is on the Camp May road to Pajarito Ski Area. An old rancher who was born on the Baca Land and Cattle Co. in the 1930's told me that he had never seen Wild Iris on that hill and he was in his 80's. This site was an aspen stand that was severely burned when fire came over the ridge on May 10, 2000 and Los Alamos had to be evacuated. These plants showed up after the burn and I photographed them in the spring of 2001. To me, the message of the Iris is simple… there is hope in tomorrow.

Wild Iris in the Cerro Grande Fire on the Camp May road.
Photo by Jim Paxon.

Anyone who knows me understands that I am the eternal optimist. I am always looking for the pony underneath the pile of "horse-doo" on Christmas morning! I believe that we *CAN* turn our national fuels and fire risk situations around. We have the research and the technology needed. Mother Nature is willing to work with us, if we will in fact go to work… now! The sons of Arizona, Drs. Covington, Pyne and Swetnam, et al are ready to help as well with solid studies and conclusions. To get started, all it takes is the determination of each of us to do our part. Then the sun that sets on burned sticks can rise on healthy forests.

Snags in winter sunset on the Rodeo-Chediski Fire. Photo by Dewayne Saxton.

Personal property fire risk reduction is a major part of this plan, but it takes all the partners, including your neighbors next door, implementing Firewise to reduce the risk to an acceptable level in our wildland urban interface (W.U.I.). Remember, as I said during the fire, *"There are only two kinds of mountain communities... those who have had a fire and those that are going to!"* So many communities are just not paying attention to the plight and condition of their neighborhoods and surrounding forests... until they receive that climax fire-visit. Even then, once the black is replaced by the green of grass and flowers and the dead sticks begin to fall, our attention turns to other matters. All interests must come to the table. All interests must participate and be part of the solution in order for the process to not be stalled in appeals and litigation.

I would give almost anything for my dire predictions to be wrong, but to be so, we must accelerate our forest treatments and each of us must shoulder personal responsibility for our communities and our own "home in the woods!" Would you rather feed a small dragon and control him or fight a huge, multi-headed monster and lose?

The choice is up to us. In the course of time, this choice may end up being a matter of life and death... for the forest, for the wildlands and God forbid, for forest families and their neighbors.

206

POEM BY PENELOPE WOODS

While Our Forest Burned

We watched and waited as it grew
We watched it in the sky and we watched it on TV
We watched it in denial
We watched with waning optimism and waited for the call
Then it came
The monster forced us out – this White Mountain family of ours
How do we choose what pieces of our past to take?
How much can we fit in our cars?
We abruptly gain a new perspective on what really matters in life
One by one, thousands upon thousands, the full moon guided us down the mountain
The midnight caravan!
Like a string of red Christmas lights
Weaving slowly around the canyon
Not a sound to be heard
Not a word to be said
Questions racing in our heads – words we didn't dare utter out loud
Where will we go?
What will we do?
Have we seen the last of our homes?
Will friends soon become memories?
We haven't a clue
All of us displaced and scattered, yanked from our routines
Yet all united – this White Mountain family of ours
Our futures cling with promise to the words of the fire boss
As he loyally reports on our fates
We endear ourselves to him – how can we not?
While desperately searching for a glimmer of light in his weary and burning eyes,
We listen hard for an encouraging tone in his voice, a half-smile on his face, anything at all
Feeling our pain, he skillfully weighs his words, being ever so cautious not to give us false hope
Always reminding us that the fire is in control, not the thousands who are chasing it
Not for a moment can they let their guard down
Not for a moment can we abandon our faith
So we watch and we wait and we pray for those noble and nameless heroes on the fire lines and in the
   air, fighting to save us from doom
We pray that, unharmed, they can hold back the flames
We pray for our forest and our homes and our families and our friends and our livelihoods
We pray that we can soon go back to it all
Days go by – we watched and we waited
We watched the media, the mayors of our towns, the governor of our state, and the president of our
   country, all there, while we remain in refuge far removed
We witness the spirit of compassion and generosity of our neighbors, near and far
They share our grief – they truly care
Unknowing, we feel fear, anxiety, anger, sadness, helplessness, and confusion
But most of all, we feel hope that our mountain will be spared

Finally, our beloved fire guru stands at the podium and announces, "This is an auspicious day!"
It is safe for us to go home
They say there was no explanation why the fire didn't burn the town – it was fully expected
But we all know why – it's very simple – our prayers held it back
We have been blessed with a miracle
With a renewed appreciation for all that we have and for this magnificent place where we live,
With a deep gratitude in our hears for our firefighters that words cannot express
We curl up in our beds and listen to the familiar sounds of our own surroundings
But our sign of relief is interrupted by our sorrow for those others of us
Those who no longer have a home or business to go to
To them, we say, have faith – things fall apart so that things can fall together
This is an opportunity, a second chance for us all; let's begin
You are not alone – we are one – this White Mountain family of ours!

GLOSSARY

Air Tanker: A fixed wing aircraft equipped to drop retardant on or close to fires. Heavy air tankers carry between 2,000 and 3,200 gallons of retardant

Area Command: An oversight team who manages resources for more than one incident management team working on a fire or group of fires (complex)

Anchor & Flank: Basic firefighting tactic that works from safe point (anchor) where the fire has diminished and cooled and fireline can be built/dug along both flanks of fire until the head can be hooked or pinched off.

Black Line: Fire's edge that is no longer burning and cooled down. Another basic firefighting tactic is to build fireline right against the black or the edge, which works until flames exceed four feet.

Burnout: Sometimes called "backfiring." When line cannot be built directly against the fire's edge, the indirect line must be burned out from the dug fireline, to rob the fire of fuels and secure that piece of line.

Chaparral: A plant community of low, often volatile vegetation. In Arizona we have oak and Manzanita fields that burn vigorously.

Cold Trailing: Final Attack or mop-up practice of searching for latent heat with the back of one's hand. When heat is felt, the location is dug up and water and stirring dirt are applied until the fire (heat) is extinguished.

Contained: When a fire or portion of is no longer growing. Usually when a secure fireline has been completed and the line is black.

Controlled: When there is no growth nor risk of fire escaping it is called controlled. It is also the point in time when emergency funding for working that fire ends.

Creep Fire: Fire burning with minimal flame length and moving very slowly in an erratic pattern.

Crowning: When fire gets up into the tops of trees and runs through the crowns in solid flames, much faster and more intense than fire burns on the ground.

Direct Attack: Building fireline right against the edge of the fire. Common vernacular is 'building line with one foot in the black."

Dog Hair: Trees so thick that they are like the hair on a dog's back when standing up.

Drip Torch: Handheld canister with a wick filled with a mixture of diesel and gasoline. A burning wick drip flaming liquid fuel onto fuels at ground level.

Engine: A ground vehicle with a water tank, hose systems and means of pumping water. Categories are from a one ton vehicle with 150-200 gallon capacity (Type 6) up to structural giants (pavement queens or Type I) with large tanks and high volume pumps.

Engine: A ground vehicle with a water tank, hose systems and means of pumping water. Categories are from a one ton vehicle with 150-200 gallon capacity (Type 6) up to structural giants (pavement queens or Type I) with large tanks and high volume pumps.

Engine, Type 3: Minimum 500 gallon capacity tank and 120 gallon per minute (g.p.m.) pump at 250 pounds per square inch pressure (p.s.i.) and usually has a crew of five firefighters. These are 2.5 ton chassis and are mostly all wheel drive.

Engine, Type 6: Minimum 150 gallon capacity tank and 30 gallon per minute (g.p.m.) pump at 100 pounds per square inch pressure (p.s.i.) and usually has a crew of three firefighters. These are four-wheel-drive vehicles on one ton chassis.

Escaped Fire: Fire that is not under any sort of control, or where it was contained, it has "gone over the hill."

Extended Attack: When initial attack goes beyond the first burning period and exceeds the capability of the initial attack resources.

Faller: Sawyer, Cutter or one who falls (cuts down) trees.

Fire Brands: Embers or burning particles that are lofted and fall to earth out in front of the flamefront.

Fire Crew: An organized group of trained and equipped firefighters, usually 20 person. Type I crews are extremely physically fit and trained (hotshots). Type II crews are regular and call-when-needed crews such as SWFF (Southwest Firefighters).

Fire Visit: In natural fire regimes, the periodic occurrence of fire passing across a landscape, usually low intensity and of short duration.

Flank of the Fire: The side of the fire's perimeter

Flamefront: The leading edge of the fire (Head) where the greatest heat and spread of the fire occurs.

Fuel Depot: Also known as a "jackpot." Concentration of woody fuels that will burn intensely with high energy and usually throw off embers or firebrands. Firefighters also refer to houses and structures as fuel depots.

Fusee: Similar to road flares, used to ignite fuels in burnout operations.

Head of the Fire: The front or fastest moving part of the fire, usually directionally influenced by slope and wind, where the greatest amount of heat and movement of the fire occurs.

Heel of the Fire: Usually close to the origin or start of the fire, where the fire is coldest and initiation of line building can begin safely (anchor).

Hotshots: Also known as Type I or Inter-agency Hotshot Crews (I.H.C.). There are 93 crews nationwide. Hotshots are physically fit, well trained and experienced. Crews are self-contained with tools, saws, food, water and vehicles, can respond immediately and work for a minimum of 48 hours with little or no support.

Hundred Hour Fuels: Fuels from ¼" to 3" diameter and usually woody type.

I.C. (Incident Commander): In the old Large Fire Organization, the Fire Boss. The individual responsible for decisions and managing all aspects of an incident (fire).

Iced out: When a smoke plume reaches a certain elevation and forms a thunderhead on top. Often the cloud will take the shape of a blacksmith's anvil. The air at the top cools rapidly, forming ice crystals that then begin to fall down toward earth through the interior of the smoke column. As the cooler air accelerates in its descent, the descending wind-speed at ground level increases dramatically, "splashing" the ground with fire and scattering flames and embers in a violent explosion, in all directions.

Initial Attack: First resources to respond to a new wildfire, that work to contain the fire within the first burning period.

Indirect Attack: When heat becomes too intense and flames exceed four feet, firefighters can no longer work right next to the edge of the fire. They must fall back a safe distance and dig fireline. Then to secure the line, burnouts are done to remove fuels between the dug fireline and the edge of the fire.

L.C.E.S.: Lookout, Communications, Escape Routes and Safety Zones. A quick checklist to continually assess fire conditions. If conditions change drastically, firefighters can withdraw in a timely manner and not face life-threatening conditions.

Ladder Fuels: Fuel arrangement that provides continuous pathways for fire to get into the crowns of trees, for example, grass and weeds lead into low brush with close by small trees that are under medium sized trees that are against the biggest or dominant trees. Fire can easily climb the "ladders" into crowns and then spread uncontrollably at a much faster speed than fire on the ground would.

Large Fuels: Also 1,000 hr. fuels. Logs and pieces of woody fuels greater than 3: diameter.

McLeod: Sometimes known as a "duff rake" it is a hoe/rake like device with long handle and a 12" cutting edge on one side and 3" long rake teeth on the other. Excellent tool to use in removing ground vegetation, sod and leaf litter.

Medium Fuels: Also 100 hr. fuels. Usually woody type fuels from ¼" to 3" diameter.

Mega Fires: Very large, fast moving fires that usually burn in excess of 100,000 acres and threaten communities.

Mopup: Also known as "Final Attack." The extinguishment of all burning materials within a buffer zone inside the actual constructed fireline.

One Hour Fuels: Also Fine Fuels. Less than ¼" diameter. Grass, weeds, dead leaves and pine straw that enables fire to carry or spread. Fine fuels are the most sensitive to changes in humidity. A cloud will increase moisture as direct sun will desiccate or decrease fuel moisture.

Plume Dominated: Smoke from the vertical convection column of a fire that rises almost straight up and forms a thunderhead on top. Plume dominated fires are fuel and slope induced and minimally affected by wind. Often the plume will ice out on top. When the smoke column cools, it can no longer support the weight of burning embers. The cooler air drops through the interior of the column like an elevator falling down the elevator shaft. The falling air accelerates and hits the ground scattering fire and embers in all directions, often with gale force, causing a blowup.

Probability of Ignition: Chance that an ember or firebrand will cause ignition if it lands on a burnable surface. Expressed in tenths referring to percentages, i.e. P.I. of 1 has only a 10% chance of starting a new fire. Conversely P.I. of 10 means that 100% of the embers can start new fires.

Pulaski: A combination cutting and trenching tool that combines an axe head on one side and a grubbing hoe on the other. Developed around 1915 by Ed Pulaski, who survived the Big Blowup of 1910 near Wallace, Idaho and parts of Montana that burned more than 3,000,000 acres in four days and killed 85 people, 78 of them firefighters.

Retardant: Also known as "slurry." Chemicals and dye that are mixed with water and delivered to the fire by air tanker or helicopter. Basically a form of agricultural fertilizer that reduces the flammability of anything that the retardant coats. Retardant also uses emollients that reduce the evaporation of plain water.

Red Flag Warning: A weather alert issued by National Weather Service. Usually indicates sustained winds greater than 25 m.p.h. with gusts in excess of 35 m.p.h., high temperatures with low humidity where fire conditions will be extreme.

Safety Zone: An area that is cleared of fuels and flammable materials and large enough to allow firefighters to withdraw to and not have to use their fire shelters to maintain safety

S.E.A.T: Single Engine Air Tanker. Crop Duster type airframe converted to air tanker configuration. SEAT's carry up to 1,000 gallons of retardant and are extremely precise in their delivery.

Slash: Debris left after logging or a natural disturbance such as blow-downs. Slash is dead woody material concentrated and very flammable.

Slopover: An event where fire crosses a fireline and burns out of control. Firefighters will attempt to build fireline and contain the spread of the slopover.

Snag: A standing dead tree.

Spot fire: A fire out in front or to the side of the main fire, usually started by lofted embers that land on burnable fuel beds.

S.W.C.C.: Southwest Coordination Center in Albuquerque that serves Arizona, New Mexico and West Texas.

Temporary Flight Restriction (T.F.R.): Federal Aviation Administration restriction on airspace over a fire that defines spatial limits of area and elevation that cannot be used except by fire affiliated aircraft.

Thousand Hour Fuels: Also Large or Heavy fuels. Woody fuels greater than 3" diameter.

Torching: A tree or small group of trees that burns from the ground all the way to the tops of the trees all at once. Torching contributes to the lofting of embers.

Underburn: A fire that consumes surface fuels, but not overhead or aerial fuels.

Unified Command: Fires that involve more than one jurisdiction and have joint commanders that share the command responsibilities. There is still one staff and one Incident Action Plan (I.A.P.).

W.F.S.A., (Wildland Fire Situation Analysis): Analysis used by Agency Administrators and Incident Management Teams to determine fire suppression strategies. Several alternatives, costs, results and probabilities of success are analyzed.

W.U.I. (Wildland Urban Interface): Area where communities and structures meet woodland or forested areas where fires have the propensity to burn.

A "smoke dog" or "dragon", depending on your perspective. Photo by Jean Burr.

South Show Low, June 22nd, 2002. Photo by Steve Campbell.

END NOTES

Chapter 1: Ancient Ones

a. Ferguson, W.M. and Rohn, A.H. <u>Anasazi, Ruins of the Southwest in Color</u>. 1987. University of New Mexico Press, Albuquerque.

b. Plog, Stephen. <u>Ancient Peoples of the American Southwest.</u> 1997. Thames and Hudson, London.

c. http//wmat.us/wmahistory.shtml

d. http//Huachuca-www.army.mil/history/museum.html

e. Interview—Edgar Perry at Hondah. March 6, 2006.

f. http//www.indians.org/Welker/originfire.html

Chapter 2: Recipe for Disaster

a. Pyne, S. <u>Fire, A Brief History.</u> University of Washington Press, Seattle. 2001.

b. Beale, E.F. "Traveling the Wagon Road From Ft. Defiance to the Colorado River." Report to 35 Congress, First Session, Senate Executive Document 124, 1858.

c. Cooper, C.F. "Changes in Vegetation, Structure and Growth of Ponderosa Pine Forests Since White Settlement." Ecological Monographs 30:129-164, 1960.

d. Dieterech, J.M. "Chimney Spring Forest Fire History." USDA Forest Service Research Paper RM-220, 1980 p.8.

e. Covington, W. W. et al. Historical and anticipated changes in forest ecosystems of the inland west of the United States. Journal of Sustainable Forestry1994. Ch 2, p. 13-63

f. Interview w/ Hiram A. "Doc" Smith, February 7, 2007.

g. Arizona Fire History. Southwest Coordination Center *http://gacc.nifc.gov/swcc/fire/history*

h. Interview, Wally Covington, Flagstaff, January 10, 2007.

i. Olberding, Susan. "Fort Valley, the Beginnings of Forest Research" Forest History Today, Spring 2000.

j. Wedge prepared by Laboratory for Tree Ring Research from a tree on Black Mountain in the Gila National Forest.

k. Interview Dr. Tom Swetnam, Tucson, March 22, 2006.

l. Pyne, S.J. <u>Smokechasing,</u> U. of A. Press, Tucson, Az. 2003

m. Pyne, S.J. <u>The Year of the Fires</u>, Penguin Books, New York. 2002.

n. Reaves, Joseph A. Arizona Republic, June 30, 2002. "Hell Comes to the White Mountains—A Chronology.

o. Interview w Show Low City Manager, Ed Muder. January 30, 2007.

p. Interview w/ F.S. District Ranger Ed Collins, February 22, 2007.

Chapter 3: Firefighters

a. Wallington, Neil. <u>World Encyclopedia of Fire Engines and Firefighting.</u> Anness Publishing, Ltd. 2004

b. Brunacini, Alan. Phoenix F.D. Chief (Ret.) Interview, January 13, 2007.

c. Swetnam, Tom. Aspen Fire Essay, guest editorial. Arizona Daily Star. August 10, 2003

d. Pyne, Stephen. <u>Year of the Fires, the Story of the Great Fires of 1910.</u> Penguin Books, New York. 2002

e. Mineer, Roger. Interview, January 24, 2007.

f. Pyne, Stephen. <u>Smokechasing.</u> 2003. University of Arizona Press, Tucson.

g. Sunset Magazine. July 1993.

h. Lewis, Merriwether. From "Journals of the Expedition under the Command of Captains Lewis and Clark, edited by Nicholas Biddle, 1814, Heritage Press, New York.

i. Matthews, M. "To Carry a Fire Shelter or Not?" Article in Wildland Firefighter Magazine. February 2007 p. 18.

j. Thomas, D. and Cook, W. The Dude Fire Staff Ride. Article in Fire Management Today, Volume 62, Number 4, Fall 2002.

k. Fatality Report Summary for 2006, National Interagency Fire Center, January 2007. www.nifc.gov

l. Huggard, C. J. & Gomez, A. R. Forests Under Fire, A Century of Ecosystem Mismanagement in the Southwest. 2001. University of Arizona Press p. 185

m. 2002 Fire Season Summary. National Interagency Fire Center. www.nifc.gov

Chapter 4: ICS
a. NIFC Paper, "The History of I.C.S., October 1994.

Chapter 5: Before the Monster Awoke
a. Deiterech, J.M. "Chimney Spring Forest Fire History." USDA Forest Service Research paper, RM-220, 1980.

Chapter 6: Ignition – and the Devil Danced!
a. Interview with George Leech dated Dec. 16, 2007.
b. Interview and letter from Frank Hayes, dated December 18, 2006
c. Tucson Citizen Newspaper, July 27, 2002 article by Gabrielle Fimbres
d. Times article quote.
e. Interview with Gene Kelly, former Mayor of Show Low, March 15, 2007
f. Interview with Paul Watson, Pinetop Fire Chief (Ret.), January 27, 2007
g. Interview with Roger Mineer, Lakeside Fire Chief, January 24, 2007
h. Holdcroft, Gary P. Walking Through the Ashes, Oct. 2004, Self Published. (p.30)
i. Interview with Ken Butler, January 13, 2007

Chapter 7: Lost & Desperate
a. Summary Statement of Special Agent Daniel Hawkins (redacted), dated (redacted).
b. Deposition of Jerry Clifton to Special Agents of B.I.A. dated (redacted).
c. Deposition of Scott Clifton to Special Agents of B.I.A. dated (redacted).
d. Interview with Jerry Beddow, March 1, 2007.
e. Interview w/ Chief Mel Epps (Ret.), Heber-Overgaard Fire Dept., December 7, 2006.

Chapter 8: Two Weeks of "Hell" in the White Mountains
a. NICC Summary—Incident Management Report for June 18, 2002.
b. Interview w/ Roy Hall, February 1, 2007.
c. Interview w/ Kirk Rowdibaugh, Arizona State Forester, March 6, 2002.
d. Interview and Letter from Chief Don Howard, Summit Fire Dept., march 5, 2007.
e. Holdcroft, Gary P. Walking Through the Ashes, Self Published, Oct. 2004. p.63.
f. Interview w/ Engineer Darin Whiting, Show Low Fire Dept., February 16, 2007
g. Interview w/ Chief Mel Epps, Heber-Overgaard Fire Dept., December 7, 2006.
h. Interview w/ Abbie Crozier, Cellular One, January 23, 2007.

Chapter 9: Evacuation of Show Low, Pinetop-Lakeside, Hondah, McNary & Forest Lakes
a. Interview w/ Bob Worsley at Legacy Ranch, January 31, 2006.
b. Interview w/ Bill Beecroft at Legacy Ranch, February 1, 2006.
c. Interview w/ Frank Hayes, Air Attack Group Supervisor, December 1, 2006.
d. Interview w/ former Show Low Mayor Gene Kelly, March 15, 2007.
e. Interview w/ former Pinetop-Lakeside Mayor Ginny Handorf, March 2, 2007.
f. Interview w/ Abbie Crozier, Cellular One, January 23, 2007.
g. Interview w/ Tom Brown, SLFD Chaplain, January 16, 2007.
h. Interview w/ Ed Muder, Acting City Manager of Show Low, January 30, 2007.
i. Interview w/ Frank Hayes, ATGS, December 1, 2006.
j. Interview w/ Gary Martinson, Owner of Bison Ranch, January 25, 2007.
k. Phoenix fire engines 1st time out of valley, Fire Times, June 25, 2002. p.2.
l. White Mountain Independent Special Report—Rodeo-Chediski Fire, tabloid published July 7, 2002.
m. Ibid, p 6.
n. Interview w/ Chief Mel Epps (Ret.) H-O F.D., December 7, 2006.
o. Interview w/ Bill Beecroft, February 1, 2006.
p. Interview w/ Martin & Eunice Kent, September 1, 2002.
q. White Mountain Independent Special Report—Rodeo-Chediski Fire, tabloid published July 7, 2002, p. 9.
r. Summary of Treatments, Ft. Apache Fire & Forestry, B.I.A. 2003.

Chapter 10: Rick Lupe, Hero
a. Interviews w/ Roy Hall, Deputy Director for Fire & Aviation Management, SW Region, USFS. February 1 & 20, 2007.
b. Interview with Marco Minjarez, Prevention Specialist, Ft Apache Fire (former Superintendent of Ft. Apache Hotshots) April 10 and July 23, 2007.
c. Sawtooth Prescribed Fire Fatality Investigation conducted by Bureau of Land Management, published August 7, 2003.
d. Interviews w/ Wendell Peacock, B.I.A. Spokesman for the Lupe Family, January 20 & 25, 2007.
e. White Mountain Independent, Special Report—Rodeo Chediski Fire tabloid published July 7, 2002, p. 9.
f. Congressional Record, October 29, 2003.
g. Interview w/ Richard Genck, September 20, 2003.

Chapter 11: Presidential Support
a. White Mountain Independent, Special Report—Rodeo-Chediski Fire, tabloid published July 7, 2002. p. 9.

Chapter 12: On the Scoreboard
a. American Indian Report Magazine, September 2003. p.14.
b. http://www.dolanellis.net/original_songs/wildfire.htm

Chapter 13: Repatriation & Celebration
a. White Mountain Independent, Special Report Rodeo-Chediski Fire, tabloid published July 7, 2002. p. 16.
b. Interview w/ former Show Low Mayor Gene Kelly, March 15, 2007.

Chapter 14: Final Attack
None.

Chapter 15: Post Fire
a. Navajo County Assessor's Office Summary received by letter March 10, 2006.
b. White Mountain Apache Tribe News Release, September 11, 2002.
c. White Mountain Independent, October 21, 2003 p.10
d. AzCentral.com news March 13, 2004.
e. California Division of Forestry and Fire Website http//cdfdata.fire.ca.gov

Chapter 16: Reflections
a. Interview w/ District Ranger Ed Collins, Lakeside Ranger District, Apache-Sitgreaves National Forest, February 22, 2007.

My mentor for Manhood – Poppa Garrett

About the Author

Jim Paxon was born and raised in Lubbock, Texas, and has had a lifelong love affair with Nature. His respect for the way things work and happen without any forethought on Man's part has only strengthened as he grew up. He's a plainspoken man with considerable knowledge and experience with Mother Nature's use of fire as a tool for maintaining the perfect balance in the forest and on the open range. It is hoped that his story of the Rodeo-Chediski Fire will resolve some issues for many people, and help everyone to gain a new understanding of the way Nature works.

As a founding member of the Arizona Wildfire Academy, Jim continues to train firefighters for the future. Jim is active as a consultant, working with Northern Arizona University's Ecological Restoration Institute, NBC's Channel 12 – KPNX, The Arizona Republic, and Arizona's ecologically-oriented governor, Janet Napolitano. He works with Show Low and other Arizona communities in reducing fire risk.

Jim spent many years in Truth or Consequences, New Mexico, but since Rodeo-Chediski, he and his bride, Debbie, now call Show Low, Arizona home.